Test Equipment for the Radio Amateur

THIRD EDITION

Clive Smith, PhD, BSc(Eng), G4FZH

Radio Society of Great Britain

Published by the Radio Society of Great Britain, Cranborne Road, Potters Bar, Herts EN6 3JE.

First published 1974
Third edition 1995

ISBN 1 872309 23 2

Cover design: Geoff Korten Design.
Cover photo: Clive Smith.
Illustrations: Derek Cole, Ray Eckersley, Roy Pettit and Bob Ryan.
Production and typography: Ray Eckersley, Seven Stars Publishing.

Printed in Great Britain by Bell & Bain Ltd, Glasgow.

Contents

Acknowledgements

I would like to thank George Benbow, G3HB, for being my mentor in the preparation of this book and my wife Helen, G4KNQ, for reading the various parts of the book as it was produced. Thanks should also go to the various people involved in the preparation, especially Ray Eckersley, G4FTJ.

G4FZH

Preface

There is increasing pressure on radio amateurs to be able to make measurements, not only to conform to licence conditions, but to try and minimise problems due to electromagnetic incompatibility in a congested world with a myriad of electronic devices. It is also hoped that the inclusion of PCB and component layouts will tempt radio amateurs to be more adventurous in making their own equipment and re-learn the art of construction.

This third edition of a very popular book has been completely updated. Obsolete equipment and techniques have been removed and replaced where appropriate with more up-to-date test methods and equipment. Where equipment has been retained from the earlier editions, components have been updated where necessary. Emphasis has been placed on the simpler type of equipment which is easier to make or more affordable to the radio amateur.

The book details equipment that can be built, made from kits or which can be bought relatively cheaply. There is in fact quite a lot of equipment available from the various radio rallies which abound around the country. It is often a case of realising what a piece of equipment is and not being charged an 'arm and a leg' for it. A list of possible second-hand equipment has been included as an appendix – this list is by no means comprehensive and it would be foolish to give any indication of price.

The previous edition of this book has been used for the general layout and some of the articles – this is acknowledged here rather than in the references for each individual chapter.

The author is willing to help in the procurement or finding the equivalents of any components which may prove difficult to obtain. He is also willing to give assistance if required, but please remember that amateur radio is a hobby and one still has to earn a living!

Clive Smith, G4FZH

Abbreviations and units

AC	Alternating current
AF	Audio frequency
AFC	Automatic frequency control
AM	Amplitude modulation
ARRL	American Radio Relay League
BCD	Binary-coded decimal
CMOS	Complementary metal-oxide semiconductor
CW	Carrier wave
DC	Direct current
DFM	Digital frequency meter
DIL	Dual-in-line
DO	Dip oscillator
DPM	Digital panel meter
ECW	Enamelled copper wire
EHT	Extra high tension
FET	Field effect transistor
FM	Frequency modulation
FSD	Full-scale deflection
FSK	Frequency shift keying
HF	High frequency (3–30MHz)
HRC	High rupture capacity
HT	High tension
IC	Integrated circuit
IF	Intermediate frequency
JFET	Junction FET
LCD	Liquid crystal display
LED	Light-emitting diode
MOSFET	Metal-oxide semiconductor FET
PCB	Printed circuit board
PEP	Peak envelope power
PLL	Phase-lock loop
PSD	Phase-sensitive detector
PSU	Power supply unit
PTFE	Polytetrafluoroethylene
PTT	Press-to-talk
QRP	Low power
RAE	Radio Amateurs' Examination
RF	Radio frequency
RIS	Radio Investigation Service
RMS	Root mean square
SM	Silver mica
SSB	Single sideband
SWG	Standard wire gauge
SWR	Standing wave ratio
TTL	Transistor-transistor logic
UHF	Ultra high frequency (300–3000MHz)
VCO	Voltage-controlled oscillator
VFO	Variable frequency oscillator
VHF	Very high frequency (30–300MHz)
VSWR	Voltage standing wave ratio

Electrical units

A	ampere	current
F	farad	capacitance
H	henry	inductance
Hz	hertz	frequency
s	second	time
S	siemen	admittance, conductance, susceptance
V	volt	voltage
Ω	ohm	resistance, reactance, impedance

Division of measuring units

G	giga	10^9
M	mega	10^6
k	kilo	10^3
m	milli	10^{-3}
μ	micro	10^{-6}
n	nano	10^{-9}
p	pico	10^{-12}

Chapter 1

Introduction

1.1 General

Test equipment can be used for many purposes but the main reasons it is required by the radio amateur are to:

(a) comply with the licence conditions and, in the UK, to demonstrate such compliance to the Radio Investigation Service (RIS);
(b) help maintain equipment in good running order; and
(c) help in repairing equipment when a failure has occurred.

Sadly it is used less in items (b) and (c) as the radio equipment becomes more sophisticated, the test equipment becomes more complex, increasing legislation requires more stringent testing and the skills needed are fast diminishing. It may then be asked "Why bother to produce a book at all?"

It is hoped that through the following pages it will be possible to help the radio amateur appreciate what can be carried out with relatively simple or less-expensive test equipment. It will also help to return some of the skills or knowledge associated with using test equipment and keep the radio equipment in good running order, thus minimising repair bills. An aspect that one is up against is the throwaway attitude of some of the major suppliers of radio equipment. It is fairly obvious that the equipment is so designed and packaged that repair or maintenance by the average radio amateur is definitely discouraged – a shame, as one learns a great deal by probing into equipment.

There is one area where test equipment is very useful and that is for the 'home-brewer'. Here it is necessary to be able to use test equipment to ensure that the equipment built performs to the specifications expected.

1.2 Typical test equipment

Which test equipment should the radio amateur have as a *minimum*? This is a difficult question to answer but the following are suggested:

- Multimeter
- SWR/RF power meter
- Power supply (12V DC but 5V DC also useful)
- Dip oscillator
- Selection of various cables and wires
- Selection of plugs and sockets
- Insulated pointer (for prodding into circuits)

Also desirable are:

- Frequency counter
- Oscilloscope
- Audio frequency generator

Hopefully some of the projects described in this book will encourage the radio amateur to increase his or her stock of test equipment.

1.3 Equipment tolerances

All equipment has a tolerance on its calibration and therefore readings taken from equipment have an error. In high-quality test equipment this error is small, as it is with equipment that is frequently calibrated. Probably the most important reading that an amateur takes is that of frequency. If at all possible, check the frequency counter with one that has just been calibrated against a frequency standard or get it calibrated. Remember also that calibration does not last for ever and rough handling is likely to destroy the calibration quicker than anything.

1.4 Tools

Which tools should the radio amateur have as a *minimum*? This is again a difficult question to answer. All tools should preferably have insulated handles, and the following are suggested:

- Screwdrivers, large and small, flat-bladed
- Screwdrivers, large and small, cross-point
- Pliers, large and small
- Wire cutters, large and small
- Soldering iron, large and small
- Solder, multicore
- Adjustable spanner, medium
- Box spanners, various BA and/or metric sizes
- Insulating tape

1.5   The shack

It is generally desirable to have an area set aside for the operation of the radio equipment. For permanently installed pieces of test equipment, eg power meters, there should be a permanent position for them to allow easy access for both reading and connecting/disconnecting them. It should also be possible to provide a temporary working surface on which test gear can be placed.

1.6   The workshop

It is desirable to have an area set aside where equipment can be partly dismantled and left in that state. It should be ideally an area that can be locked away from unwanted helpers (eg children and pets!). The dining room table is not normally considered as fulfilling these requirements. There should also be a safe electrical mains supply with preferably a master cut-out switch that will isolate all supplies in the case of an emergency.

1.7   Safety

In most walks of life there has recently been much more conscious effort put into the design of equipment and the provision of notices and documentation in order to ensure the safety of personnel. For first aid, the reader is referred to reference [1]. There is a good chapter on safety in reference [2] and it is worth reading parts of Chapter 37 in reference [3].

This concept should be always used in the use of any equipment, especially when electrically powered. Electricity cannot be seen or heard but its effects can be devastating. Some use of test equipment merely requires putting additional equipment in line with other plugs and sockets (eg power meters), but other equipment may need the connection to points where lethal voltages exist. In this case adequate precautions should be taken for both the person carrying out the testing *and* for other persons, eg friends, members of the family (children) and pets.

The way legislation is going may also mean that the way is open for courts to decide on compensation etc. The use of equipment in public demonstrations should be seriously considered and the necessary safeguards required. Always make sure that all connections to the mains are correct and secure, and make sure that no 'whiskers' of wire protrude for the unwary finger!

One golden rule is never to work alone on electrical equipment. Voltages below about 50V can normally be worked on without too many precautions, but above this voltage more and more care must be taken, especially in the case of valve linear power supplies where there may be voltages of 2000V or more. Also, be careful of large capacitors – they do not lose their charge immediately and are capable of giving severe shocks.

It is therefore best to consider any voltage above 50V

as dangerous and act accordingly. Probably the three most important precautions are:

1. Ensure that all equipment is satisfactorily earthed – the integrity of the earthing system should be checked periodically.
2. Switch off and disconnect from the mains supply before attempting the investigation or repair. However, it must be appreciated that sometimes the fault must be investigated under live conditions and then special care must be taken.
3. Beware of capacitors – they may be charged, especially high-value ones. It is always wise to use bleed resistors but these still require a finite time to discharge the capacitor. It is wise to discharge capacitors with an insulated and earthed wand before working or soldering to them.

Using a low-voltage but high-current power supply must not allow anyone to be lulled into a false sense of security. The high-current capability of many supplies is quite capable of melting metal if a short occurs – be careful if a ring is worn on the fingers.

The RSGB has put a set of safety recommendations together for the amateur radio station. Most of these apply equally well when testing and when replacing faulty components (or making a change). Those most relevant for this book are:

1. All equipment should be controlled by one master switch, the position of which should be well known to others in the house or club.
2. All equipment should be properly connected to a good and permanent earth (see Note A).
3. Wiring should be adequately insulated, especially where voltages greater than 500V are used. Terminals should be suitably protected and labelled.
4. Transformers operating at more than 100V should preferably be fitted with an earthed screen between primary and secondary windings.
5. Capacitors of more than $0.01\mu F$ capacitance operating in power packs, modulators etc (other than for RF bypass or coupling) should have a bleed resistor connected across them. The value of the bleeder resistor should be low enough to ensure a rapid discharge. A value of $1/C$ MΩ is recommended (where C is in microfarads). The use of earthed probe leads for discharging capacitors in case the bleed resistor has failed is recommended (see Note B). Low-leakage capacitors (such as paper and oil-filled types) should be stored with their terminals short-circuited to prevent static charging.
6. Indicators (eg lamps or LEDs) should be installed showing the power condition of the equipment. These should be clearly visible at the operating and test position. Replace failed indicators as soon as possible.

LEDs are more reliable than filament types and consume less power.

7. Double-pole switches should be used for breaking mains circuits on equipment.

8. All equipment should be protected by fuses or similar. Always use fuses of the correct rating and connected on the equipment side of the switch. Switch OFF equipment before changing fuses. (See also Note C.)

9. In metal-enclosed equipment install microswitches or similar so that when a lid is opened power is removed (especially if high voltage). Check their operation occasionally. Sometimes they need to be bypassed when fault-finding/repairing. This should be done in an obvious manner so that the equipment cannot be returned to normal service with the bypass still in existence.

10. Test probes and indicators should be of the insulated variety.

11. A rubber mat should be used when the equipment is installed on a floor that is likely to become damp.

12. If at all possible, switch off equipment before adjustments or faults are investigated. Switch off when making the repair. If adjustments are made or faults investigated on live equipment, use one hand only (possibly keeping the other in the pocket). Use good-quality tools with insulated handles.

13. Do not wear headphones when probing in live equipment.

14. Make sure that all metalwork is properly earthed – this includes microphones and morse keys.

15. Avoid the use of meters with metal zero-adjusting screws in high-voltage circuits. Beware of live shafts projecting through panels, particularly when metal grub screws are used in control knobs.

16. Be careful not to touch or short test points.

Note A: Owing to the common use of plastic water pipe (mains or internal), never assume a metal water pipe is earthed. Steps must be taken to ensure that the earth connection is of sufficiently low resistance to provide safety in the event of a fault. Checks should be made whenever repairs are made to the mains water system in the building.

Note B: A 'wandering earth lead' or an 'insulated earthed probe lead' is an insulated lead permanently connected at one end to the chassis of the equipment: at the other end a suitable length of bare wire is provided with insulated handle so that any points with stored charge can be discharged.

Note C: If necessary use high rupture capacity (HRC) fuses where large surges are likely to occur on switching on.

1.8 RF hazards

Exposure to RF presents additional hazards. Certainly from VHF upwards one must be wary of possible damage to body tissues if prolonged exposure occurs at relatively high powers. The following guidelines are therefore suggested:

1. Do not work or test antennas with power applied unless absolutely necessary. See also the following item.

2. With high-power operation (including testing), try to avoid unnecessary exposure in the proximity of antennas. This poses both a danger to body tissues as well as the danger from high-voltage RF.

3. If at all possible, operate RF amplifiers (especially at VHF and UHF) with the covers on. If testing necessitates their removal then keep exposure to a minimum.

4. At UHF and up into the microwave region *never* look into the open end of a piece of waveguide *nor* point it at anyone.

5. Use well-shielded dummy loads.

1.9 References

[1] *First Aid Manual*, 6th edn, St John, Red Cross and St Andrew's, ISBN 0-86318-978-4.

[2] *Microwave Handbook*, Vol 2, ed M W Dixon, G3PFR, RSGB, 1991.

[3] *ARRL Handbook for the Radio Amateur*, any edition from 1986 onwards, ARRL.

Chapter 2

Current and voltage measurements

2.1 Introduction

Many measurements on electrical/electronic equipment require the determining of current or voltage, and the measurement of any one of these parameters may well give a clue to the operating condition of an electrical circuit.

Items of equipment often use meters to display various electrical quantities. A meter will give an indication of either current or voltage in a circuit but this measurement can be an indication of another electrical parameter, eg resistance, signal strength, power or VSWR.

2.2 Equipment

The four items of equipment most commonly used to perform these measurements are:

1. The analogue meter.
2. The digital meter.
3. Solid-state bar indicators.
4. The cathode-ray tube.

Fig 2.2.1. Photograph of analogue and digital multimeters

Each of these items has its own particular characteristics, and the choice may well depend on personal preference, what is available, accuracy or measurement being undertaken.

This chapter will deal with items 1, 2 and 3, which give a value for a parameter, while Chapter 3 deals specifically with the cathode-ray tube/oscilloscope which gives a graphic representation of a particular electrical waveform. Fig 2.2.1 is a photograph of typical analogue and digital multimeters.

Table 2.2.1 compares analogue and digital meters. It assumes that the analogue meter has no electronic circuit associated with it as this may alter its characteristics. It should also be borne in mind that the input to a digital meter may be affected by input amplifiers and attenuators.

2.3 The analogue meter

The meter is referred to as *analogue* as it can display an infinite variety of values. The basic analogue meter consists of a pointer indicating a value on a scale which must then be interpreted. The two most common forms of meter are the *moving-coil* and *moving-iron* types. They both rely on the production of a magnetic field by a current passing through a coil which reacts with a permanent magnetic field or a piece of iron. Fig 2.3.1 shows a selection of meters.

Various current, voltage and resistance-measuring functions are often combined into a single meter known as a *multimeter* – see Section 2.16. It is important to understand the underlying principles so that they can be applied to situations where it is not desirable to permanently couple a multimeter, eg a power supply output, or to more specific applications. This is the approach taken in this section.

There are other types of meter but these are far less common, difficult to obtain or now possibly obsolete, although they may turn up at radio rallies. Typical of these is the *RF ammeter* which uses a thermocouple to measure the power dissipation in the load. These are still available new but are expensive.

2.4   The moving-coil meter

This meter operates on current, the voltage measurements being derived from this parameter. It consists of a coil of wire wound on a former which is mounted on a spindle in pivots and located within the magnetic field of a permanent magnet. Attached to the spindle is a pointer which passes across a scale. A small balance weight is added to counteract the weight of the pointer. A typical arrangement of this meter is shown in Fig 2.4.1.

Fig 2.3.1. Photograph of various meter movements

The current being measured is passed through the coil and produces a magnetic field which reacts with that of the permanent magnet. The current is fed to the coil by means of two hair springs. These hair springs provide a load against which the resultant torque created by the interaction of the magnetic fields acts. The pointer deflection is proportional to the current passing through the coil. The hair springs also return the pointer to a zero position when current flow ceases.

In order to damp the coil system, it is usual to wind the coil on an aluminium former which acts as a short-circuited single-turn coil and in which eddy currents oppose the movement. The degree of damping is also dependent on the value of any external resistance placed in parallel with the coil.

It is good practice to place a short-circuit across the terminals of any sensitive instrument when not in use or if being moved.

A screw adjustment, accessible from outside the instrument, allows a small adjustment of the hair springs so that the pointer can be accurately zeroed. As this adjuster connects with the springs it may be electrically live if made from a conducting material – *beware!*

Instruments are normally balanced to work in stated positions – horizontal, vertical or 45°. It is usually permissible to use an instrument in other than its intended position but the zero may need to be adjusted and there may be small additional errors due to pivot friction. The type of panel material (eg ferromagnetic or aluminium) may also affect the meter reading.

Table 2.2.1. Comparison of analogue and digital meters

Feature	Analogue meter	Digital meter
Operation	Current	Voltage
AC or DC	DC moving coil (AC with rectifiers), AC/DC moving iron	DC (AC with rectifiers or converters)
Display	Electromechanical	Semiconductor
Power supply required	None (taken from circuit under test)	DC supply
Best sensitivity	50µA FSD typical	199.9mV typical
Circuit loading	Depends on circuit and sensitivity of meter	Input >10MΩ, may affect high-impedance circuit
RF interference	None	Possible due to internal oscillator

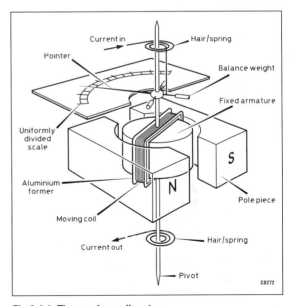

Fig 2.4.1. The moving-coil meter

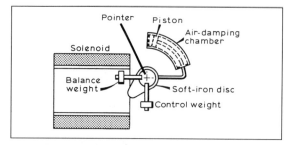

Fig 2.5.1. Attraction-type moving iron meter

The moving-coil instrument will only respond to DC currents. The scale is linear and can be divided into various subdivisions and with various legends.

A meter is normally specified by the current required for *full-scale deflection* (FSD), the resistance of the coil, instrument shape and size. The first two parameters are important when changing the range a meter can cover or making it respond to voltage. The common range of moving-coil meter movements is from 50µA to 10mA FSD. The arc through which the pointer moves (and hence scale length) may vary from 90° to 270°, 90° and 120° being the most common. In addition there are some meters which have a centre-zero position.

2.5   The moving-iron meter

This meter relies on the attraction or repulsion of a piece of ferromagnetic material with the magnetic field produced by a fixed coil. Fig 2.5.1 shows the basic construction of an attraction type.

In the attraction type a small piece of iron is drawn into the core of the coil when the current flows. It does not matter which way the current flows in the coil – magnetic attraction always takes place.

In the repulsion type there are two pieces of iron rod within the coil: one fixed, the other movable and attached to the pointer. When a current passes through the coil, both rods are magnetised in the same direction and, since like poles repel, the moving part is repelled by the fixed part. It therefore does not matter which way the current flows in the coil – the result is always the same. Moving-iron instruments therefore respond to both AC and DC.

Control of movement in both types is by hair springs and damping is usually achieved by a vane in a cylinder containing air. The scale is non-linear, the graduations being very close at low values of current. At higher values of current the graduations become more even but still basically non-linear. The typical meter movement starts at about 100mA FSD while the frequency range extends to about 60Hz.

These meters are not too common in radio equipment but may be used and found in power supplies, including mains measurements.

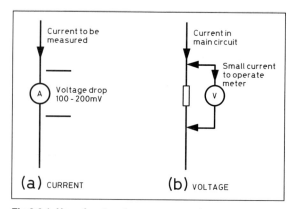

(a) CURRENT   **(b)** VOLTAGE

Fig 2.6.1. Use of meters for measurement

2.6   Extending the range of analogue meters

The meters referred to above come in various fixed arrangements and may not suit the ranges it is desired to measure. Scales are commonly in the range 0–3 or 0–10 or multiples thereof. It is possible by the addition of resistors to extend the range of meters, still using the original scaling. There is no reason why the scale should not be redrawn – it is possible to use transfers or, if one is skilful, to redraw it. Fig 2.6.1 shows the basic arrangements for voltage and current.

A meter basically requires current to operate, so let the extension to read higher values of current first be considered. The FSD of the meter cannot be changed so it is necessary to shunt some of the current to be measured around the meter. The typical circuit is shown in Fig 2.6.2. Here, assuming the maximum current to be measured is I, then the shunt resistance is given by:

$$R_{shunt} = \frac{R_m I_{FSD}}{I - I_{FSD}}$$

where I_{FSD} is the full-scale deflection of the meter and R_m the resistance of the meter. It would be normal to choose I to be a multiple or submultiple of the maximum scale reading so that only a multiplying factor is required of

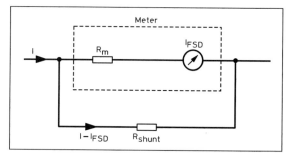

Fig 2.6.2. Arrangement for current shunts

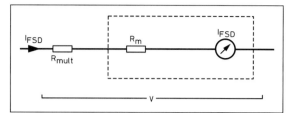

Fig 2.6.3. Arrangement for voltage multipliers

the scale reading. The power rating of the shunt would be calculated using $(I - I_{FSD})^2 R_{shunt}$.

2.6.1 Example

It is desired to use a 100μA FSD meter to measure a maximum current of 500μA. The resistance of the basic movement is 2000Ω. Calculate the shunt resistor value.

Substituting these values in the above formula gives:

$$R_{shunt} = 500\Omega \text{ with a power rating of } 80\mu W$$

An alternative way of considering this is to determine the multiplying factor n of the scale. Using the previous definitions of resistors, the formula for the shunt becomes:

$$R_{shunt} = \frac{R_m}{n - 1}$$

Applying this to the above example, then $n = 5$ and the same value of shunt is found. However, the power rating of the shunt must still be determined.

To use a meter as a voltmeter means that the maximum voltage to be read should provide the value of I_{FSD}. The circuit used in this case is shown in Fig 2.6.3. The equation for the series resistor R_{mult} is given by:

$$R_{mult} = \frac{V}{I_{FSD}} - R_m$$

The power rating for the resistor is given by $I_{FSD}^2 R_{mult}$.

2.6.2 Example

A 50μA movement meter with a coil resistance of 3000Ω is required to measure voltages up to 30V. Calculate the multiplier resistor value.

$$R_{mult} = 597k\Omega \text{ with a power rating of } 1.5mW$$

These simple calculations show the basis on which the familiar multimeter is based and how it is designed. The switch on the multimeter merely switches in different shunt and multiplier resistors. Remember, these calculations only apply to DC for the moving-coil meter.

2.7 Meter sensitivity

The sensitivity of a voltmeter is usually expressed in ohms/volt (Ω/V). This is merely the reciprocal of the full-scale current sensitivity I_{FSD} of the basic meter. Hence, a

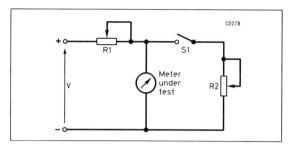

Fig 2.9.1. Circuit for determining meter coil resistance

1mA meter used as a voltmeter would be described as 1000Ω/V and a 50μA meter as 20,000Ω/V.

2.8 Effect on circuit readings

Putting a voltmeter across a resistor may upset the circuit conditions due to the loading effect of the meter. For example, putting a meter which requires 50μA across a resistor through which only 100μA flows will disturb the circuit significantly. Putting the same meter across a resistor through which 10mA flows will have little effect. How can this be gauged or guarded against?

Consider a 20,000Ω/V meter. When set on the 10V range, this will have a resistance of $10 \times 20,000 = 200k\Omega$. It is suggested that any resistance across which this voltmeter is placed should have a maximum value of one-tenth of this, eg 20kΩ. This rule-of-thumb method can be used for any range. The smaller the percentage, the more accurate will be the reading.

For ammeters the point that must be considered is the voltage drop across the ammeter in relatively low voltage circuits (ie $I_{FSD} \times R_m$). For example, a 0.5V drop across an ammeter is unacceptable in a 12V circuit, but it is immaterial in a 100V circuit. A meter must therefore be chosen that has as low a coil resistance as possible. This reduces the in-circuit voltage drop and keeps any shunt resistance value as high as possible. If possible, use an ammeter of I_{FSD} equal or just greater than the range required.

2.9 Measuring resistance of a meter coil

A good-quality meter will have its I_{FSD} and coil resistance marked on it somewhere, often on the scale plate. However, when visiting radio rallies or junk sales for example, meters may be acquired with only the I_{FSD} value given. The problem then is how to obtain the coil resistance value. It must be ensured that the meter is not overloaded in performing this test and so damaged – this is likely to be the case if a commercial ohmmeter is connected across a meter.

To overcome this problem, the value can be determined by the indirect method shown in Fig 2.9.1. The expected range for different movements is:

50μA	1800–3000Ω
100μA	1200–1800Ω
1mA	70–200Ω
10mA	5–15Ω

Connect the circuit, choosing a value of resistor R1 and voltage *V* to give a reasonable deflection on the unknown meter. With S1 open, adjust R1 to give full-scale deflection. Close S1 and then adjust R2 to give half-scale deflection on the meter. Disconnect the voltage source, remove R2 and measure it with an ohmmeter. This will be the value of the meter resistance.

2.10 Choice of meter

This can be fraught with problems and needs an understanding of the circuit being tested. For the typical DC circuits that are common in amateur work the moving-coil meter will be needed for probably 95% of all applications. The effect on the circuit has already been discussed in Section 2.8.

For voltage measurements the meter should take only a small current compared with that flowing in the circuit, ie the current that the power supply can provide. Make the current drawn by the voltmeter circuit less than 5% of the current that can be supplied in the main circuit. The smaller the percentage, the more accurate will be the reading.

For current measurements the voltage drop across the ammeter must be kept as low as possible. Choose a meter that has a low as coil resistance as possible and an I_{FSD} equal or just greater than the range required. Try to keep the voltage drop less than 5% of the supply voltage.

For mains circuits of 100V or above the moving-iron meter represents a more viable alternative and tends to be cheaper.

2.11 Making shunts

It is possible to make shunts. For values of 0.1Ω or greater it may be possible to make them by series/parallel combinations of standard *off-the-shelf* resistors. If this is not possible or not desired, then the alternative is to make them from wire. This can be resistance wire (not too easy to get hold of) or standard enamelled copper wire.

A wire table is given in Chapter 13 which gives the diameter of wire, the current-carrying capacity and the resistance per unit length. Compute the resistance required, choose a wire capable of carrying at least the required current and then calculate its length. This wire should then be wound on a former such as a 1W or 2W carbon resistor of high resistance. Always use as thick a wire as possible in order to minimise the heat rise in the shunt due to the I^2R loss.

If it is possible to get constantan resistance wire then the following characteristics may be useful.

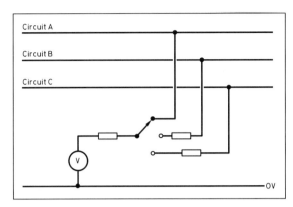

Fig 2.12.1. Switched voltage measurements

| 24swg | 0.56mm dia | 1.93Ω/m |
| 32swg | 0.27mm dia | 8.04Ω/m |

2.12 Meter switching

In order to save cost (and sometimes panel space), it may be worthwhile for a meter to serve several functions. This is more likely to be necessary in valve circuits for measuring grid and anode currents and voltages; these normally require different ranges for the various parameters being measured. For convenience two meters would be used: a voltmeter and an ammeter. In all instances a break-before-make switch should be employed, and care should also be exercised in selecting the switch when high-voltage circuits are involved.

A problem arises when the resistance of wire and switch contacts may affect the value of low-value shunts. The switching in of different multiplier resistors is of little consequence as these tend to be high-value resistances.

2.12.1 Voltmeters

Voltages are normally measured with respect to 0V or earth. This means that one end of the voltmeter is fixed – see Fig 2.12.1. Knowing the characteristics of the meter, the various values of series resistance can be calculated. It is suggested that the lowest value is usually wired directly in series with the meter and then the other values chosen such that this value plus the additional one equals the value calculated. This is shown in Fig 2.12.1, assuming that circuit A is the lowest voltage to be measured. Thus, some current limiting always exists in series with the meter.

2.12.2 Ammeters

For the purposes of this section a meter is assumed to have an FSD of 1mA and coil resistance of 100Ω. Fig 2.12.2 shows how switching could be arranged for the measurement of current on three ranges. Switch or

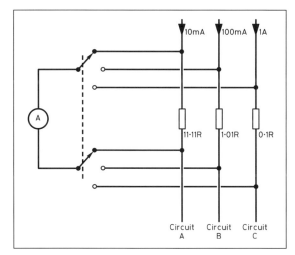

Fig 2.12.2. Switched current measurements

conductor resistance is unlikely to be a problem with circuit A, it may be a problem on circuit B and certainly will be on circuit C.

One solution is to use a non-switchable meter for any current range which requires a low shunt value, typically less than about 0.5Ω. A different approach is to consider the meter as measuring volts across a resistor. The problems of measuring a voltage and the current taken must then be considered as previously discussed. If a 50μA meter was used, then it must be possible to develop a minimum voltage drop of about 150mV, and for a 1mA movement it should be about 100mV. It should be equal to or greater than $I_{FSD} \times R_m$. The circuit used for this arrangement is given in Fig 2.12.3.

2.13 AC measurements

If an alternating current is passed through a moving-coil meter there will normally be no deflection since the meter will indicate the mean value – in the case of a waveform symmetrical about zero this is also zero. If, however, the AC current is rectified so that the meter sees a series of half-sine pulses (full-wave rectification), it will indicate the mean value ($2/\pi$ or 0.637 of the peak value).

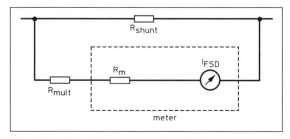

Fig 2.12.3. Current measurement by volt-drop method

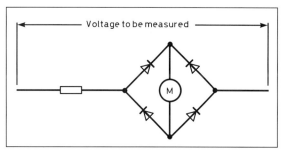

Fig 2.13.1. Typical arrangement for AC measurements

Commercial instruments using moving-coil instruments for AC sine-wave measurements therefore incorporate a rectifier arrangement (see Fig 2.13.1) and the scale is adjusted to read RMS values (0.707 of the peak value). They will read incorrectly on any waveform that does not have these relationships. The moral is: do not use the meter on any waveform other than a sine wave. This arrangement is normally only used for voltage measurements – AC current measurements pose additional problems and are not considered further.

Moving-iron instruments, as previously mentioned, do respond to an AC current and can be used for measurements without rectifiers. This type of meter unfortunately has a square law characteristic and so the scale tends to be cramped at the lower end. Moving-iron meters normally have a full-scale reading of about 20% more than the normal value to be displayed. They are not used for multimeters.

Other AC measurements can be accomplished by means of electronic voltmeters or oscilloscopes.

ICs do exist (eg AD536, 636, 736, 737, SSM2110) which will provide the RMS of any waveform but their frequency range is limited.

2.14 Meter protection

Meters are relatively expensive and are easily damaged if subjected to excessive current. Damage can be prevented simply and cheaply by connecting two silicon diodes in parallel (anode to cathode) across the meter terminals (Fig 2.14.1) and this should be regarded as standard practice. No perceptible change of sensitivity or scale shape need occur.

A characteristic of silicon diodes is that they remain of very high resistance until the anode is some 400mV above the cathode, at which point they start to conduct and the resistance falls to a low value. Since the voltage drop across the average meter is around 200mV, it follows that a silicon diode connected across the meter will have no effect even when the meter shows full-scale deflection. If, however, the meter is overloaded to twice the FSD and the voltage across the meter rises to 400mV,

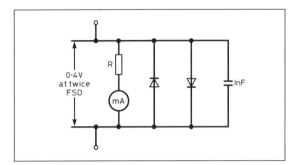

Fig 2.14.1. Meter protection using diodes

the diodes will begin to conduct and shunt the meter against further increase of fault current.

Most meters will stand an overload of at least twice the FSD without damage but, in order to ensure the protection afforded by parallel diodes without affecting the meter, it is wise to include a series resistor as shown in Fig 2.14.1. The series resistance ensures that the voltage drop across the meter/resistor combination is 200mV minimum. Parallel back-to-back diodes are used because excessive current in either direction can damage the meter.

2.14.1 Example

What series resistor should be added to a 1mA FSD meter with a coil resistance of 100Ω?

At 1mA FSD the voltage drop across the meter is 1mA × 100Ω = 100mV. Thus the drop across the series resistor should also be 100mV, and this requires a resistance of 100Ω. This then means that the meter is protected for currents in excess of 400mV/200Ω = 2mA.

If an additional series resistor is to be included when shunts are used to increase the current range, they should be placed across this combination and the series resistance taken into account when making the calculations.

2.14.2 Choice of diodes for protection

For most cases, small-signal silicon diodes such as the OA202, 1N914 or 1N4148 are satisfactory as they have the advantage of having an inherently high reverse resistance, ie a low reverse leakage current, as this shunts the meter circuit. However, it is important that under the worst fault conditions the diode will not fail and go open-circuit, thus affording no protection. An example of this with small-signal diodes would be in a high-voltage supply where a large current could flow in the event of a short-circuit of the power supply. In these cases a rectifier diode should be used such as the 1N400x or 1N540x series.

The reverse current of these diodes may be a few microamps and, depending on the current to be measured, may have a slight effect on the sensitivity of the meter circuit.

Zener diodes can be used for meter protection, particularly those with avalanche characteristics (ie a sharp knee), which applies to diodes of 6.2V or more. However, there is rarely any advantage in the use of zener diodes, and in fact there could be a disadvantage as they usually show some reverse leakage. They are useful for meters which will not stand overload significantly greater than their FSD or which have a basic voltage drop larger than the turn-on voltage of a silicon diode. If zener diodes are used they should be connected in series as shown in Fig 2.14.2.

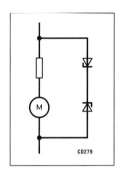

Fig 2.14.2. Use of zener diodes for meter protection

2.14.3 Precautions when using diode protection

Although diode protection should be applied as routine in order to safeguard instruments, it can cause some unusual effects if measurements are made with an AC signal imposed on a DC signal. This AC component, providing it is symmetrical, should not introduce any error. However, if the AC is large enough it may bring the diodes into conduction at the peak of the cycle, thus introducing a dynamic shunt on the meter. This can be partly confusing when back-to-back diodes are used, as the meter sensitivity will drop without any offset reading to warn what is happening. These effects are most likely to occur when measuring rectified mains or when RF is present.

2.14.4 Protection when RF may be present

Whenever a meter is to be used when RF may be present, and this includes even a power supply output voltmeter, it is wise to shunt the meter with a capacitor, typically a 1000pF ceramic type, as shown in Fig 2.14.1.

If strong RF fields will be present, eg in a transmitter, it would also be wise to shield the meter and possibly feed it via shielded cable. These protection methods should culminate in the scheme shown in Fig 2.14.3.

2.15 Resistance measurement

This item has been included in this chapter as it may form part of a multimeter. For further details of resistance measurement see Chapter 9.

Resistance may be measured using a meter (mA or µA), a battery and an application of Ohm's Law. Two common arrangements are shown in Fig 2.15.1. It will be seen that each circuit comprises a battery in series with a meter, a resistor RV1 and the unknown X. An additional refinement is added in the circuit of Fig 2.15.1(b), in the form of RV2 which is to adjust the

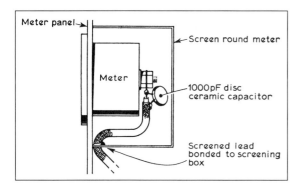

Fig 2.14.3. Screening and bypassing a meter in a transmitter

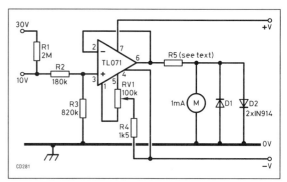

Fig 2.17.1. Basic high-impedance DC voltmeter

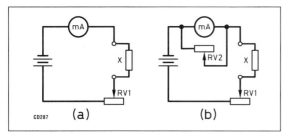

Fig 2.15.1. Two common arrangements for measuring resistance

sensitivity of the meter to compensate for any drop in battery voltage.

To use and calibrate, the terminals across which X will be connected are shorted together and RV1 adjusted until the meter reads full scale. When the unknown X is connected across the terminals, the meter reading will be less than full scale. Calibration of the meter scale can be carried out using a series of known-value high-accuracy resistors. The scale is non-linear. Alternatively a graph relating meter current to resistance can be prepared.

2.16 Multimeters

A number of shunts and multipliers selected by a switch can be used in association with a single basic meter to

form a multi-range meter (normally called a *multimeter*) measuring current and voltage and, if containing an internal battery, resistance as well. Fig 2.16.1 shows a multi-range instrument for DC voltage and current. It is based on a 50µA movement of resistance 2700Ω.

The cost of multimeters is quite variable but there are many good low-cost units on the market. The ideal multimeter should have a basic sensitivity of 20kΩ/V on DC (a basic movement of 50µA) and cope with AC values.

2.17 Analogue electronic instruments

This section deals with instruments that have active circuits preceding a pointer-type instrument. The circuit is included in order to increase the sensitivity of an instrument, increase the input impedance and the frequency range. Not all of these may be achieved with one instrument – it depends on what it is has been designed for.

Full-scale deflections can be achieved by a few millivolts or microamps. Input impedances up to about 50MΩ can be achieved which reduces the loading on a circuit under measurement. In conjunction with diode probes, accurate AC measurements can be made in excess of 100MHz.

The typical analogue electronic meter uses operational amplifiers to provide high input impedance, buffering and amplification if necessary. It is quite common for the op-amp to drive a meter with a 1mA movement. Fig 2.17.1 shows a circuit for measuring with a 10V and 30V range. The TL071 op-amp has very high input impedance and is used in a unity, non-inverting gain mode. On the 10V range the input resistance is R2 + R3; on the 30V range it is R1 + R2 + R3. These resistors also act as attenuators. The arrangement

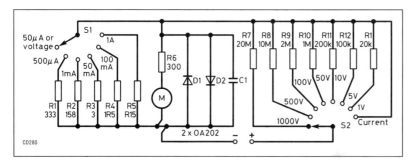

Fig 2.16.1. Basic DC multimeter: current to 1A, voltage to 1000V

with R2 always in series with the input is preferred as it provides some protection for the op-amp. RV1 and R4 provide offset balance null due to the op-amp providing a small DC bias at the output. R5 limits the current through the meter and can be varied to suit various meter sensitivities – it might be better split into two components in the ratio of about 75% fixed and 25% variable. The use of a reasonable output voltage and the 1mA meter means that the effect of the meter resistance is almost negligible. For a 1mA meter movement it is suggested that R5 is about 8.2kΩ – a fixed 6.8kΩ resistor in series with a 2.2kΩ trimmer could be used. D1 and D2 are used to protect the meter movement as explained earlier in this chapter.

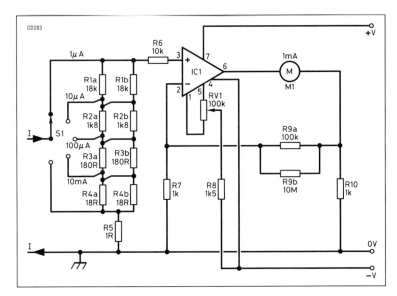

Fig 2.18.1. DC micro/milliammeter

To measure current, it is necessary to measure the voltage drop across a resistor through which the current flows, and the amount of voltage drop that can be tolerated was discussed earlier in this chapter. It is suggested that any voltage drop should be kept below 200mV in order to minimise any disturbance to the circuit being measured. For the arrangement shown, 1mA flowing through 100Ω is 0.1V. This voltage is somewhat on the low side and must be amplified before being applied to the meter circuit. Fig 2.17.2 shows a suitable non-inverting amplifier. The gain of this is given by (R1 + R2)/R2 and with the values shown comes to approximately 82 (ie 8.2V/0.1V). The value of R3 for a typical 1mA movement should be approximately 8.2kΩ, again possibly achieved by using a 6.8kΩ resistor in series with a 2.2kΩ trimmer.

The circuits discussed so far have been for DC only.

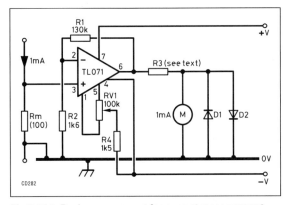

Fig 2.17.2. Basic arrangement for current measurement

The problem for AC circuits is to convert the signal to DC and then measure it. The other problem is the voltage drop across the rectifying diodes. This can be achieved with a precision rectifier which consists of op-amps with diodes in the feedback loop in order to minimise the effect of the diode forward voltage drop – see Section 2.19.

2.18 A DC micro/milliammeter

2.18.1 General

This circuit (Fig 2.18.1) will measure current from under 1μA to 10mA in five ranges. It uses the principles outlined earlier by converting the current to a voltage and using an operational amplifier to amplify the signal and drive a meter. The advantage of this arrangement is that the voltage dropped across the resistor is low – in this case 10mV maximum on any range. If the circuit is battery powered then it can be used floating, but with a split mains supply the current is usually referenced to ground with the arrangement suggested.

Because of the resistance values required in the input it is necessary to construct them from two parallel units.

Table 2.18.1. Components list for the DC micro/milliammeter

R1a, 1b	18k, 0.5W, 1%	R8	1k5, 0.5W, 5%
R2a, 2b	1k8, 0.5W, 1%	R9a	100k, 0.5W, 1%
R3a, 3b	180R, 0.5W, 1%	R9b	10M, 0.6W, 1%
R4a, 4b	18R, 0.5W, 1%	RV1	100k skeleton pot
R5	1R, 0.5W, 1%	IC1	TL071
R6	10k, 0.5W, 1%	M1	1mA FSD meter
R7, 10	1k, 0.5W, 1%	S1	1-pole, 5-way switch

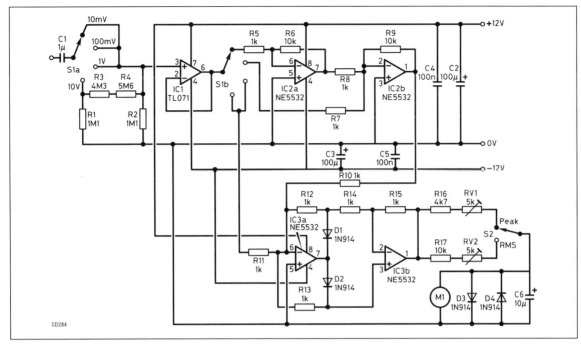

Fig 2.19.1. High input impedance AC voltmeter

The op-amp used should have a very low input bias current – that for the TL071 is quoted as 30pA.

2.18.2 Construction and calibration

Construct the circuit as shown and apply a split power supply. No special precautions are required. A PCB layout is given in Appendix 2. With no input, adjust trimmer RV1 to obtain zero deflection on the meter. The unit is now ready for use.

2.19 A high-impedance AC voltmeter

2.19.1 General

The meter presented here is for analogue signals and is reasonably accurate from 10Hz up to about 0.5MHz. It has four ranges, corresponding to 10mV, 100mV, 1V and 10V, the output meter being switchable to read either RMS or peak for a sine-wave input. The input impedance is 1MΩ shunted by a few picofarads which depends on the method of wiring, sockets used etc.

2.19.2 Circuit description

The circuit diagram is given in Fig 2.19.1. The input is buffered by IC1, a FET input op-amp. R1 to R4 form a constant input resistance network and provide an attenuation of 10 on the 10V range. Amplifiers IC2a and IC2b each have a gain of 10, the 10mV and 100mV signals being routed via them. Switch S1 selects the

correct amplification or attenuation for the ranges such that a 1V signal is presented to the precision rectifiers formed by IC3a/b. The DC output from these rectifiers is then scaled for peak or RMS by networks R16/RV1 and R17/RV2, the resulting output driving meter M1. IC2 and IC3 are formed by dual op-amps type NE5532 which have a 10MHz unity gain bandwidth product.

2.19.3 Construction and calibration

Providing the components listed are used, there should be little problem in constructing the circuit and getting it to work. To assist, a PCB layout pattern is given in Appendix 2. The unit should be well screened in a metal box and with no possibility of extraneous pick-up. To calibrate, a sine wave of known amplitude should be ap-

Table 2.19.1. Components list for the high-impedance AC voltmeter

R1, 2	1M1, 0.6W, 1%	C2, 3	100μ, 25V
R3	4M3, 0.6W, 1%	C4, 5	100n, 50V ceramic
R4	5M6, 0.6W, 1%	C6	10μ, 6.3V
R5, 7, 8,		D1–4	1N914 or similar
10–15	1k, 0.6W, 1%	IC1	TL071
R6, 9	10k, 0.6W, 1%	IC2, 3	NE5532
R16	4k7, 0.5W, 5%	S1	3-pole, 4-way rotary
R17	10k, 0.5W, 5%		switch
RV1, 2	5k trimmer	S2	SPCO switch
C1	1μ, 50V	M1	100μA FSD

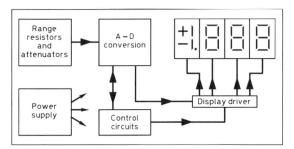

Fig 2.20.1. Block diagram of digital meter

Fig 2.21.1. Photograph of typical digital panel meter

plied to the input, the correct range selected and RV1 (peak) and RV2 (RMS) adjusted for the correct reading.

2.20   The digital meter

The digital meter is fast becoming more common and its price is now comparable with the analogue equivalent in most instances. It provides a very accurate meter at reasonable price. Its disadvantages are that the smallest digit can only jump in discrete steps, response time depends on sampling rate, and it requires a power supply.

The digital voltmeter works by converting an input analogue voltage to a digital signal that can be used to drive either an LED (light-emitting diode) or LCD (liquid crystal display) – see Fig 2.20.1. The conversion technique used is either a straightforward A-to-D converter or the dual ramp technique. A digital voltmeter is often quoted as having, for example, a 3½-digit display. This means that it will display three digits 0–9, with the most significant being only a 0 (normally suppressed) or a 1, ie a maximum display showing 1999.

There are quite a few ICs made by various manufacturers which provide a basic digital voltmeter, external components being required for extending the range, overvoltage protection and displays. These ICs provide outputs suitable for driving LEDs, LCDs or providing BCD outputs for further processing etc.

The best approach for a digital display is to use a panel meter module (which includes the above ICs) and comes with a 3½ or 4½-digit display and capable of accepting a 200mV signal. These are relatively cheap and provide a good basis for making various types of metering system.

The digital form of the multimeter is readily available at reasonable cost and it is not worth the exercise of making one of these meters. The approach here, as for the analogue meter, is to understand the basic principles and how to apply them to specific situations.

2.21   The digital panel meter

This will normally be a module based on an LCD which either plugs into a DIL socket or is on a small PCB – see

Fig 2.21.1. It has a full-scale reading for a 199.9mV DC input, works from 5V or 9V DC supplies (depends on model), consumes very low current (eg 150–300µA on a 9V supply) and has an input resistance of at least 100MΩ. The panel meter will provide an accuracy of 0.1% or better, but this does not take into account any external signal-conditioning circuits such as amplifiers or attenuators. In addition to these parameters, some of the displays will also show units such as 'µ', 'm', 'V', 'A', 'Ω', 'Hz' etc (referred to as *annunciators*). They can be purchased with and without back-lighting.

The main design consideration in using these units is to get the parameter to be measured to a DC voltage in the range 0–199.9mV. This can include the use of amplifiers, attenuators and rectifiers.

The following designs are based on the Anders OEM22 module which is readily available [1]. The panel meter consists of an LCD driven by a 7136 IC which contains an A-to-D converter and LCD drivers. The unit can be driven from 5V (5mA), providing two links are made on the board or direct from 9V (300µA). This latter is amenable to the PP3 battery (or its mains substitute – see Chapter 12).

2.22   A practical digital voltmeter

Fig 2.22.1 shows the arrangement for a digital voltmeter for DC voltage ranges of 200mV, 2V, 20V and 200V. The unit requires a 9V DC supply such as shown in Chapter 12.

R1 to R5 form a potential divider network with switch S1a selecting the correct input; ie the maximum voltage to the panel meter is to be 199.9mV. R6 and D1/D2 provide protection for the panel meter should the wrong range be inadvertently selected. S1b selects the position of the decimal point while S1c selects the annotation to be shown. The link *must* be cut to the BP line on the panel meter.

It is hoped that sufficient information is provided for

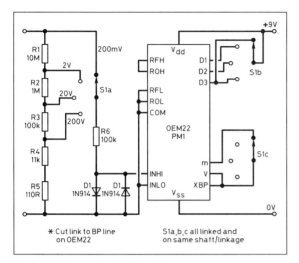

Fig 2.22.1. A practical digital voltmeter

Table 2.22.1. Components list for the digital voltmeter

PM1	Anders OEM22 panel meter	R3	100k, 0.5W, 1%
S1	3-pole, 4-way rotary switch	R4	11k, 0.5W, 1%
D1, 2	1N914 or similar	R5	110R, 0.5W, 1%
R1	10M, 0.6W, 1%	R6	100k, 0.6W, 5%
R2	1M, 0.5W, 1%		

the reader to adapt this design to cope with other ranges. An amplifier is required ahead of the meter input for inputs lower than 200mV.

2.23 A practical digital ammeter

This uses the same principle as the analogue milli/microammeter, but this time the voltage drop to be developed by the current passing through the measurement resistor must be 200mV for full scale. The circuit in Fig 2.23.1 is therefore applicable for a meter measuring 200µA to 200mA in decade ranges.

R1 to R4 form the load across which the voltage is developed from the current being measured. R1 to R3 involve resistors in parallel to make up the correct value required. Switch S1a selects the input, S1b selects the decimal point positions and S1c selects the correct annotation for the range being used. The combination R5, D1 and D2 provides protection for the panel meter input. The unit can be powered from a PP3 battery or equivalent.

2.24 RF diode probe

This device allows the scope of a DC voltmeter to be extended to measure AC voltages up into the tens of megahertz or even 100MHz region. The probe essentially rectifies the AC immediately and then only has to pass a DC voltage to the meter. The diode is often the limiting

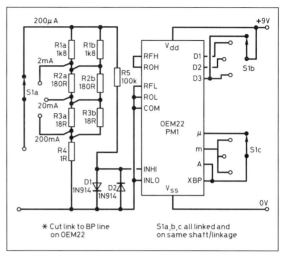

Fig 2.23.1. A practical digital ammeter

Table 2.23.1. Components list for the digital ammeter

R1a, 1b	1k8, 0.5W, 1%	R5	100k, 0.5W, 5%
R2a, 2b	180R, 0.5W, 1%	PM1	Anders OEM22 panel meter
R3a, 3b	18R, 0.5, 1%	S1	Rotary switch, 3-pole, 4-way
R4	1R, 0.5W, 1%	D1, 2	1N914 or similar

factor: to get high-speed operation the diode junction must be narrow and hence this reduces the breakdown voltage. Using a BAT46 Schottky barrier diode, the maximum input voltage is about 35V RMS, and with the 1N914/1N4148/OA91 it is about 45V RMS. With a Schottky diode the forward voltage drop is of the order of 0.2 to 0.3V but with a silicon type it is about 0.6V. The probe should be mounted in a small metal cylinder which is well screened and the resulting DC signal fed via a coaxial cable to the DC meter – see Fig 2.24.1.

A typical circuit is shown in Fig 2.24.2 with component values for feeding a 50µA meter movement. The advantage of arranging the capacitor and rectifier in this manner is that the capacitor also acts as DC blocking.

An alternative, when the circuit is to be fed into a DC voltmeter of high input impedance such as an electronic

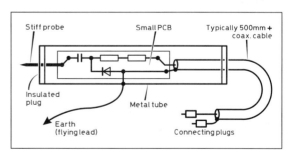

Fig 2.24.1. Typical construction of an RF probe

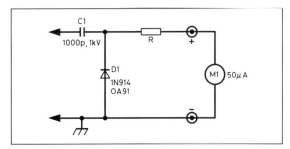

Fig 2.24.2. RF probe circuit. For R = 270k + 12k, the meter scaling is 0–10V, and full-scale, power in 50Ω is 2W. For R = 820k + 27k, the meter scaling is 0–30V, and full scale, power in 50Ω is 18W

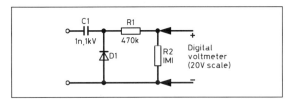

Fig 2.24.3. RF probe for digital voltmeter

analogue meter or a digital meter, is shown in Fig 2.24.3. The input resistance of the meter should be such that it is 10 times the value of R2. Also, the value for the series resistor R1 is approximately 41% of the combined resistance R2 in parallel with the meter input resistance. This then allows the meter to read the RMS value of the RF signal. The values shown are suitable for a meter with an input resistance of at least 10MΩ. For a meter of input resistance of 1MΩ, reduce the values of R1 and R2 by a factor of 10.

To measure higher voltages and hence higher power levels, one suggestion is to use a resistive divider across the load. Fig 2.24.4 shows a divide-by-10 unit suitable for a 50Ω system. Remember, the actual voltage is 10 times the value as read on the meter.

2.25 An RF millivolt probe

The RF diode probes previously described are limited to voltages in excess of about 1V as a result of the diode forward voltage drop. A method to extend measurements down to a few millivolts is to use the IC transistor array CA3046 which has a minimum gain-bandwidth product of 300MHz. The concept is to amplify the RF signal before detection.

The suggested arrangement is shown in Fig 2.25.1. The 14-pin DIL device

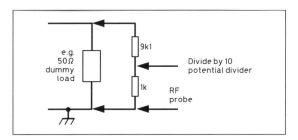

Fig 2.24.4. Suggested method for higher voltages

should be mounted in a small screened case with a probe for the RF input in the usual manner. Every effort should be made to keep stray capacitance to a minimum and no IC socket should be used. The input impedance should be about 50kΩ in parallel with 3pF. With the arrangement of two symmetrical DC darlington pairs the maximum offset voltage will be less than 1mV.

The working range will be from about 1mV to 4V and the device is intended as an add-on unit for a voltmeter. Calibration can be carried out in the several-volt region using one of the earlier electronic DC voltmeters. Useful measurements should be possible to frequencies in excess of 100MHz.

2.26 Temperature measurement

Fig 2.26.1 shows a circuit that measures temperature using a digital panel meter. The temperature sensor is an LM35DZ, a three-terminal device [2] which gives a linear output voltage of 10mV/°C over the range 0–100°C. The output at 100°C is therefore 10mV × 100 = 1000mV. This is too large for direct connection to the panel meter and so must be attenuated by a factor of 10 such that

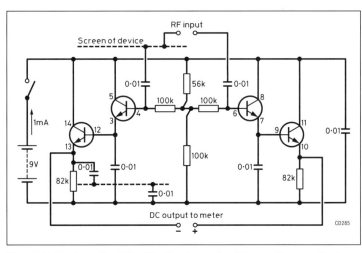

Fig 2.25.1. Peak-reading RF millivoltmeter probe. All capacitors are disc type. The numbers refer to pins on the CA3046 which is a 14-pin DIL device

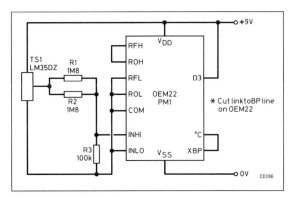

Fig 2.26.1. Circuit diagram of temperature meter

Table 2.26.1. Components list for temperature meter

PM1	Anders OEM22 panel meter	R1, 2	1M8, 0.6W, 1%
TS	LM35DZ	R3	100k, 0.6W, 1%

100mV input is equivalent to 100°C. This attenuator is formed by the resistors R1, R2 and R3. If the temperature sensor is mounted in a small tube and fed remotely it can be used for measuring temperature of components and heatsinks etc. The manufacturer quotes the sensor as having an accuracy of ±0.9°C typical. If a type LM35CZ is substituted it is quoted as having a range of −40 to 110°C.

2.27 Bar indicators

Another method of indicating the value of a parameter is the use of solid-state indicators. These consist of a row of LEDs which will illuminate when a certain value has been exceeded, the differing thresholds being set by the driver IC. The indicators can be separate LEDs or a bar indicator, which consists of a row of LEDs with possibly a common cathode or anode. The indicators come in a variety of forms and may consist of typically two, three, four, five, 10, 30 or 101 elements. They can run in two modes: the *dot mode* where a LED is illuminated indicating that value or *bar mode* where all LEDs below that value are also illuminated – this function is selectable on the driver IC. In the dot mode there is a slight overlap so that at no point are all LEDs extinguished.

There are three common driver ICs [3] for these displays, each controlling 10 LEDs. These ICs are:

- LM3914   Control in linear steps
- LM3915   Control in 3dB steps (logarithmic)
- LM3916   VU scale

As an example, a block diagram of the LM3914 is shown in Fig 2.27.1. The resistors R1 to R9 set the various threshold levels for the comparators that drive the LEDs. The input signal is buffered and then applied to the

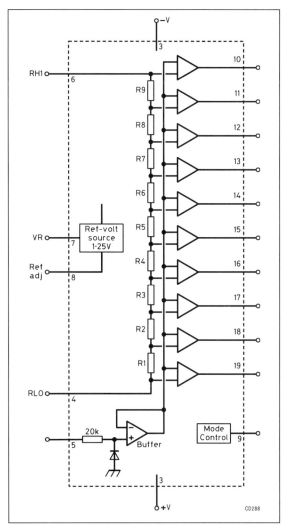

Fig 2.27.1. Typical bar graph driver integrated circuit

comparators. V− is normally ground (0V) and the maximum supply voltage V+ is 25V. The input signal is restricted to the range not less than V− and 1.5V below V+. Mode select gives either dot or bar displays.

The voltage reference source need not be used or it can be modified as shown in Fig 2.27.2. With VR being connected to RHI and REF ADJ being connected to 0V, along with RLO, then the reference voltage (1.25V) is divided along the R1 to R9 chain; in the linear model this represents increments of 125mV. If it is modified then the equation of Fig 2.27.2 holds, the current through R1 being given by R1/VR – it should lie between 80µA and 5mA. Note also that the current drawn out of the reference pin determines the LED current, it being about 10 times this current. This current should include both the current

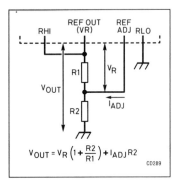

$$V_{OUT} = V_R \left(1 + \frac{R2}{R1}\right) + I_{ADJ} R2$$

CD289

Fig 2.27.2. Modifications to reference output

through R1 and R2 plus that through the divider chain. An external voltage can be used to set the divider reference, and it is suggested that the maximum voltage on the divider chain does not exceed V+, ie 1.8V. It is also advisable to keep this voltage below 12V. A method to compensate for this is to divide down the input signal so that the comparison is carried out at a lower voltage. In the bar mode, current consumption for the LEDs should be kept to a minimum because of total IC dissipation – keep the LED current to about 10mA. For further details see the IC data sheet.

2.28 5V level detector

This circuit (Fig 2.28.1) is suitable for monitoring signals in 0.5V steps up to 5V – it can cope with DC levels and slowly varying AC signals. The unit is in bar-mode display with pin 9 tied to +V, but for dot display it is

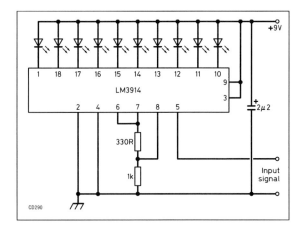

Fig 2.28.1. 0–5V level detector

open-circuit pin 9. The input signal is applied via pin 5 and ground. Precautions in using the circuit are adequate decoupling, keeping leads to the LEDs short and a common grounding point.

2.29 References

[1] *OEM22 Data Sheet*, Anders.
[2] *LM35DZ Data Sheet*, National Semiconductors.
[3] *RS Data Sheets 3835 and 7792 for LED driver ICs and bargraph modules*.

Chapter 3

The oscilloscope

3.1 General

The oscilloscope is a general-purpose instrument for examining electrical waveforms, but it can also be used for various sets of measurements, depending on how it has been set up. It is the intention of this chapter to explain how an oscilloscope works, how it can be used for taking measurements and the operation of the various controls. Its limitations are also discussed.

The cost of a new oscilloscope capable of displaying two waveforms and coping with frequencies up to about 20MHz is about £350 upwards. It may be possible to pick up a second-hand one or an obsolete model at a radio rally or surplus store for somewhat less than this. However, the cost does bear a close relationship to the performance – this will be understood better as one progresses through this chapter.

There is quite a lot to know about oscilloscopes: how they are used, the various facilities offered and their limitations. At first there seems to be a bewildering set of controls: they are all useful, although not all are needed in the first few steps. The oscilloscope allows measurements of voltage and time, and from these can also be determined waveform shape, phase and frequency. Further use of the oscilloscope in the amateur radio field is covered in the relevant chapters.

3.2 The basic oscilloscope

Fig 3.2.1 shows a photograph of a dual-trace oscilloscope. Fig 3.2.2 shows the absolute basics for an oscilloscope, which consists of a display (usually a cathode-ray tube) that depicts an electrical signal. These signals have been processed in some way (eg amplified) for them to be suitable for display. The oscilloscope also contains an oscillator (or *timebase*) which causes the display beam to traverse the display face in the horizontal plane.

In addition a power supply is required to provide the amplifier and timebase with low-voltage supplies and the tube with a high voltage (in the kilovolt region). The

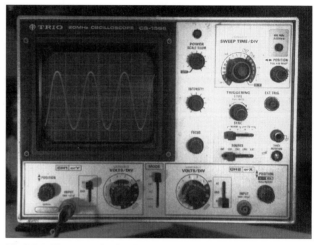

Fig 3.2.1. Photograph of a dual-trace oscilloscope

screen is split into two directions, the 'X' (or horizontal) and 'Y' (vertical direction).

Some oscilloscopes can display a single trace while others can display two traces or even more with adapters. The single-trace oscilloscope has a cathode-ray tube

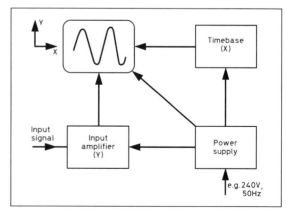

Fig 3.2.2. Basic block diagram of an oscilloscope

19

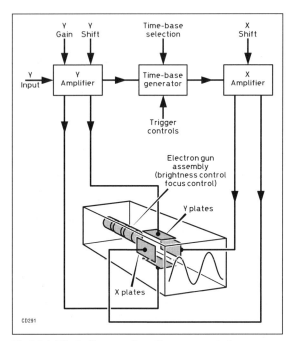

Fig 3.3.1. Block diagram of oscilloscope controls

with a single electron gun firing at the phosphor. The two-trace oscilloscopes fall into two categories – the *dual-trace* and the *dual-beam*. In the dual-trace oscilloscope there is a single electron gun but the control of it is split between the two traces to be shown, first one and then the other, but using the same timebase. In the dual-beam type there are two electron guns in the same cathode-ray tube which are independent of each other, and hence the two beams can have different timebase settings.

3.3   The oscilloscope block diagram

Fig 3.3.1 shows a fuller block diagram of an oscilloscope and the main controls available. The cathode-ray tube consists of an evacuated glass tube with the inner face coated with a phosphor. Electrons are produced by the electron gun and fire at the phosphor which glows when hit. The electron beam has to be made to move on the screen in sympathy with the signal to be displayed. The vertical (or Y) deflection is the amplitude of the signal being viewed and the horizontal (or X) movement is by a timebase oscillator which causes the beam to move across the screen and then to fly back to the start without leaving a trace on the screen (*blanking*).

The Y-signal (input) must be able to cope with a variety of inputs from DC to signals in the megahertz region. It must also be able to cope with various amplitudes from millivolts to tens of volts. In order to produce a display, signals of reasonably high voltage must be applied to the tube. For this reason the signal is amplified; in order to

take measurements the amplifier is calibrated and varied by a control on the oscilloscope calibrated in volts/division or millivolts/division – sometimes per centimetre. The measuring divisions are marked on a clear plastic sheet placed in front of the tube face and known as a *graticule*.

The horizontal axis is calibrated in time – seconds/division, milliseconds/division and microseconds/division. This then requires the timebase to be variable with an external control; there are two features associated with this. The timebase must always start at the same point of the waveform being examined on each trace (ie it is *triggered*) and at the end of the trace it must be *blanked* so that it can return to the start for the next display. Unless the display is continually refreshed it will just fade away.

In addition to these controls there will be brightness and focus, ie a nice sharp image is required.

3.4   Basic oscilloscope controls

This section goes through the typical controls on an oscilloscope and briefly describes their function.

Y-gain (voltage/div) – changes gain of vertical amplifier so that suitable size can be positioned on the screen.

Y-position – allows position of trace to be varied vertically in order to place trace at convenient point on the screen.

AC/DC/GND – coupling of input signal: DC allows signal plus any DC to be displayed, AC removes DC component from display, and GND allows input to be grounded internally in the oscilloscope in order to zero position the trace.

CH1/CH2/ALT/CHOP/ADD – selects the signal to be displayed: channels 1 or 2 separately, both channels on an alternate basis, both channels but chopping between them during a single scan or ADD where the signals are both added together (Note: Y2 often has an INVERT facility as well, which would then allow a subtract facility).

Timebase (time/div) – changes the speed at which the beam traverses the screen and thus affects the number of cycles of an input signal being displayed on it.

X-position – allows horizontal shift of the trace in order to put it in a convenient position for taking measurements.

X-magnification – normally allows a ×10 magnification if required, equivalent to a faster time on the timebase.

Trigger level – determines the trigger level of the input signal. This can be put to AUTO or set to a given level. The input signal triggers the timebase so that a stationary waveform appears on the screen.

Source – selects the source for the trigger circuit, ie internal, channel 1, channel 2, line (mains) or external.

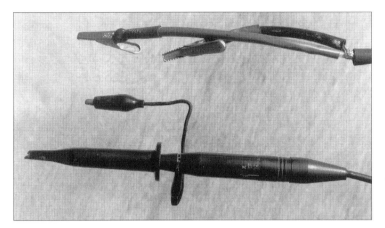

Fig 3.5.1. Photograph of oscilloscope probes

Focus – controls the focussing of the beam; adjust for a sharp image.

Intensity – controls the intensity of the image displayed on the screen.

Cal – an output for calibration purposes, usually at a frequency of 1kHz with a fixed amplitude, often 0.1V peak.

3.5 The oscilloscope probe

To connect an oscilloscope to a circuit under test, a lead with connections at one end and a plug for the oscilloscope at the other is required. Such leads are often referred to as *probe leads*.

Fig 3.5.1 is a photograph of two types of lead. The simplest is one which has the oscilloscope connector at one end (normally a BNC plug) and a pair of crocodile clips at the other; the cable is coaxial. One of the crocodile clips is connected to the centre, while the other is on a short length of flexible wire is connected to the braid. The braid connection is the normal earth, while the actual signal being examined is connected via the centre. These form a very basic probe but suffer from the fact that the crocodile clips are large, clumsy and often uninsulated. The input impedance is of the order of 1MΩ shunted by about 60pF or more due to the cable.

The better arrangement is the lead with a probe. This is usually plastic covered (ie insulated), has the choice of several attachments in order to form the best clip for connecting to the circuit and has a small earth lead with a miniature crocodile clip. It is connected via a coaxial cable to the BNC connector. The input impedance is about 1MΩ shunted by 40pF. A variant on this type is one which has a divide-by-10 arrangement which attenuates the input voltage by a factor of 10 and so allows a larger value to be measured and displayed on the screen. This arrangement also increases the input impedance to 10MΩ shunted

by about 15pF and hence decreases the loading on the circuit being measured.

3.6 Voltage measurements

Consider the oscilloscope screen display as depicted in Fig 3.6.1. This is obviously a sine wave but its voltage may be defined in different ways. The easiest voltage measurement to take is the *peak-to-peak value*. The vertical displacement (Y) is six divisions from peak to peak. One must then take into account the setting of the Y-controls: say these are at 0.5V/div. The peak-to-peak voltage is therefore $6 \times 0.5 = 3$V, the peak value is half of this, ie 1.5V, and the RMS value is $1/\sqrt{2}$ (or 0.7071) times this value, ie 1.06V.

Consider Fig 3.6.2. What is the magnitude of this waveform if the Y-gain is set to 2V/div? Note that for pulse-type waveforms it is usually the equivalent peak-to-peak amplitude that is quoted. The answer is 12V.

3.7 Frequency measurements

There are two possible methods that can be used here. The first method for making a frequency measurement is similar to that for voltage above, except that now the horizontal (X) axis is used with its setting. One problem with something like a sine wave is estimating a point on a curve. Measure from like point to like point, eg the two negative peaks in Fig 3.6.1. The distance between the two negative peaks is eight units. If the X or timebase setting is 0.5ms/div, then this represents a period of $8 \times 0.5 = 4$ms. The frequency is the reciprocal of this, ie 1/4ms or 250Hz.

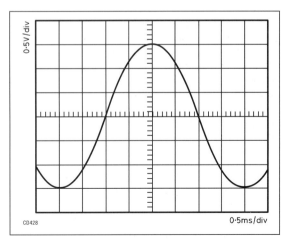

Fig 3.6.1. Typical sine wave

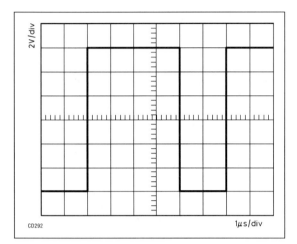

Fig 3.6.2. Typical pulse waveform

Repeat the exercise for Fig 3.6.2, assuming the timebase setting is 1μs/div (the answer is 166.667kHz).

It should be noted from this exercise that the period of a rectangular waveform is easier to estimate than that of a sine wave because of the well-defined edges.

Another parameter that can be easily measured for a pulse waveform is the *mark-to-space ratio*, ie the ratio of when it is high to when it is low. In the case shown it is a measure of the durations on the screen and is 4:2 (which is the same as 2:1).

The *duty cycle* can also be ascertained: this is the ratio of it being high (ie active) to the duration of the whole pulse. In this instance it is 4:6, ie 2:3 or, expressed as a percentage, 66.7%.

The second method, which is only valid for sine waves, requires the oscilloscope/equipment to be set up as shown in Fig 3.7.1. It will display what are known as *Lissajous figures*. The timebase should be switched off and an X-input arranged via one of the Y-inputs (usually Y2). The known source should be adjusted until a stationary pattern is obtained on the oscilloscope screen.

Fig 3.7.2(a) shows typical Lissajous figures for some common ratios.

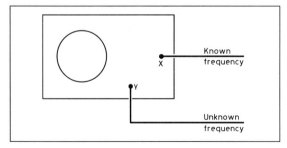

Fig 3.7.1. Second method of frequency determination

For the less-common ratios, see Fig 3.7.2(b). The number of loops in both horizontal (N_H) and vertical (N_V) planes should be counted. The unknown frequency can then be calculated by:

$$f_{unknown} = \frac{N_V}{N_H} \times f_{known}$$

Always regard the frequency measurement made on an oscilloscope as an approximate value – a frequency counter is much more accurate.

3.8 Phase measurement

There are two possible methods that can be used here. The first to be described allows both signals to be displayed simultaneously together with the associated phase shift. This method can cope with any shape of waveform, the upper frequency limit being dependent on the oscilloscope and any small phase shifts introduced between the two input channel amplifiers. The two signals to be examined are applied to the two input channels, Y1 and Y2. Try to adjust gains so that the waveforms are approximately equal (Fig 3.8.1 shows a typical display) and for most accurate results have the input selection set to CHOP. The phase shift can then be calculated. Remembering that one cycle is equivalent to 360°, then the phase shift (in degrees) is given by:

$$\frac{B}{A} \times 360°$$

The second method is most suitable for the audio frequency range or just above, and assumes a sine-wave input. The method relies on one signal being applied to the X-input – see Fig 3.8.2.

To start with, connect both inputs (X and Y) to the same input signal, and adjust the signal level so that a suitably sized display is obtained and there is a straight line at approximately 45°. Then connect the output signal of the

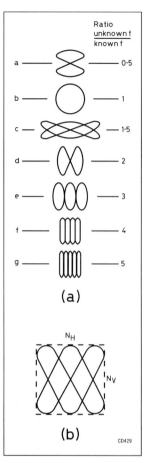

Fig 3.7.2. Lissajous patterns: (a) known ratios; (b) unknown

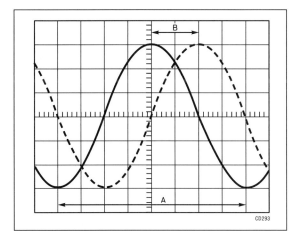

Fig 3.8.1. Phase measurements

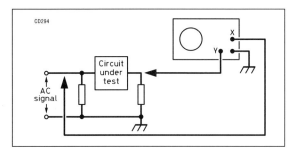

Fig 3.8.2. Second method for phase measurement

circuit under test to the Y1-input and various displays may be obtained as shown in Fig 3.8.3. This figure shows how the resulting waveform can be interpreted and how the phase angle can be obtained.

3.9 Differential voltage measurements

Occasionally one may have to make a voltage measurement between two points in a circuit, neither of which is grounded, for example the voltage V_{AB} in Fig 3.9.1. This can be accomplished in two ways. The first is to measure A with respect to ground and then B with respect to ground. The difference between these two values is equal to V_{AB}. This is satisfactory for DC and if any AC waveforms at A and B are identical in shape. It is also the only method available for a single-trace oscilloscope.

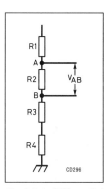

Fig 3.9.1. Differential voltage measurement

The second method is applicable for both dual-trace and dual-beam oscilloscopes. There will be controls on the oscilloscope that will allow display of Y1 + Y2 and Y1 − Y2. In the latter case one must use the INVERT control on channel Y2 and then the ADD facility – this will then give Y1 − Y2. Make sure that the gain settings on both Y1 and Y2 are the same, the Y1 − Y2 display is set up and, for the dual-beam oscilloscope only, both timebases are set identically. Put one probe (Y1) on A and the other (Y2) on B – the display will then show V_{AB}. The magnitude and time readings are then as described earlier.

3.10 Equipment limitations

The oscilloscope, although the most general-purpose tool available for electronic work, is not perfect and has limitations. These are especially true in the radio field with the higher frequencies involved.

The Y-amplifiers (plus the tube) limit the frequency response of the oscilloscope. This means that after a certain point the oscilloscope calibration is not valid, although comparative measurements can still be made above this point providing the frequency is not changed. Above about 30MHz the cost of oscilloscopes rises quite sharply – don't buy a 20MHz oscilloscope and expect to examine a 144MHz waveform! Another problem that should

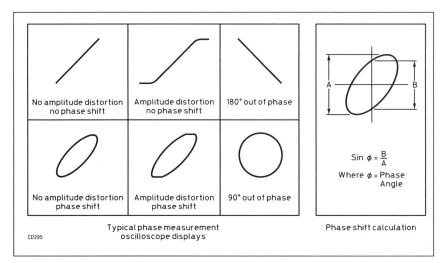

No amplitude distortion no phase shift

Amplitude distortion no phase shift

180° out of phase

No amplitude distortion phase shift

Amplitude distortion phase shift

90° out of phase

Typical phase measurement oscilloscope displays

$\sin \phi = \dfrac{B}{A}$

Where ϕ = Phase Angle

Phase shift calculation

Fig 3.8.3. Phase-shift measurements

be considered is that of the display of rectangular wave-forms, which consist of a series of harmonics in fixed ratios. The higher harmonics will exceed the oscillo-scope's bandwidth, and the effect is that the displayed waveforms will progressively become rounded as their frequency rises, eventually tending to a sine wave.

The capacitance of the oscilloscope and/or its probe may affect the circuit under test if the capacitance in the circuit is of the same order as the oscilloscope input (20–40pF), eg a tuned circuit. The effect on a rectangular pulse is that the capacitance may try to round the waveform slightly.

The input voltage specification of an oscilloscope is normally quoted as x volts DC plus peak AC. Typical of these figures are 400V DC plus the peak AC signal that can be displayed. Exceeding this will damage internal components of the oscilloscope. Although a divide-by-10 probe can be used (see Section 3.5) to extend the volt-age range, such probes have a voltage limit (typically 600V DC) and may have to be derated as frequency rises – check the specification.

For most semiconductor applications the voltage limit never causes a problem, but with high-voltage valve cir-cuits one must pay due regard to the limitations.

Chapter 4

Frequency measurements

4.1 General

The measurement of frequency is of prime importance to the radio amateur in order to ensure that transmission occurs only within the authorised bands and hence complies with the licence conditions.

Although synthesisers are becoming the vogue in radio equipment, there are still a large number of transmitters with variable-frequency LC oscillators. With synthesisers the digital display is usually driven by the binary digits that set up the division ratios and not the actual frequency produced. It is therefore imperative that high-accuracy frequency measurements can be made – to a higher accuracy than any other measurement the radio amateur has to make.

In making the measurements, the problem is *how accurate is the test equipment*? In this section it is all based on crystal oscillators and so will be reasonably accurate but, as in other walks of life, nothing is perfect. Crystal oscillators will show signs of changing in frequency with varying temperatures, ageing and power supply variations. The last of these is easy to accommodate, the first could be cured by the use of crystal ovens (with increased building costs and power consumption) but the ageing is more of a problem. Is it at all possible to test the test equipment against any standard signal source? The answer to this is "yes".

The use of a standard frequency to check another frequency is almost invariably carried out by observing the frequency difference between two signals, adjusting this to be in the audio range and reducing this beat frequency to as close to zero as possible. This can either be accomplished using a meter or aurally.

4.2 Standard frequency services

There are various standard frequencies transmitted throughout the world and these can be harnessed in order to check other equipment against them. Typical of these transmissions are shown in Table 4.2.1 [1, 2].

These standard frequencies are maintained to an accuracy of typically one part in 10^{11}. However, if the

Table 4.2.1. Standard frequency services

CHU	Canada	3330, 7335, 14,670kHz
FFH	France	2500kHz
IBF	Italy	5000kHz
JJY	Japan	2500, 5000, 10,000, 15,000kHz
MSF	UK	60kHz
LOL2	Argentina	5000, 10,000, 15,000kHz
RWM	Russia	4996, 9996, 14,996kHz
VNG	Australia	4500, 7500, 12,000kHz
WWV	USA	2500, 5000, 10,000, 15,000, 20,000, 25,000kHz
WWVB	USA	60kHz
WWVH	USA	2500, 5000, 10,000, 15,000, 20,000, 25,000kHz

sky-wave is used, there could be a large error in reception due to Doppler shift and fading of the signal. These problems can be avoided by using a low-frequency transmission such as those from MSF or WWVB. Timing information is also impressed on the signals in either GMT or UTC.

In addition, in the UK the BBC maintains the accuracy of the Droitwich 198kHz (formerly 200kHz) carrier to high accuracy – 1 part in 10^{11}.

4.3 A 198kHz frequency calibrator

4.3.1 Introduction

The circuit described in this section will produce an accurate 1MHz output plus outputs at 10kHz, 12.5kHz, 25kHz and 100kHz. In addition there is a 1kHz sinewave output. In the event of failure of the received 198kHz carrier the circuit will automatically switch over to an internal reference. The design uses principles from reference [3].

Fig 4.3.1 shows the block diagram of the unit. The 198kHz carrier is divided by 396 to give a 500Hz output and the internal 1MHz VCO is divided by 2000 to give 500Hz. These two signals are then compared in a phase comparator. The resulting 'locked' 1MHz signal is divided by various ratios to give the different outputs. On cessation of the received 198kHz carrier, the internal 1MHz crystal oscillator takes over as the reference.

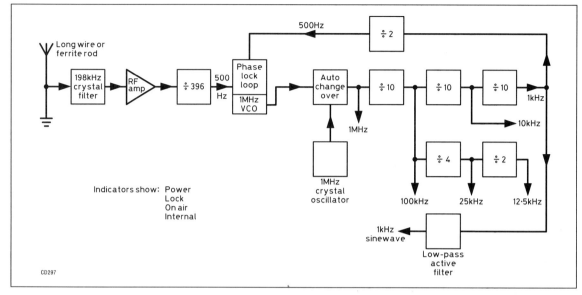

Fig 4.3.1. Block diagram of frequency calibrator locked to Droitwich (198kHz)

4.3.2   Circuit description

The circuit diagram is shown in Fig 4.3.2. The incoming 198kHz signal from the antenna (ferrite rod or long wire) has its sidebands stripped off by the narrow-band filter XL1. The resulting signal is then amplified by IC1 and IC2, IC2b acting as a voltage comparator with hysteresis which gives a square-wave output. The resulting signal is then divided by a dual BCD counter (IC3) which is reset on the 99th pulse. Part of IC4 detects this condition, while the remainder ensures synchronous operation between the two independent BCD counters of IC4. The signal is then divided by four in IC5 to produce a square wave at 500Hz for the phase-lock loop IC6. The phase-lock loop also has a free-running 1MHz voltage-controlled oscillator which is divided by 2000 (IC9 and IC10) to produce a 500Hz signal for the phase comparator. The two 500Hz signals are compared in IC6, the resulting 1MHz VCO output being locked to the 198kHz Droitwich signal. IC9, IC10 and IC11 also divide the 1MHz signal to give the additional outputs at 10kHz, 12.5kHz, 25kHz and 100kHz.

A crystal-controlled oscillator is formed by XL2 and IC8a. IC8b/c act as a detector as to which output is used, the 1MHz output chosen being via IC8d. A 1kHz rectangular-wave output from IC10 is filtered by the active low-pass filter IC12a, the resulting output being buffered by IC12b and producing a 1kHz approximate sine wave. D2, C9 and R15 provide a DC output to drive a meter M1 to give an indication of relative received signal strength. D1, R14 and C8 provide a DC output to indicate presence of the 198kHz carrier.

4.3.3   Construction

It is possible to use either a long wire antenna or a ferrite rod antenna. C1 and VC1 can be omitted for the long wire. If a ferrite rod antenna is used this should be the type with a long-wave coil. The value of this coil is normally about 4mH but can vary according to supplier. VC1 should be fitted but it may be necessary to provide a capacitor C1 in order to achieve a resonant circuit. IC sockets should *not* be used for IC1 and IC2. The case of XL1 should be connected to ground.

The unit requires 12V DC at about 100mA. The whole circuit should be enclosed in a metal box with well-decoupled power supply lines. The circuit should stand off any conducting plane by about 25mm (1in). A PCB and component layout are given in Appendix 2.

4.3.4   Alignment

On receipt of a signal at 198kHz (the ON AIR and LOCK indicators should be illuminated), tune VC1 and VC2 for maximum steady meter indication – this must be carried out with less than full-scale deflection.

To set the internal crystal oscillator, use a calibrated frequency counter as follows. Temporarily stop reception of the 198kHz signal and the LED indicator should show INTERNAL. Switch S1 to 1MHz and adjust VC3 to get the frequency as close as possible to 1.000000MHz. The standard is now set up.

4.3.5   In use

Adjust the position of the calibrator/antenna for maximum received signal strength. *Observe the indicators:*

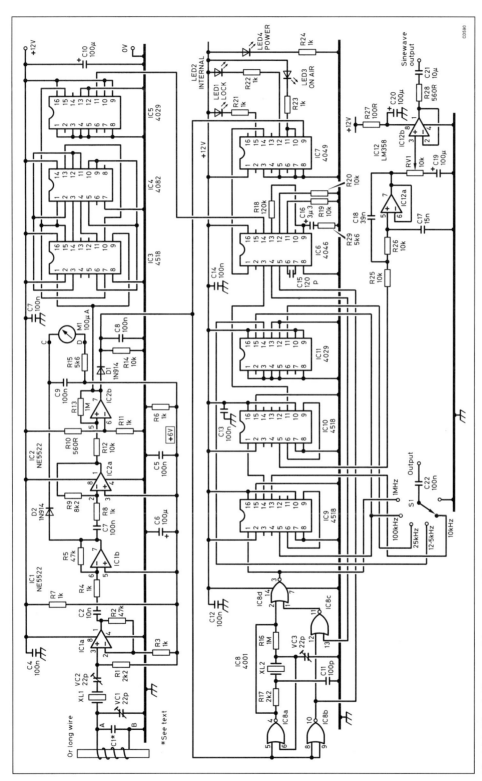

Fig 4.3.2. Circuit diagram of frequency calibrator

Table 4.3.1. Components list for the 198kHz frequency standard

R1, 17	2k2	C11	100p polystyrene
R2, 5	47k	C15	120p polystyrene
R3, 4, 6,		C16	3μ3, 25V tantalum
7, 8, 11,		C17	15n polyester
21–24	1k	C18	39n polyester
R9	8k2	C21	10μ, 50V non-elec
R10, 28	560R	VC1–3	22p trimmer
R12, 14,		D1, 2	1N914 or similar
19, 20,		LED 1,3	Red
25, 26	10k	LED2	Yellow
R13, 16	1M	LED4	Green
R15	5k6	IC1, 2	NE5532
R18	120k	IC3, 9, 10	4518
R27	100R	IC4	4082
R29	5k6	IC5, 11	4029
RV1	10k pot	IC6	4046
C1	See text	IC7	4049
C2, 3	10n, 50V	IC8	4001
	ceramic	IC12	LM358
C4, 5, 7,		XL1	198kHz crystal filter
8, 22	100n, 50V	XL2	1MHz crystal
	ceramic	Antenna	See text
C6, 10,		M1	Meter, 100μA FSD
19, 20	100μ, 25V elec	S1	1-pole, 12-way or 2-
C9, 12–14	100n ceramic		pole, 6-way

All resistors are 0.25W, 5% unless specified otherwise.

the green LED should be illuminated to show power applied. If receiving 'off-air', two red LEDs will be lit continuously. If any sign of a flicker is occurring, this indicates occasional going 'out of lock' – the received signal is inadequate. If the yellow LED illuminates, then the calibrator is running on the internal reference.

The various outputs are available for calibrating other test gear.

4.4   Digital frequency counters

This type of frequency meter utilises integrated circuits to count electronically the number of cycles of an input waveform in a given counting period. Although these digital integrated circuits are themselves complex, the principle of operation of the digital frequency meter (DFM) is quite simple: it consists of five major circuits, *the input wave-shaping circuit, clock, gate, counter* and *display*. Fig 4.4.1 shows a basic block diagram of a DFM.

The input wave-shaping circuit takes the input waveform, amplifies it and converts it to a rectangular waveform of sufficient magnitude to operate the counting circuits.

The clock produces a series of pulses which determine the basic counting period of the DFM. The pulses are typically 10ms, 100ms or 1s long and derived from a crystal-controlled oscillator (typically 1MHz or 5MHz). The pulses are thus of high accuracy and applied to the gate which can be considered as an on/off switch operated by the clock.

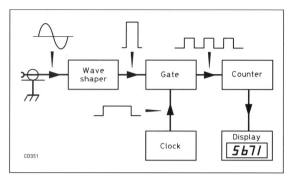

Fig 4.4.1. Simplified block diagram of digital frequency meter

When the clock pulse opens the gate, an input train of pulses from the wave-shaping circuit is sent to the counting circuits. The counting circuits count the number of input pulses for the duration that the gate is open, then this count is frozen and the binary count decoded and used to drive decade displays.

The accuracy of a DFM depends on the accuracy of the clock signal. Accuracy can be increased if the clock oscillator is housed in a crystal oven (thermostatically controlled) and compared with a standard frequency source for calibration. The resolution of a DFM is the smallest digit a display exhibits, usually 1Hz. The resolution will change according to the frequency range in operation and the length of the clock signal.

The DFM can also be made to display the period of an input waveform. In this case one period of the input allows the number of standard pulses to be counted (eg 1μs or 1ms). The number counted in one period is then the time for a period.

4.5   Prescaling

To increase the frequency range of a DFM, it is common to put components that perform *prescaling* ahead of the input – Fig 4.5.1. These components consist of an amplifier, wave-shaping circuit and high-speed frequency divider (the *prescaler*). Prescaling will divide the input frequency by a known amount (eg 2, 10, 64 or 100), and the resulting signal is then applied to the basic frequency counter. It should be borne in mind that prescaling reduces the resolution of the counted frequency. For example, a frequency counter without prescaling may measure

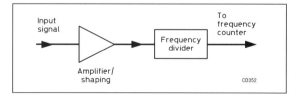

Fig 4.5.1. Prescaling

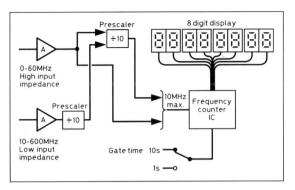

Fig 4.6.1. Block diagram of frequency counter

to 1Hz but, if prescaling of 10 is introduced, then the same counter will only read to 10Hz.

The counter following has prescaling which extends its limit up to 600MHz; for prescalers and amplifiers to extend the frequency range above this the reader is referred to reference [4].

4.6   A 600MHz digital frequency counter

4.6.1   Introduction

This frequency counter is capable of operating up to about 600MHz with a sensitivity of 50mV or better. It is based on an eight-digit frequency counter IC which will count to 10MHz. The range is increased by the use of prescalers which divide the incoming frequency down to the 10MHz range. Fig 4.6.1 shows a block diagram of the system. It offers three input ranges, 0–6MHz (typically 10MHz),

0–60MHz and 10–600MHz. It is possible to build a 0–60MHz counter and then add the additional components later to increase the capability to about 600MHz.

The *gate time*, ie the count period, can be switched between 1s and 10s. At the 1s position the counter offers a seven-digit display, while at the 10s position it provides an eight-digit display. The decimal point is switched to denote the megahertz position, all digits to the left of it representing megahertz. The supply requirement is 5V at approximately 300mA.

References [5], [6] and [7] provided the basic information for the design; for extension in frequency ranges and sensitivity the reader is referred to reference [4].

4.6.2   Input circuit up to 60MHz

The circuit diagram is shown in Fig 4.6.2. The input impedance is approximately 1MΩ, with junction FET TR1 acting as a buffer. The signal is then fed to IC3 which contains a group of transistors capable of operation up to 1GHz. This provides amplification and an output capable of driving logic circuits. The output transistor TR2 is a high-speed PNP switch which translates the ECL output logic level of IC3 to a TTL-compatible level.

4.6.3   Input circuit 10–600MHz

This circuit is shown in Fig 4.6.3 and has an input impedance of approximately 50Ω. IC1 is a monolithic amplifier with 50Ω input and output impedances, and operates up to 1GHz with a gain of some 16dB. The resulting output is fed to IC2 which is a high-speed divide-by-10 counter capable of operating up to at least 575MHz with

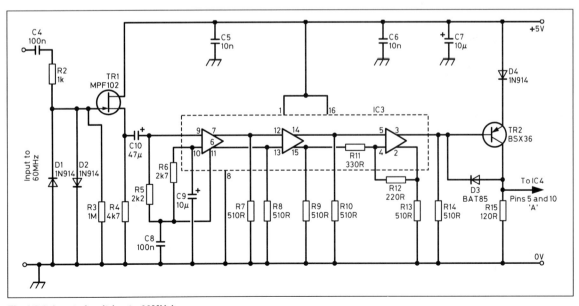

Fig 4.6.2. Input circuit (up to 60MHz)

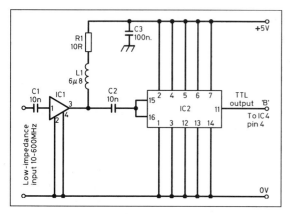

Fig 4.6.3. Input circuit (10–600MHz)

a sine-wave input. The output selected is TTL compatible. The circuit will operate without IC1 but of course is not as sensitive. Although a Mini-circuits monolithic

broad-band amplifier is used, it is possible to use those from other manufacturers such as Avantek.

4.6.4   Control, counter and display circuit

Fig 4.6.4 shows all of the remaining digital side of the frequency counter and displays. The initial stages of the frequency counter consists of the input selection and prescaling circuits.

IC4 and IC5 are both 74F fast TTL in order to cope with the speed. IC4 is a multiplexer which is controlled by DC signals supplied via S1a and determines the route of signals from the input amplifiers to the counter IC. IC5 is a divide-by-10 circuit which provides prescaling for all signals above 10MHz. IC6 is the heart of the digital frequency meter and provides all the count circuits, decoders and drivers for the eight-digit LED display. Timing is derived from a 10MHz crystal oscillator.

Switches S1b/c determine the position of the decimal point in conjunction with the gate time selection switch

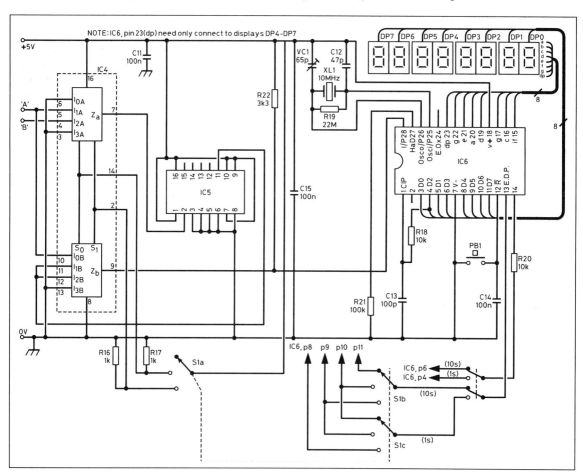

Fig 4.6.4. Control, counter and display circuit

Table 4.6.1. Components list for the 600MHz digital frequency counter

R1	10R	C13	100p polystyrene/
R2, 16, 17	1k		ceramic
R3	1M	VC1	65p trimmer
R4	4k7	XL1	10MHz crystal
R5	2k2	D1, 2, 4	1N914, 1N4148
R6	2k7	D3	BAT85
R7–10,		TR1	MPF102
13, 14	510R	TR2	BSX36, 2N5771,
R11	330R		fast PNP switch
R12	220R	LD0–7	Double 7-segment
R15	120R		LED display (4 off),
R18, 20	10k		common cathode,
R19	22M		0.5in
R21	100k	IC1	MAR-1
R22	3k3	IC2	SP8680B
C1, 2, 5,		IC3	MC10116
6	10n ceramic disc	IC4	74F153
C3, 4, 8,		IC5	74F160
11, 14,		IC6	ICM7216D
15	100n ceramic disc	L1	6µ8 RF inductor
C7, 9	10µ, 16V tant	PB1	Pushbutton switch
C10	47µ, 6V tant	S1	4-pole, 3-way rotary
C12	47p polystyrene/	S2	DPDT toggle, PCB
	ceramic		mounting

All resistors are 0.25W, 5% unless specified otherwise.

(S2) for the various inputs. PB1 is a reset button for the counter.

4.6.5 Construction

A double-sided PCB and component layout is provided in Appendix 2. If the reader wishes to make his or her own board, it is essential that an earth plane is provided on the copper side for the two input circuits in Figs 4.6.2 and 4.6.3. It is wise to use good layout practice for the digital circuits, especially where they can run up to 100MHz. Adequate decoupling is also essential.

Do not use IC sockets for IC1, IC2, IC3, IC4 and IC5. The dual LED displays should be mounted on single-row sockets. The PCB is double sided and through connections are made mainly via component leads, including IC sockets. The sockets may therefore have to stand off the board slightly in order to solder on the top side. It is suggested that turned-pin sockets are used. There are three through connections to be made with wire links.

Where necessary, clearance must be made around holes on the earth plane where connection is not made to the earth plane – use a sharp drill or cutter for this.

If a counter is only required up to 10MHz then the output of the circuit of Fig 4.6.2 can be fed straight to pin 28 of IC6, omitting IC4 and IC5 and the range switch S2. If an input is required only up to 60MHz then omit the components associated with the 600MHz input amplifier and alter the stop on S1 for only two positions.

4.6.6   Calibration

Using a highly accurate frequency counter which is calibrated against a standard, feed the same input signal into both counters and adjust VC1 for the same reading. Alternatively the frequency standard of Section 4.3 could be used.

4.7   The heterodyne frequency meter

The measurement of frequency was more difficult before frequency counters were readily available, and the heterodyne frequency meter represented one solution. This provides crystal-controlled frequency markers with a calibrated VFO (or receiver) to interpolate between them plus a means of mixing the unknown frequency with the VFO to produce an audible output. A well-known instrument of this type which was abundant on the surplus market was the American-made BC221; these may occasionally still be found at radio rallies.

4.8   References

[1] *Radio Data Reference Book*, G R Jessop, G6JP, and R S Hewes, G3TDR, 5th edn, RSGB, 1985.

[2] *ARRL Handbook for the Radio Amateur*, ARRL, 1988 onwards.

[3] 'A Droitwich-locked frequency reference', N Belham, G2BKO, *Radio Communication* June 1984.

[4] *Microwave Handbook*, Vol 2, ed M W Dixon, G3PFR, RSGB, 1991.

[5] 'A frequency counter for a 144MHz transmitter', N B Pritchard, *Radio Communication* May 1979.

[6] *Data Sheet for ICM7216A/B/D*, Harris Semiconductors.

[7] *Data Sheet for 8680B*, Plessey Semiconductors.

Chapter 5

Wavemeters and analysers

5.1 Introduction

This chapter covers equipment which is suitable for making measurements on circuit elements, oscillators and transmitter outputs, and which falls into three groups as explained below.

Absorption wavemeters usually require no DC supply. They function by absorbing energy from a circuit close by and using this energy to drive some form of indicator such as a moving-coil meter.

The *dip oscillator* contains active circuits and requires a DC power supply. The oscillator contained within energises an adjacent circuit, and when energy is absorbed by this circuit it is indicated by a dip in a meter reading.

Both of the above circuits are unlikely to have an accuracy of better than 5–10% and so cannot be used to check for operation near band edges. However, they are very useful for:

(a) checking tuning of resonant circuits;
(b) giving an indication of whether a transmitter has an output or that an oscillator is oscillating;
(c) giving an indication of harmonic generation; and
(d) use as a relative field strength meter. The indications given are not absolute but relative, ie the indicator is not calibrated.

The *spectrum analyser* is a much more sophisticated instrument compared to the above. It is capable of analysing a waveform, showing the frequency components present and the actual levels referenced, for example, to the carrier.

5.2 A simple absorption wavemeter for 65–230MHz

The absorption wavemeter shown in Fig 5.2.1 is an easily built unit covering 65–230MHz. (For a lower-range unit, the dip oscillator described in the following section can be used.)

Construction is straightforward and all the components, apart from the meter, are mounted on a Perspex plate of thickness 3 or 4mm and measuring 190×75mm. Details of the tuned circuit are shown in Fig 5.2.2(a) and should

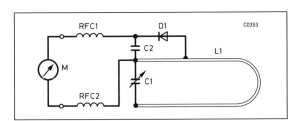

Fig 5.2.1. Circuit diagram of simple absorption wavemeter for 65–230MHz

be closely followed. The layout of the other components is not critical provided they are kept away from the inductor.

For accurate calibration a signal generator is required but, provided the inductance loop is carefully constructed and the knob and scale are non-metallic, the dial markings can be determined from Fig 5.2.2(b).

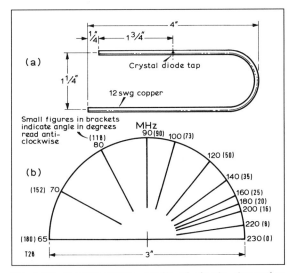

Fig 5.2.2. Constructional details of simple absorption wavemeter showing (a) inductor L1 and (b) dial plate. Metric equivalents are: ¼in = 6.3mm, 1¼in = 31.8mm, 1¾in = 44.5mm, 3in = 76.2mm and 4in = 101.6mm.

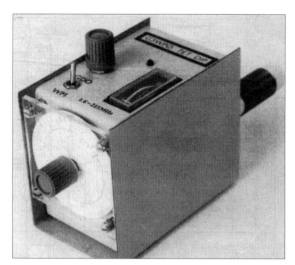

Fig 5.3.1. Photograph of G3WPO Mk2 FET dip oscillator

Table 5.3.1. Components list for the FET dip oscillator

R1	10k	C1	Toko Polyvaricon, 2×266p
R2, 7	39k	C2, 3,	
R3, 5	56k	8, 9	10n, 50V ceramic
R4, 6,		C4, 5	12p, 5%, ceramic disc
18, 19	100k	C6, 7	10p, 5%, ceramic disc
R8	220R	C10, 11	10n mylar
R9	2k2	D1	3mm red LED
R10, 11	47R	ZD1	5V6, 400mW zener
R12, 21	1k5	TR1, 2	3SK88
R13	3k3	TR3–5	BC238 or similar NPN
R14	470R	L1	See text for details
R15, 16	33k	L2, 3	470µH, eg Toko type 7BS
R22	1k	M1	200µA meter
VR1	470R, vertical	S2	Single-pole switch
	mount preset	PR1	Piezo-resonator, eg Toko
RV1/S1	100k lin with		PB2720
	on/off switch		

Shaft coupler, 6:1 slow motion drive
Wire, 0.2mm diameter enamelled copper
Nuts and bolts, various
Six 5-pin DIN plugs and sockets – see text
PP3 battery connector

All resistors are 0.25W, 5% unless specified otherwise.

In operation the unit should be loosely coupled to the circuit under test and the capacitor tuned until the meter indicates resonance (a maximum). A more sensitive meter should be used (eg 50µA or 100µA) for low-power oscillators etc. The wavemeter can also be used as a field-strength indicator when making adjustments to VHF antennas. A single-turn coil should be loosely coupled to the wavemeter loop and connected via a low-impedance feeder to a dipole directed towards the antenna under test.

5.3 FET dip oscillator

The original version of this appeared in *Radio Communication* in November 1981, but the revised Mk2 version which is described here (Fig 5.3.1) is from 1987 [1]. The specification is:

- Dip and wavemeter function
- Coverage of 0.8–170MHz
- Audio and meter indications
- Battery operation

5.3.1 Circuit description

The circuit diagram is given in Fig 5.3.2. The instrument is based on a Kalitron oscillator which is formed by the two MOSFETs TR1 and TR2. The frequency determining components are C1 and L1 (the plug-in coil). Resistor Rs is included as part of the plug-in coil and is a gain-setting resistor. The RF from the oscillator is detected by D2 and D3 which are Schottky barrier diodes with a good frequency response and lower forward voltage drop compared with devices such as the ubiquitous 1N914. The detected DC is applied to the base of amplifier TR5 which controls the current flowing through the meter M and the audio multivibrator formed by TR3 and TR4. The

frequency of the multivibrator is determined by C11/R19 and C10/R18.

As the current through TR5 increases, the note from the piezo-resonator increases, as does the meter reading. The meter and audio levels are set by the sensitivity control RV1. The multivibrator commences oscillation at about mid-scale on the meter and has a readily detectable note which drops sharply as resonance of the RF circuit is reached.

In use as an absorption wavemeter, S2 removes the voltage supply to the oscillator. The received signal is then rectified by D2 and D3 and applied to the meter drive/audio circuits which are still powered. There is an increase in meter reading and audio frequency as resonance is reached.

The circuit runs from a 9V supply (eg PP3 battery) with R8 acting as a current-limiting resistor. Current consumption between bands varies and is between 5 and 15mA. LED D1 acts as a reminder of the equipment being switched on.

5.3.2 Construction

The case and mechanical details are given in Fig 5.3.3 and Fig 5.3.4 gives the details for the dial plate, dial cursor and scale. The wiring details are given in Fig 5.3.5.

A commercial kit is available for this equipment but a PCB and component layout are given in Appendix 2.

5.3.3 Coil construction

These consist of five-pin DIN plugs fitted into rigid electrical plastic conduit which acts as a coil former. Details

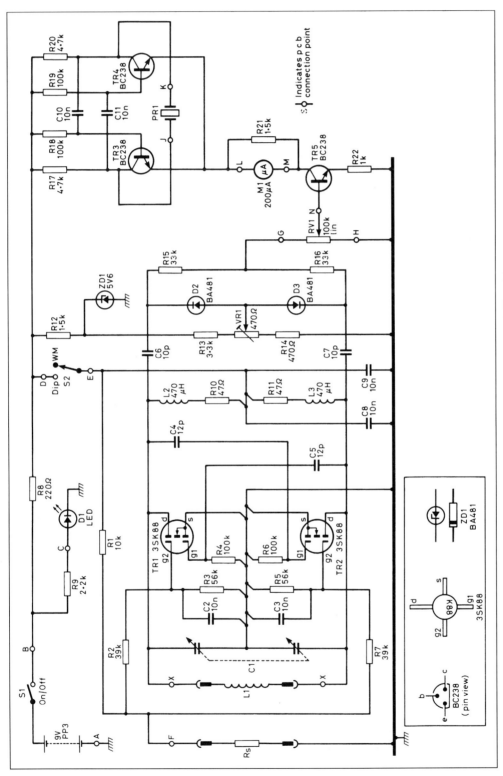

Fig 5.3.2. Circuit diagram of FET dip oscillator. The plug-in coil details for R_s and L1 are given in Fig 5.3.6

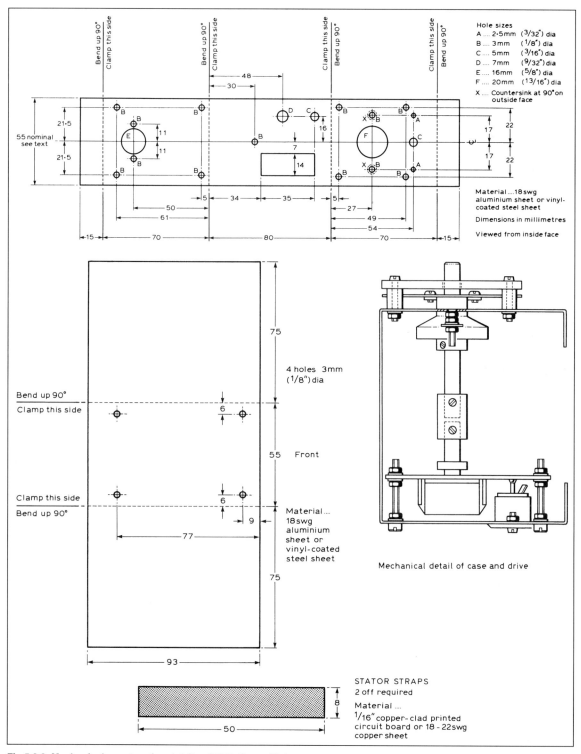

Hole sizes
A .... 2·5mm (3/32") dia
B .... 3mm (1/8") dia
C .... 5mm (3/16") dia
D .... 7mm (9/32") dia
E .... 16mm (5/8") dia
F .... 20mm (13/16") dia
X .... Countersink at 90°on outside face

Material....18swg aluminium sheet or vinyl-coated steel sheet

Dimensions in millimetres

Viewed from inside face

4 holes 3mm (1/8") dia

Front

Material....
18swg aluminium sheet or vinyl-coated steel sheet

Mechanical detail of case and drive

STATOR STRAPS
2 off required

Material ....
1/16" copper-clad printed circuit board or 18 - 22swg copper sheet

Fig 5.3.3. Mechanical construction details of FET dip oscillator

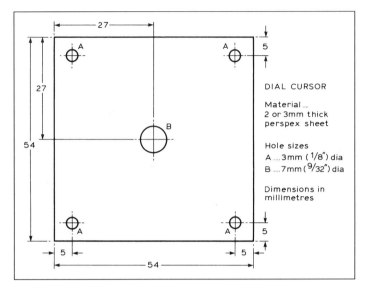

Fig 5.3.4(a). Dial cursor for FET dip oscillator

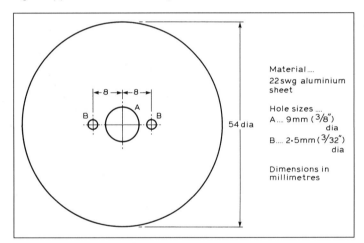

Fig 5.3.4(b). Dial plate for FET dip oscillator

of the coils are given in Fig 5.3.6. Only the actual plug end is used and it is glued into the plastic tube. The lowest four range coils are wound directly onto the formers, while the two highest ranges are wound within the former which then acts as a protective plastic shroud.

5.4   A VHF dip oscillator

This dip oscillator [2] covers the band 29–460MHz in four overlapping ranges with plug-in coils. The ranges are:

Range A 29–55MHz	Range C 97–220MHz
Range B 50–109MHz	Range D 190–460MHz

The circuit is given in Fig 5.4.1 and photos in Fig 5.4.2.

5.4.1   Circuit description

The circuit is based around a Kalitron oscillator formed by two junction-type FETs TR1 and TR2.

The frequency-determining components are the split-stator capacitor C1 and the plug-in coil L1.

The resulting RF signal is then detected by a balanced diode detector D1 and D2, and used to drive meter amplifier TR3. The original design used either a 2N5245 or a TIS88 for TR1 and TR2 but it should be possible to substitute a BF256A or similar N-channel junction FET.

The power can be turned off to convert the instrument to a sensitive absorption wavemeter, and when headphones are plugged into the jack J1 it becomes a modulation monitor.

In this design the existence of spurious dips and 'suck-outs' in the various ranges is very much associated with the quality of the two RF chokes L2 and L3. These are each of 15μH.

If troubles of this kind are experienced other inductors can be tried. It is very difficult to find components with no strong resonance over the whole of a wide band but the prototype instrument, using the inductors with the two series-damping resistors R4 and R5, nevertheless seemed to minimise the problem.

5.4.2   Power supply

This is normally provided by a PP3 battery, the current drain being about 10mA (including the LED). The PP3 replacement mains supply as described in Chapter 12 could be substituted.

5.4.3   Construction

Construction can either be on tag strip (Fig 5.4.3) or using a PCB as given in Appendix 2. The most important points are to keep the leads to the tuning capacitor as short as possible, using copper strip to keep the inductance low. Also, keep all other RF leads short, especially any that are associated with the sources of TR1 and TR2.

The original version, as shown in the photographs, was constructed in an aluminium box forming about a 50mm (2in) cube and a design for making this is given in Fig 5.4.4. Following this construction is, however, a matter of personal choice.

The tuning capacitor C1 with a tuning scale drum is driven by a 6:1 reduction drive. A home-made 22mm

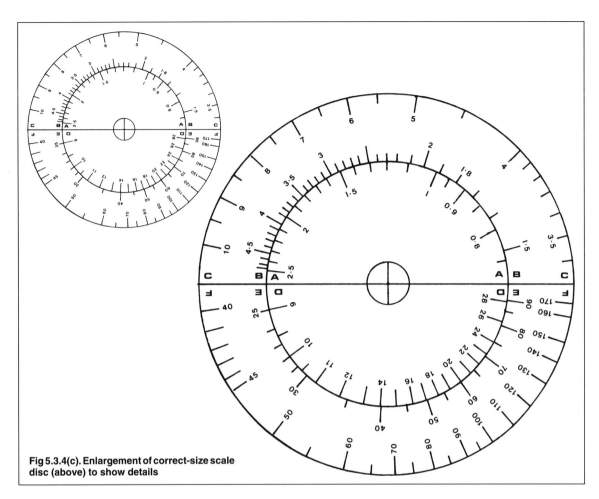

Fig 5.3.4(c). Enlargement of correct-size scale disc (above) to show details

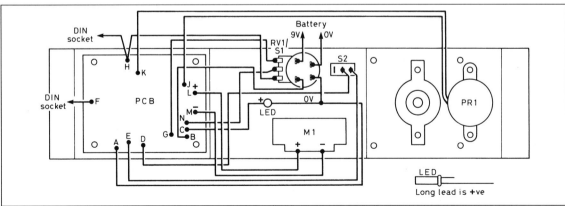

Fig 5.3.5. Wiring diagram for G3WPO Mk2 dip oscillator

(0.875in) wide card or plastic scale is fitted to the drum.

The coil socket and the coil mounting strips are made from 3mm (0.125in) thick PTFE sheet, although polythene or even polystyrene is acceptable (Fig 5.4.4). Two Belling-Lee 4mm sockets (similar to O-Z pattern) are mounted on the socket strip.

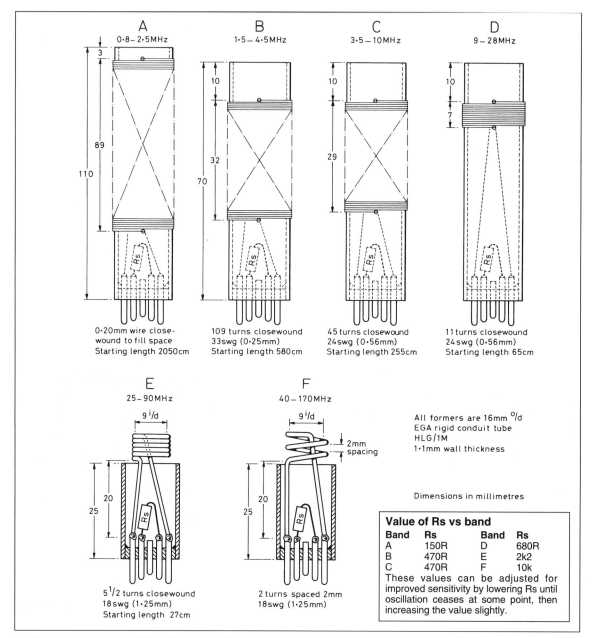

Fig 5.3.6. Coil details for G3WPO Mk2 dip oscillator

5.4.4   Coil construction

The coil for the lowest frequency range, A, is wound on a short piece of 12.5mm (0.5in) diameter polystyrene rod and then glued in place – see Table 5.4.2.

Connecting and supporting legs (each 44.5mm or 1.75in long) are made from 14swg enamelled copper wire. The next range coil, B, is self-supporting and wound directly with 14swg wire, also with connection pieces 44.5mm (1.75in) long.

Range C has a simple rectangular loop of 13swg enamelled copper wire, while the highest frequency range D requires the two plug sections to be further shortened (see Fig 5.4.4) and then a strip of copper wire or beryllium/copper sheet is soldered straight across their ends.

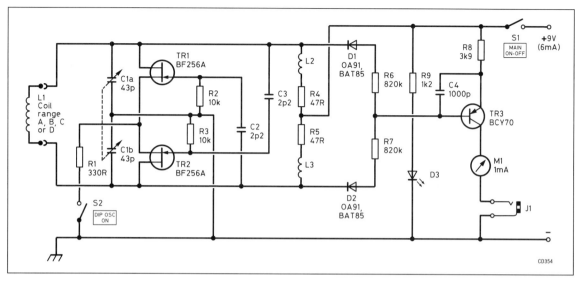

Fig 5.4.1. Circuit diagram of the VHF FET dip oscillator

Fig 5.4.2. VHF dip oscillator. Top: front panel. Right: inside view

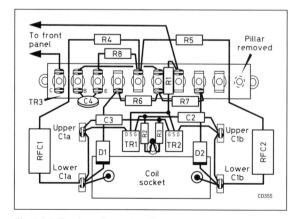

Fig 5.4.3. Tag board construction

Table 5.4.1. Components list for the VHF dip oscillator

R1	330R	D3	Low-current red LED
R2, 3	10k	C1	43p + 43p variable
R4, 5	47R	C2, 3	2p2 ceramic
R6, 7	820k	C4	1000p ceramic
R9	1k2	TR1, 2	BF256A
L1	See text	M1	1mA FSD meter
L2, 3	15µH inductor	S1, 2	On/off switch
D1, 2	OA91, BAT85	J1	Jack socket to suit

PP3 battery connector
Belling-Lee 4mm OZ similar plugs and sockets

All resistors are 0.25W, 5% unless specified otherwise.

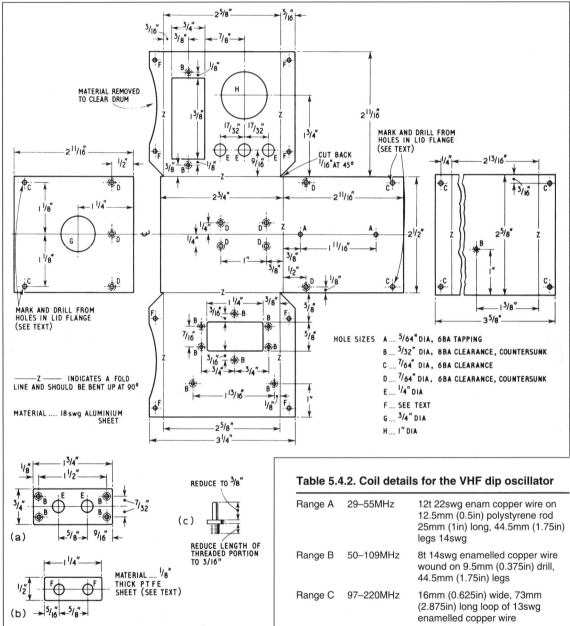

Fig 5.4.4. Mechanical details for VHF dip oscillator

Table 5.4.2. Coil details for the VHF dip oscillator

Range A	29–55MHz	12t 22swg enam copper wire on 12.5mm (0.5in) polystyrene rod 25mm (1in) long, 44.5mm (1.75in) legs 14swg
Range B	50–109MHz	8t 14swg enamelled copper wire wound on 9.5mm (0.375in) drill, 44.5mm (1.75in) legs
Range C	97–220MHz	16mm (0.625in) wide, 73mm (2.875in) long loop of 13swg enamelled copper wire
Range D	190–460MHz	8mm (0.3125in) wide, 17.5mm (0.6875in) long 26swg (or near) copper or beryllium/copper strip soldered directly across plug ends

5.5   Calibration of dip oscillators

The easiest way to check the calibration of a dip oscillator is to listen for the output on a general coverage receiver, an amateur receiver or scanner. This probably allows a good check on the calibration into the VHF range. Additional points can be found by using the second-channel response provided that the IF is known (the second-channel response is $2 \times$ IF removed from the normal response).

Another method is to use the resonances of lengths of

Fig 5.6.1. Using the dip oscillator

feeder cables, providing that the velocity factor for the particular cable is known so that the physical length corresponding to the wanted electrical half- and quarter-waves can be found.

5.6   Using the dip oscillator

Although the dip oscillator has a wide range of uses for measurements on both complete equipment and individual components, these all rely on its ability to measure the frequency of a tuned circuit. In use, the coil of the dip oscillator is coupled indirectly to the circuit under test with maximum coupling being obtained with the axis of the coil at right-angles to the direction of current flow. Coupling should be no greater than that necessary to give a moderate change on the dip oscillator meter. This is shown diagrammatically in Fig 5.6.1.

If the tuned circuit being investigated is well shielded magnetically (eg a coaxial line), it may be difficult to use inductive coupling. In such cases it may be possible to use capacitive coupling by placing the open end of the line near to one end of the dip oscillator coil. A completely enclosed cavity is likely to have some form of coupling loop, and the dip meter coil can usually be coupled inductively by means of a low-impedance transmission line such as a twisted pair with a coupling loop.

When used as an absorption wavemeter, the oscillator is not energised and the tuned circuit acts as a pick-up loop. This arrangement is useful when looking for the harmonic output of a multiplier or transmitter, or for spurious oscillations.

5.6.1   Determination of the resonant frequency of a tuned circuit

The resonant frequency of a tuned circuit is found by placing the dip oscillator close to that of the circuit and tuning for resonance. No power should be applied to the circuit under test and the coupling should be as loose as possible consistent with a reasonable dip being produced on the indicating meter.

The size of the dip is dependent on the Q of the circuit under test, a circuit having a high Q producing a more pronounced dip than one only having low or moderate Q.

5.6.2   Absorption wavemeter

By switching off the power supply in the dip oscillator and then using in the normal way, the instrument may be used as an absorption wavemeter. In this case power has to be applied to the circuit under test. Resonance is determined by maximum deflection on the meter caused by rectifying the received RF.

The absorption wavemeter can also be used to check for harmonics and spurii.

5.6.3   Capacitance and inductance

Obviously, if an instrument has the ability to measure the frequency of a tuned circuit, it can also be used for the determination of inductance and capacitance, provided that one of these components is known or a substitution made. If one component is known then use of the resonance formula is all that is required, ie:

$$f = \frac{1}{2\pi\sqrt{LC}}$$

Otherwise, carry out the following steps. To measure capacitance connect a close-tolerance capacitor C_s (eg 1%) in parallel with a coil (any coil will do providing it will resonate at a frequency within the range of the dip oscillator). This circuit is coupled to the dip oscillator and its frequency f_1 megahertz is noted. The unknown capacitor C_x is then connected in place of the known value and the new resonance f_2 megahertz is noted. The unknown capacitance is then given by:

$$C_x = \frac{f_1^2 C_s}{f_2^2}$$

A similar substitution can be made for inductance, assuming a known close-tolerance inductor is available. In this case replace C_s and C_x by L_s and L_x respectively.

5.6.4 Signal generator

For receiver tuning, the dip oscillator may be used to provide an unmodulated carrier wave by tuning the oscillator to the desired frequency and placing it close to the antenna terminal. The amplitude of the signal may be controlled by adjusting the distance of the dip oscillator from the antenna terminal.

5.6.5 Checking crystals

The frequency at which a crystal is oscillating can be checked by using the dip oscillator as an absorption wavemeter as described above. It is also possible to check in a similar manner the harmonic on which a crystal is oscillating.

5.7 Wide-range UHF cavity wavemeter

5.7.1 General

Measurement of frequencies above 500MHz becomes difficult using conventional lumped-circuit type wavemeters, so that it is an advantage to use a cavity design. Cavity wavemeters are often constructed to cover relatively narrow bands but for amateur purposes it is desirable to cover several bands if possible, thus providing continuous coverage and allowing their use for second harmonics. The wavemeter described here has been designed to cover from around 400MHz to 2.5GHz using a single cavity with an adjustable inner quarter-wave ($\lambda/4$) element.

Basically, the direct measurement of a $\lambda/4$ element is used to find the wavelength at which it is resonant. An equivalent circuit of the wavemeter is shown in Fig 5.7.1. It consists of input coupling, a resonant circuit formed by the $\lambda/4$ line/cavity and output coupling with detection and meter drive (output probe).

When a $\lambda/4$ circuit is energised, a current maximum will occur at the shorted end and a voltage maximum at the open end as shown in Fig 5.7.2. A current resonance indicator must therefore be coupled to the low-impedance end of the circuit, ie as near as possible to the shorted end. Also, as the input will normally be the output of an oscillator or transmitter, and this will also dictate coupling at the low-impedance end, ie near the short-circuit.

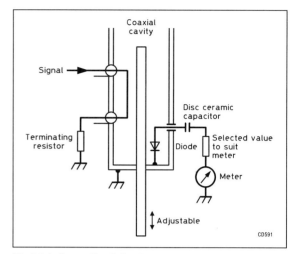

Fig 5.7.1. Generalised circuit arrangement

Both these couplings should be relatively loose so as not to foreshorten the length of the inner conductor by capacitive loading so that the mechanical length of the inner conductor is substantially the electrical length of $\lambda/4$. There will, however, be some apparent shortening of the inner conductor compared with the free space value due to the stray field from its end to the continuing outer cylinder. This will be most noticeable at the highest frequencies and may be as much as 4mm at 2.5GHz.

The characteristic impedance of the cavity is of no significance in the case of a frequency meter and may be of a value convenient to the materials available. It may be either circular or square in section. The sensitivity will naturally depend to a large extent on the meter used. With a 50µA FSD meter, satisfactory indications at levels down to 5mW may be observed.

In the design illustrated in Fig 5.7.3, the outer consists of a 25mm inside diameter tube with an adjustable-length inner conductor of 6.35mm (0.25in) diameter. The outer in this case has a narrow slot running most of the outer tube length so that the position of the inner conductor

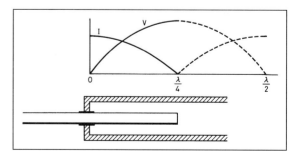

Fig 5.7.2. Current (I) and voltage (V) distribution in a quarter-wave cavity

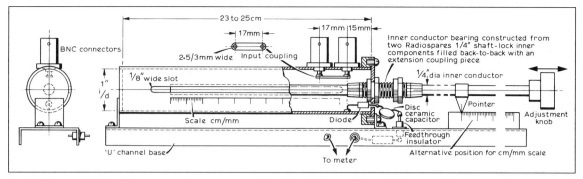

Fig 5.7.3. Layout of the wide-range cavity wavemeter. Note: 1in = 25.4mm, 1/8in = 3.175mm, 1/4in = 6.35mm

may be observed directly and the calibration scale can be fixed along the slot (similar to a slotted line). An alternative method of fitting a calibration scale to the extension of the inner conductor outside the cavity is also indicated in the diagram.

5.7.2 Construction

As mentioned, the precise dimensions of the cavity are not critical, though it can be made for 50 or 75Ω if materials permit and may be either round or square in cross-section.

For convenience, the inner conductor should be 6.35mm in diameter and the outer tube 25mm inside diameter. The material may be copper or brass but the latter is more rigid and may be more suitable for the inner conductor. The outer may be for preference copper as it may well be made from a length of water pipe. It is important to provide a reliable sliding contact for the inner conductor. If 6.35mm material is used then two conventional shaft locks should be connected back-to-back, preferably with an extension tube between them, to provide a long bearing. The input coupling is at the shorted end and consists of a strip drilled and then soldered directly to the connectors.

5.7.3 Using the wavemeter

For frequency measurement, the indicator should be connected to one port of the wavemeter and the other port connected to the output of the source whose frequency is to be measured. In the case of a source that is likely to be sensitive to load impedance, it may be preferable to connect the wavemeter via an attenuator or directional coupler, since the wavemeter when tuned to frequencies other than that of the source output will appear as a variable reactance.

Slide the inner of the wavemeter slowly out while watching the indicator for a peak reading. In the case of a wavemeter that is poorly constructed there may be a residual reading while still far off the resonant frequency.

This is usually due to overcoupling between the input and output circuits. The resonance peak will in this case be preceded by a sharp dip in this residual reading.

It is possible with this type of wavemeter to obtain more than one indication due to it resonating not only at $\lambda/4$ but also at all odd multiples of $\lambda/4$. For example, when measuring the output of a 1296MHz source, a reading will also be obtained when the wavemeter is tuned to 432MHz. This characteristic can be used when calibrating the wavemeter since it is possible to obtain several calibration points. These can be plotted on a graph and, by interpolation, the frequencies between can be calibrated. Obviously the more frequencies available when calibrating, the more accurate the overall calibration will be.

5.8 Cavity wavemeter for 2.3GHz

5.8.1 General

This wavemeter is a fixed-frequency type which, provided the essential dimension is observed accurately, can be expected to resonate within ±10MHz of the calculated frequency.

The unit (Fig 5.8.1) consists of a $\lambda/2$ cavity with two couplings, one for the oscillator and the other for the indicator. None of the dimensions are critical except for the length of the inner conductor which must be accurately turned to length with end faces truly perpendicular to the line length.

The line length for any particular frequency can be calculated from $L = C/2f$, where $C = 2.996 \times 10^{11}$mm/s (typical for the UK). From this the following lengths are suitable for various frequencies in and around the 13cm band.

f (MHz)	2250	2300	2350	2400	2450	2500
L (mm)	66.57	65.13	63.75	62.41	61.14	59.92
L (in)	2.621	2.564	2.510	2.457	2.407	2.359

The line length L must be maintained to within ±0.025mm or ±0.001in.

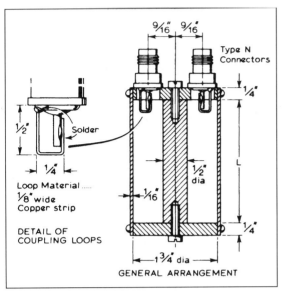

Fig 5.8.1. Mechanical details of the 13cm cavity wavemeter

5.8.2 Construction

The wavemeter should preferably be constructed from thick parts for rigidity. The two end-plates need to be about 6.3mm (0.25in) thick to allow for the fixing holes by which the outer tube is attached.

The fit between the end-plates and the outer tube should be good so that when the fixing screws are tightened there is no tendency to form gaps between the individual fixing screws. It is also important that the fit between the centre line and the end-plates is good and that the line is tightly fixed by use of a substantial fixing screw at each end – 2BA is suggested for this purpose.

The dimensions shown in Fig 5.8.1 will be found to be satisfactory but none need be rigidly adhered to except the line length. The couplings indicated are sufficiently large and should be closely copied using either N, C, BNC or TNC sockets. The UHF type SO239 is unsuitable.

With care and attention to detail the finished wavemeter can be expected to be accurate to within ±10MHz. The unloaded Q will be of the order of 1250 or about 200 when both couplings are loaded with 50Ω.

5.9 A self-calibrating wavemeter for 10GHz

5.9.1 General

The wavemeter shown in Figs 5.9.1 and 5.9.2 enables frequencies to be measured between at least 9.5GHz and 11GHz with an accuracy of ±10MHz. An important feature is that it is self-calibrating which avoids the need to refer to a precision frequency standard.

Fig 5.9.1. A self-calibrating wavemeter for 10GHz

The wavemeter consists of a rod of adjustable length set coaxially in a cavity which is loosely coupled to a waveguide which forms part of the RF system. Absorption of power occurs when the rod resonates, ie when it is electrically (not necessarily physically) $\lambda/4$ or $3\lambda/4$ long.

Because the wavelength is short at these frequencies, the tuning rates of this type of wavemeter tend to be high: in the region of 1300MHz/mm for the $\lambda/4$ mode and 440MHz/mm in the $3\lambda/4$ mode. The constructional problems that could be associated with these rates have been avoided by the use of a standard micrometer head (Moore and Wright 952M or equivalent), the spindle of which forms the resonating element.

5.9.2 Construction

The wavemeter body is made from a block of brass through which a 12.5mm (0.5in) hole has been drilled. This single hole both locates the micrometer stem and forms the cavity, thus ensuring their alignment. The micrometer spindle passes through a $\lambda/4$ choke which defines electrically the position of the 'cold' end of the resonant element more reliably than mechanical contacts such as fingering. To maintain a reasonably high Q, the gap between the spindle and the choke should be kept as small as possible, preferably less than 0.25mm without them actually touching at any point. A short probe from this choke passes through a hole in the thinned wall of the cavity and through a corresponding hole in the wall of the waveguide to couple RF.

The choke and probe are best soldered in a single operation. The choke is fitted in the micrometer end of the body with the correct orientation and the probe, formed at the end of a 305mm length of wire, is inserted through the wall. The body is then pushed over the plain end of a 12.5mm drill held vertically in a vice until the choke is in its correct position with the probe located in the hole in the choke. The body is clamped using the micrometer fixing screws and the extended probe wire supported externally. The choke and the probe are then soldered using the minimum amount of solder necessary. The probe is cut to a length of about 9.5mm and the cavity carefully cleaned.

The body of the wavemeter and the micrometer spindle may be plated with gold, copper or silver, although this is not really necessary. The plating on the spindle should not exceed 5µm otherwise difficulty may be found in reassembling the micrometer.

5.9.3   Calibration

A source of RF and a means for detecting relative power levels are required to calibrate the wavemeter. These will normally be part of the receiver or transmitter with which the wavemeter is to be used. The probe should first be trimmed to reduce 'suckout' to the minimum convenient, for example a 10% reduction in mixer current. For each of a number of unknown frequencies, the micrometer readings R_1 and R_2 (corresponding to the $\lambda/4$ and $3\lambda/4$ suckouts) should be noted. The difference between these readings is accurately $\lambda/2$ at the frequency measured. Hence:

$$f(\text{MHz}) = \frac{C}{2(R_1 - R_2)}$$

where R_1 and R_2 are in millimetres and $C = 299{,}600$ for air at 25°C and 30% humidity. A conventional calibration curve can be prepared using this technique for both modes of operation. Normally advantage should be taken of the slower tuning rate of the $3\lambda/4$ mode.

5.9.4   An alternative self-calibrating wavemeter for 10GHz

A second form of self-calibrating wavemeter is shown in Fig 5.9.3. A piece of waveguide-16 coupled to the waveguide system forms the body of a resonant cavity, the length of which can be adjusted with an RF short. As this short is withdrawn a suck-out will be observed when

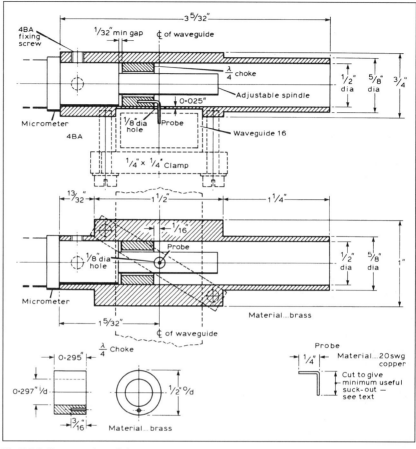

Fig 5.9.2. Construction of the wavemeter

the length of the cavity is approximately $\lambda_g/4$. A second suck-out will occur if the short is further withdrawn, the distance between the two being precisely $\lambda_g/2$.

Note: the coupling hole is in the cavity wall and the blocks forming the RF shorts should be a sliding fit within the waveguide. The 2BA drive shaft could be replaced with one having a 0BA thread which has a 1mm pitch or by a micrometer head.

5.10   Spectrum analyser

The Simple Spectrum Analyser (SSA) offers reasonable performance over the approximate range 1–90MHz. It is fairly cheap to build and utilises almost any oscilloscope for its display. It has a selectable, calibrated frequency sweep-width ranges, logarithmic signal strength calibration, a dynamic range of over 50dB and a built-in frequency marker generator. A suitable oscilloscope should have a DC-coupled Y-amplifier offering a 100mV/div sensitivity and an external input to the X-amplifier. See reference [3] for the original article.

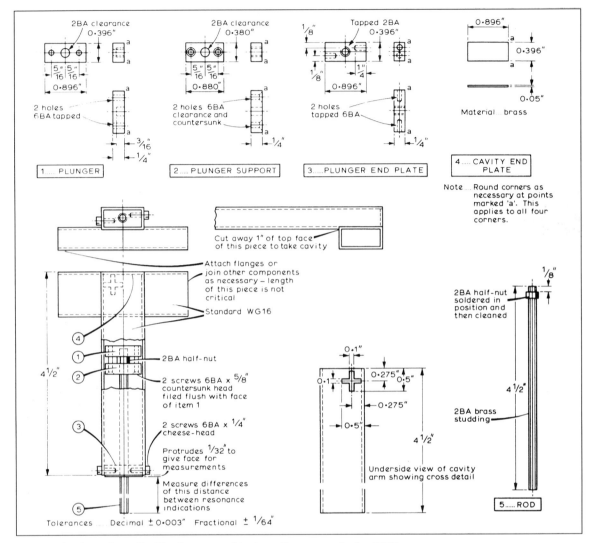

Fig 5.9.3. An alternative self-calibrating waveguide absorption wavemeter for 10GHz

What is the purpose of a spectrum analyser and how does it operate? It is essentially no more than an electronically tuneable receiver, the S-meter output of which is connected to the vertical (or Y) input of an oscilloscope. The tuning frequency of the receiver is driven by a sawtooth waveform which is also used to drive the horizontal (or X) input of the oscilloscope. If the receiver also has a logarithmic response to signal level, then relative signal strengths can be read off the oscilloscope screen – see Fig 5.10.1 for a typical display.

Spurious responses, selectivity and overload problems can occur. The overload problems can be overcome by specifying a maximum input level (for the SSA it is −20dBm) and, by using an attenuator before the analyser

input, it can cope with larger signals. The necessary selectivity is obtained by using a superheterodyne receiver design in which the image problems are minimised by using an intermediate frequency (IF) which is higher than the maximum frequency of the analyser (in this case 145MHz) which allows a readily available helical filter to be used.

This item is available as a kit; alternatively it is up to constructors to use their own methods, and for these there is a PCB and component layout in Appendix 2.

5.10.1 Overview

Fig 5.10.2 shows a block diagram of the SSA. After attenuation (if required), the input signal is fed via a

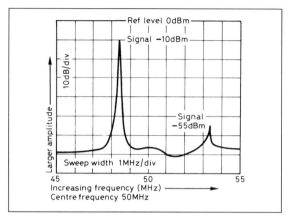

Fig 5.10.1. A typical screen display of a spectrum analyser

low-pass filter to the first (up-conversion) mixer, where the input frequency range of 0–90MHz is mixed with the varicap-tuned local oscillator which operates over the range 145–235MHz, giving a first IF of 145MHz. The signal is then passed through the helical filter to a second mixer and local oscillator, where it is down-converted to the second IF of 10.7MHz.

The signal next passes through wide or narrow IF filters, a buffer amplifier and a further wide filter before entering the logarithmic IF strip. This produces a signal strength output which is proportional to the logarithm of the input signal magnitude, hence the display can be calibrated in dBm. This output (usually termed the *video output*) is then fed to the Y-input of the oscilloscope.

The remaining parts of the SSA are straightforward. The sweep generator produces a linear ramp sweep voltage, part of which (selected by the SWEEP WIDTH control) is added to a DC voltage from the CENTRE FREQUENCY control. Since varicap oscillators do not have a completely linear voltage/frequency relationship, this sweep voltage is passed to the break-point generator, which puts a 'kink' in the sweep where it will attempt to linearise the frequency sweep over the 70–90MHz portion of the range. The output from the sweep oscillator also drives the X-input of the oscilloscope.

Not shown on the block diagram is the frequency marker generator, a simple 10MHz crystal oscillator and TTL divider which gives a low-amplitude output, rich in harmonics, and which is also fed to the analyser input.

5.10.2 Circuit detail

The SSA is divided into three separate boards. The first and most important is the RF unit (Fig 5.10.3). The input signal is routed from the front panel 50Ω BNC socket via the two front-panel switched attenuators (shown in Fig 5.10.5), to a fixed attenuator (R1, R2 and R3), which is designed to limit the maximum input to the analyser to about −20dBm and provide a consistent 50Ω input. The signal then passes through an elliptical low-pass filter (C3, C4, C5 and L1) to the first mixer which is part of IC1 (an MC3356). The MC3356 is intended to be used as a single-chip FSK receiver and has some special features which are exploited in the SSA. First, the IF amplifier has a signal strength output which is proportional to the logarithm of the input voltage and, secondly, the local oscillator and mixer will work up to at least 250MHz. The local oscillator is tuned by varicap D1 using the sweep voltage from the sweep/video board. Note that two 1nF capacitors (C8 and C30) are fitted at the anode end of D1 as a low-impedance path is vital here to enable the highest frequency to be reached. Adding C30 to one of the prototypes increased the upper frequency limit by 5MHz!

The 145MHz output from IC1a goes to the first IF filter FL1 (a three-chamber helical type). The IF output from the filter is then down-converted to the second IF of 10.7MHz in IC2 (an NE602). The local oscillator frequency of about 134.3MHz is set by L4, C2 and C13. Setting the second local oscillator below the first IF removes the 21.4MHz (2 × 2nd IF) spurious response. The NE602 requires a lower supply voltage than the MC3356 and this is obtained from a 5V regulator IC3.

Narrow (15kHz) or wide (250kHz) first IF filters (FL2 and FL3) are selected by means of miniature relays RL1 and RL2 and the front-panel switch S1 (IF BANDWIDTH). After filtering, the signal is amplified by TR1 which is run at a relatively high standing current so as to provide a good dynamic range. Although the stage does not

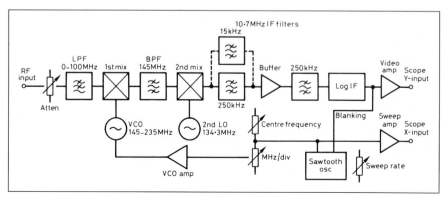

Fig 5.10.2. Block diagram of the simple spectrum analyser

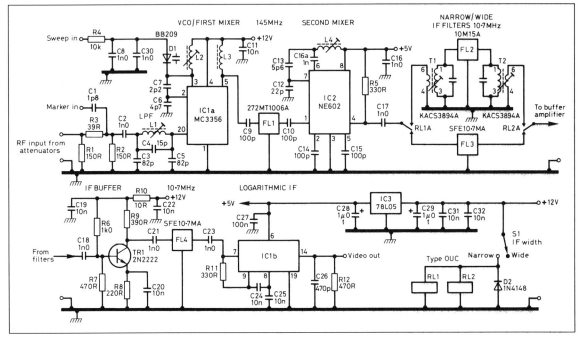

Fig 5.10.3. Circuit diagram of the RF board

provide the correct impedance terminations for the filters, in practice this is of little consequence. Removing C20 would improve the matching but with the consequential loss of over 20dB of sensitivity. The signal is then passed via a second filter (FL4) to the main IF signal processing circuit IC1b. This does one of the most difficult jobs in the analyser – it provides a DC output which is proportional to the logarithm of the IF input voltage. Here, in one circuit, the 10dB/division Y-axis calibration is achieved, with the (video) output being taken via a screened lead to the sweep/video board. The output from the FM discriminator is not used in this application.

5.10.3 Sweep generator

The sweep generator is shown in Fig 5.10.4. The ubiquitous 741 op-amp has been used throughout as they are cheap enough so that one can be liberal with them. The sweep ramp is generated by IC4 (a 555 timer), IC5 and current source TR2 with the sweep rate being controlled by a front-panel potentiometer RV1. The 555 timer also provides a fast blanking pulse output for the video amplifier. The sweep output is buffered by IC6 before being fed to the sweep-width front-panel control switch S2 (MHz/div) and the X-output at SK2.

Depending on the oscilloscope used, the inverting unity gain buffer IC7 may not be needed. If a positive voltage applied to the oscilloscope X-input deflects the spot to

the right, then IC7 can be omitted. In this case omit R22 and R23 and connect IC6 (pin 6) to the top of X-CAL preset RV2 via link LK1 (shown dotted).

The selected sweep voltage amplitude from the wiper of S2 is buffered by voltage follower IC8 before amplification by IC9. In this final stage, three important things happen:

(a) the sweep voltage gain is set to allow a calibrated frequency sweep;

(b) an adjustable DC offset (centre frequency) is added by means of a 10-turn potentiometer RV4 (CENTRE FREQUENCY COARSE) and RV5 (CENTRE FREQUENCY FINE); and

(c) an adjustable non-linearity (breakpoint) is deliberately introduced into the linear sweep ramp by means of RV6, D3 and R33.

5.10.4 Video amplifier

The video amplifier (IC11) provides a small amount of gain and, in conjunction with comparator IC10, provides the retrace blanking by shifting the retrace portion vertically downwards off the screen. Capacitor C37 across the feedback resistor R41 can be switched by S3 (VIDEO FILTER) to provide a small amount of smoothing of the 'grass' on the display if required and preset RV7 (Y-CAL) allows the output of the amplifier to be set to the required 100mV per 10dB of RF input.

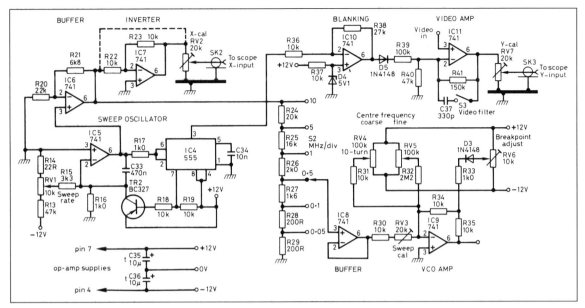

Fig 5.10.4. Video/sweep circuit

The third board, which contains the marker generator and power supply (Fig 5.10.5) needs little comment. The 10MHz oscillator is divided by 10 in IC12 to provide a comb of 10 or 1MHz markers which can be added to the input signal to allow an easy method of frequency calibration. The power supply uses standard components and is conventional.

5.10.5 Construction

The RF board is constructed on a double-sided glass epoxy PCB, one side of which is not etched and is used as an earth plane. The component placement diagram (together with drilling details) is shown in Appendix 2. Most (but not all) of the holes require the copper on the earth plane side to be cleared away around the hole with a counterbore or sharp drill. Note that the lugs of the shielding cans for FL1, T1 and T2 are used to provide earth paths for tracks underneath the board and so need to be soldered on both sides of the PCB. The small additional holes on the track layout provide locating holes for the earth plane connections of components – small ceramic capacitors these days seem very prone to disintegrate if one of their legs is bent through a right-angle! Note that if the varicap diode D1 must be mounted on the underside of the board with its cathode close to the end of L2 as shown. *No IC sockets should be used on the RF board.*

Note that this paragraph is an amendment to the original article. The effective bypassing of the varicap diode is important if maximum frequency span is to be obtained. This may be achieved by the addition of two leadless disc or trapezoidal capacitors fitted in slots cut in

the board. One should be fitted next to the track by the varicap. The track should be cut between this new capacitor and the existing two 1nF capacitors and the cut bridged with a 47kΩ resistor. The second capacitor should be fitted as close to pin 4 of IC1 as possible. The other sides of both capacitors are soldered to the ground plane. These additional components are not specified in the parts list.

The video/sweep board component placement is shown in Appendix 2. This is a single-sided PCB where the optional link LK1 (shown dotted) should be fitted as explained earlier if the X-signal does not need to be inverted. Note that resistors R24–R29 are mounted on the rotary switch S2.

The third board, containing the marker generator and power supply, is also a single-sided PCB. The component overlay is shown in Appendix 2. Sufficient space for a small heatsink for IC14 has been allowed for.

The analyser needs to be housed in a metal case in order to provide the necessary shielding from stray signals but, when choosing or making a case, remember that access to the presets on both the RF and sweep boards is required. This means that the boards should be mounted so that there is easy access to both of them. The input attenuators are constructed on slide switches S5 and S6 using short leads, and could well be fitted with a grounded screening box made of double-sided PCB.

For the CENTRE FREQUENCY COARSE control, choose a good 10-turn potentiometer and fit it with a large knob which has a cranked handle – this will save a lot of wear and tear on your fingers! The CENTRE FREQUENCY FINE control needs a good-quality, single-turn, carbon-track

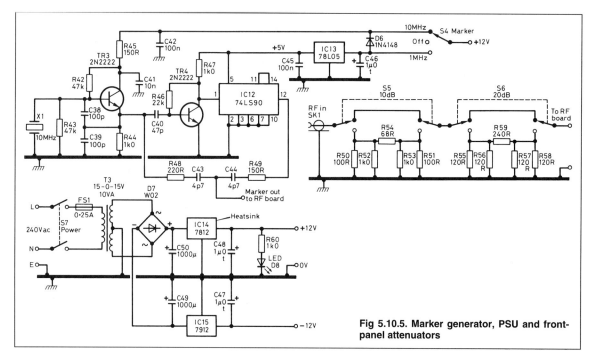

Fig 5.10.5. Marker generator, PSU and front-panel attenuators

potentiometer. The connections to the RF board from the front-panel attenuators and the marker generator should be with miniature coaxial cable such as RG174. The video and sweep connections, as well as those to S2 and the X- and Y-output sockets, should be made with a small-di-ameter screened (audio) cable.

Test the boards on the bench before finally assembling them in the case. Final setting up of the RF board should be carried out when it is fixed in the case.

5.10.6 Alignment

Start by testing the power supply and marker generator. The latter can be easily checked by listening to its harmonics on a HF receiver, or using an oscilloscope on the input and output of the decade divider IC12. Next test the sweep and video board. It should be fairly easy to check the operation of this with the oscilloscope which will be used for the final display. Do not set it up at this stage, merely confirm that the sawtooth waveform is available at the analyser X-output and that an attenuated version (with DC offset dependent on the centre frequency controls) is available at the VCO sweep voltage output.

When the RF board is complete, connect power to it and ground the tuning input. Then connect the video output to the oscilloscope (which for the moment can have its conventional timebase running) and select wide IF bandwidth. If a 145MHz source (eg a 2m handheld with a dummy load) is brought close to the input side of the

145MHz filter, the trace should deflect upwards, showing that the second mixer/oscillator and logarithmic IF strip are functioning. Adjust L4 for maximum response, reducing the input signal as required.

Now complete all of the interconnections, set the oscilloscope for external X-input and connect the X-output of the SSA to the external X-input of the oscilloscope. Adjust RV2 (X-CAL) and possibly the oscilloscope X-gain so that the available sweep is just wider than the screen. Set S2 to 10MHz/div, connect the video output of the SSA to the oscilloscope Y-input (set to 100mV/div with DC coupling) and switch on the 10MHz markers. At this stage, a few blips on the screen should be seen. When the VCO is correctly aligned, one of the blips will not disappear when the markers are switched off – this is the lower limit of the coverage or in other words 0MHz.

The next stage requires patience! Set RV4 (CENTRE FREQUENCY COARSE) to about mid-travel and unscrew the core of L2 so that it is about half-way out of the coil – by now a few marker blips should be seen as well. Adjust L4 for maximum amplitude of the blips, noting that there will be two positions where this occurs – choose the position where the core is further inside the coils, as the other corresponds to the local oscillator being on the high side of the first if. By careful adjustment of the VCO coil L2 it should be possible to see marker blips every 10MHz up to 90MHz, while still keeping the 0MHz blip. If necessary adjust L4 slightly. Coil L1 does not need adjustment – leave the core as supplied.

Table 5.10.1. Components list for the spectrum analyser

RF BOARD						
R1, 2	150R	L3	TOKO FL4 RF choke 348LS4R7	S2	1-pole, 6-way rotary switch
R3	39R			S3	SPST or SPDT toggle switch
R4	10k	L4	TOKO S18 coil 301SS0400	SK2, 3	BNC panel sockets
R5, 11	330R	T1, 2	TOKO transformer KACS3894A	**MARKER/GENERATOR**	
R6	1k	RL1, 2	Min relay type OUC	R42, 43	47k
R7, 12	470R	S1	SPDT switch	R44, 47	1k
R8	220R			R45, 49	150R
R9	390R	**SWEEP AND VIDEO BOARD**		R46	22k
R10	10R	R13, 40	47k	R48	220R
C1	1p8	R14	22R	C38, 39	100p
C2, 8, 16, 16a, 17, 18, 21, 23, 30	1n	R15	3k3	C40	47p
		R16, 17, 33	1k	C41	10n
		R18, 19, 22, 23, 30, 31, 34–37	10k	C42, 45	100n
				C43, 44	4p7
C3, 5	82p	R20	22k	C46	1μ, 35V tant bead
C4	15p	R21	6k8	D6	1N4148
C6	4p7	R24	20k	TR3, 4	2N2222
C7	2p2	R25	16k	IC12	74LS90
C9, 10	100p	R26	2k	IC13	78L05
C11, 19, 20, 22, 24, 25, 31, 32	10n	R27	1k6	X1	Crystal 10MHz, HC18U
		R28, 29	200R	S4	SPDT, centre-off toggle switch
C12	22p	R32	2M2		
C13	5p6	R38	27k	**FRONT-PANEL ATTENUATORS**	
C14, 15	100p	R39	100k	R50, 51	100R
C26	470p	R41	150k	R52, 53	1k
C27	100n	RV1	10k lin pot	R54	68R
C28, 29	1μ, 35V tant bead	RV2, 3	20k cermet preset	R55–58	120R
D1	BB209 (MV209, BB809)	RV4	100k 10-turn	R59	240R
D2	1N4148	RV5	100k lin carbon	S5, 6	DPDT slide switch
TR1	2N2222	RV6	10k cermet preset	SK1	BNC panel socket
IC1	MC3356	RV7	20k cermet preset	**POWER SUPPLY**	
IC2	NE602	C33	470n polyester layer	R60	1k
IC3	78L05	C34	10n	C47, 48	1μ, 35V tant bead
FL1	272MT1006A CBT 145MHz helical filter	C35, 36	10μ, 25V tant bead	C49, 50	1000μ, 25 or 35V electrolytic
		C37	330p	D7	W02 bridge rectifier
FL2	10M15A 2-pole 10.7MHz crystal	D3, 5	1N4148	D8	Red LED, panel mounting
		D4	5V1, 400mW zener	IC14	7812 with small heatsink
FL3, 4	SFE10.7MA 10.7MHz ceramic filter	TR2	BC327	IC5	7912
		IC4	555 timer	T3	15-0-15, 10VA mains transformer
L1, 2	TOKO S18 Coil 301SS0100	IC5–11	741 op-amps	S7	DPST on/off switch, mains
				F1	250mA fuse and holder

All resistors are 0.25W, 5% or better. Capacitors are miniature ceramic plate unless otherwise indicated.

Adjust RV3 (SWEEP CAL) and RV6 (SET BREAKPOINT) to give a linear display (as near as possible) over the 0–70MHz/80MHz range, with one marker appearing every horizontal division on the screen. Careful setting of RV6 will substantially improve the frequency above 70MHz. These adjustments interact somewhat, so it is worth repeating and persevering with them. Check with the aid of the 1MHz markers, the operation of the MHz/div (SWEEP WIDTH) switch.

5.10.7 Final adjustment

The filters on the RF board can now be adjusted. Using an internal marker blip, carefully adjust the 145MHz filter for maximum signal amplitude. Select the narrow IF filter and adjust the cores of T1 and T2 for maximum amplitude and best shape – what is displayed is the actual IF response of the analyser. When using the narrow IF filter, remember to reduce the sweep rate. If a marker is put at the centre of the screen using the centre frequency controls, reducing the sweep width with S2 should not cause the marker to move – if it does then try adjusting the oscilloscope X-shift slightly and re-centering the marker.

Finally, the calibration of the logarithmic vertical scale must be accomplished using a 50Ω signal source, such as a signal generator connected to the analyser RF input socket. Using the oscilloscope Y-shift, position the base line near the bottom of the screen. With the attenuators switched out and the oscilloscope Y-amplifier set to 100mV/div, adjust the signal amplitude to give a peak of 4 divisions or so. Now adjust the Y-CAL preset so that when the attenuation is switched in the peak falls in amplitude by one division per 10dB. If the reader has access to an accurate signal source, set the oscilloscope Y-shift so that the top of the screen corresponds to −20dBm (in a commercial instrument this is termed the *reference level*). The noise floor of the analyser is about −85dBm but note that the lowest vertical division does not quite correspond to the 10dB/div calibration of the rest of the screen.

5.10.8 Practical hints

Bearing in mind the practical limitations of the analyser – the maximum input of −20dBm (+10dBm with both attenuators in), it will show its own shortcomings if it is overloaded. The dynamic range of the analyser is over 50dB. While the absolute sensitivity will vary across its range by 6dB or so, the relative calibration of 10dB/div remains unchanged for any given frequency. When using the narrow IF setting, slow the sweep down – watching the display as this is carried out will reveal why this is necessary. While not shown on any circuit diagram, a good RF filter is recommended on the mains input in order to keep the entry of RF purely to the front-panel socket.

While the SSA is not really suitable for making intermodulation distortion measurements or looking at oscillator noise, many useful and interesting tasks await it. By connecting a few feet of wire to the input, a fascinating picture of the HF spectrum emerges – try it during the day time and then at night when the 7MHz broadcast stations are in full swing. Use the 10MHz and 1MHz markers to find the way about the spectrum.

The upper limit of the analyser should be greater than 95MHz and, if living in a good signal strength area, Band II VHF radio signals are visible. Connecting a good antenna should enable a good watch to be kept for 28MHz and 50MHz openings. If one's rig has a mixer-type VFO, try looking at the output and be prepared for a shock.

While this unit does not have quite the performance as a commercial unit (or the price tag!), when used with a modicum of care it is a very useful tool.

5.11 Commercial add-on units

These items are relatively new to the market and follow the pattern of that described in Section 5.10. They use a standard oscilloscope as the basic display mechanism. They require an oscilloscope to have X, Y mode facilities but the bandwidth of the oscilloscope is not important. The lower frequency range is about 400kHz, the upper frequency being dependent on the type, eg 100MHz, 250MHz, 500MHz. They come both in the form of a probe or a stand-alone box. Prices range from about £250 to £1000 (1993 prices).

5.12 References

[1] 'The G3WPO FET dip oscillator Mk2', Tony Bailey, G3WPO, *Radio Communication* April 1987.
[2] 'A VHF dip oscillator', A L Mynett, *Radio Communication* September 1970.
[3] 'Simple Spectrum Analyser', R Blackwell, G4PMK, *Radio Communication* November 1989.

Chapter 6

RF power measurements

6.1 Introduction

The Amateur Licence requires that output power must be measured in order to comply with its conditions. Power is normally first assessed when running into a resistive dummy load which presents the correct load to the transmitter. Such a load is required in any case to permit non-radiating adjustments to be made to the transmitter.

Power measurements when running into a dummy load can be made directly using RF voltmeters, oscilloscopes etc, taking into account their frequency limitations. The use of reflectometers is preferable for monitoring power when coupled to an antenna system as they also give an indication of what is happening on the feed system. This chapter covers both methods but the reader is also referred to Chapters 2 and 7. Modulation measurements are covered in Chapter 11.

6.2 Definitions of power

The following information is taken from the *Amateur Radio Licence Terms and Limitations Booklet* BR68 [1]. Only the relevant paragraphs have been included.

6.2.1 Notes to the schedule

(a) *Maximum power* refers to the RF power supplied to the antenna. Maximum power levels will usually be specified by carrier power. For emissions having a suppressed, variable or reduced carrier, the power will be specified by the *peak envelope power* (PEP) under linear conditions.

(e) Interpretation

(i) *Carrier power*: the average power supplied to the antenna by a transmitter during one radio frequency cycle taken under the condition of no modulation.

(iv) *Mean power*: the average power supplied to the antenna by a transmitter during an interval of time which is sufficiently long relative to the lowest frequency encountered in the modulation taken under normal operating conditions.

(v) *Peak envelope power* (PEP): the average power supplied to the antenna by a transmitter during one radio frequency cycle at the crest of the modulation envelope taken under normal operating conditions.

6.3 The effect of modulation on power output

This section deals with the basic measurement of power, without specifying measuring equipment, of either basic transmitters or an amplifier. For measurement of modulation parameters the reader is referred to Chapter 11.

In a carrier-wave situation (CW) or with a frequency-modulated signal, the output is of constant amplitude and so it is relatively easy to measure the output power. Key the transmitter and determine the RMS voltage (V_{RMS}) of the resulting carrier across a dummy load (R). The power is given by:

$$P = V_{RMS}^2/R \quad \text{watts}$$

If the signal is amplitude modulated (double sideband with carrier) then the overall output power increases. The power is divided between the sidebands and the carrier component. With 100% modulation the output power increases to 1.5 times the unmodulated condition – the power contained in each of the two sidebands is one quarter that in the carrier. It is suggested that for this form of modulation the carrier power is measured (ie no modulation) as described above. This value can be multiplied by 1.5 to give the maximum output power available.

With single sideband modulation, no power is output until modulation is applied. The output envelope is non-sinusoidal in appearance. The normal method for measuring output power is by observation of the modulation envelope and determination of the peak envelope power – this is the parameter defined by the licensing authority. Equipment for making these measurements is described in following sections.

6.4 Dummy loads

A dummy load is a resistor (or group of resistors) which has the same resistance value as an antenna system. It should be purely resistive and so should provide an SWR

53

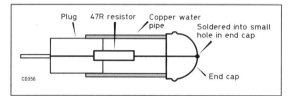

Fig 6.4.1. Typical construction of low-power dummy load

of 1:1. The dummy load is normally constructed so that it provides minimal radiation when a transmitter is operated into it. Transmitters should always be set up into dummy loads (especially if tuning HF band transceivers) before connecting them to the antenna system.

A resistor, no matter what type, will always have associated with it inherent inductance and capacitance, and the way it is mounted will also affect these values. The ideal resistor is one which has no associated capacitance and inductance and is also one which does not change its value appreciably with frequency and power dissipation. This is unfortunately difficult to arrange in the real world, and the best one can do is to choose a resistor which minimises these adverse effects. In practice, the impedance presented by the dummy load changes with frequency and hence will not provide an SWR of 1:1 – this effect is more pronounced as frequency increases. This is why any dummy load which is purchased should have some information included with it concerning frequency range and expected SWR values.

The best type of resistor to use is that made from carbon. Unfortunately it is becoming increasingly difficult to obtain resistors of this type with power ratings in excess of 2W from distributors. However, tubular carbon resistors of higher power ratings will often be seen at radio rallies. *Never* use wirewound resistors for RF. However, these may be adequate for measuring AF power.

A low-power dummy load can be made from a single 47Ω resistor with surrounding shield as shown

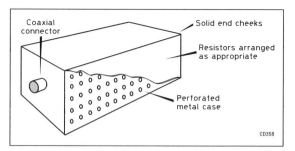

Fig 6.4.3. Possible construction of higher-power dummy load

diagrammatically in Fig 6.4.1, and this is obviously easier for those with mechanical skills and some ingenuity. To increase the power dissipation it would be possible to make the metal container a tight fit around the resistor. However, this may pose problems if conduction can occur from the resistor case. Providing a small clearance can be ensured around the resistor, then the space could be filled with heatsink compound which is thermally but not electrically conducting. Alternatively one could fill the case with cooling oil and/or put fins onto the outside of the case. The use of the metal shield prevents unwanted radiation and also provides a low-inductance path.

To increase the power rating it is possible to use resistors in parallel – Fig 6.4.2 shows a typical arrangement. These should, if at all possible, be encased in a metal shield to prevent unwanted radiation, possibly a perforated shield to permit air flow – see Fig 6.4.3. It might even be possible to build an RF probe and/or attenuator for measurements as suggested in Chapter 2.

The characteristics can be improved by arranging the resistors in a coaxial manner. Ideally the pitch circle of the resistors and centre coaxial conductor should be carefully calculated but, as this arrangement tends to be very short compared to a wavelength, non-adherence has little effect until the higher frequencies are reached. The characteristic impedance can be calculated using:

$$Z_0 = 138 \log_{10}(D/d)$$

where D is the pitch diameter of the resistors and d the diameter of the inner coaxial connector. Typical arrangements to make approximately 50Ω are shown in Table 6.4.1.

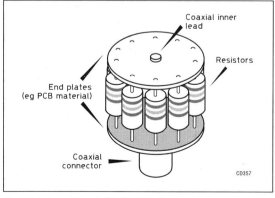

Fig 6.4.2. A multi-resistor dummy load

Table 6.4.1. Resistor values for 50Ω dummy loads

Resistance (Ω)	No in parallel	Approximate value
100	2	50
150	3	50
390	8	49
560	11	51
1000	20	50

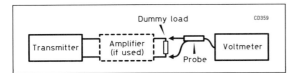

Fig 6.5.1. RF power measurement using probe and voltmeter

The overall power rating is the sum of the power ratings of each resistor used.

To obtain higher power ratings it may be possible to place the load resistors in a perforated screened container and air blow them. This could be accomplished by placing a thermal switch on the resistors and using it to switch a fan on once the temperature has risen above a certain point.

Sometimes large tubular carbon resistors come onto the surplus market, eg from firms such as Morganite. These can make excellent dummy loads. Try to form them in a coaxial manner with the feed up the centre. Again, air blowing can be used to increase the power dissipation. For higher power see reference [2].

When using a dummy load, remember that it may be possible to dissipate a much higher power for a short period of time providing a long cool-down period is allowed between application of power. A commercial dummy load may often be provided with advice on this method of use.

6.5 Use of RF voltmeters and/or probes

An RF voltmeter can be obtained, eg as surplus equipment, or a probe made as suggested in Chapter 2. In fact the commercial instrument may well use a probe. However, the measuring equipment *must* cover the frequency range in which the power measurements are being undertaken. If a peak-reading voltmeter is being used, do not forget to convert the peak voltage to RMS voltage by dividing by √2 before using the formula given in Section 6.3. *Do not forget to take into account any attenuators used.* This method of measuring power should be used for carrier power only. Fig 6.5.1 shows the basic arrangement for these measurements.

6.6 Use of the oscilloscope for power measurement

This requires the use of an oscilloscope with a timebase, and this chapter deals solely with the measurement of power, eg a voltage display on an oscilloscope. See Chapter 11 for using the oscilloscope for modulation measurements.

At 100W (CW) the peak-to-peak voltage across a 50Ω dummy load is 200V; at 400W PEP, the maximum peak-to-peak voltage that will be measured is about 400V. You have been warned!

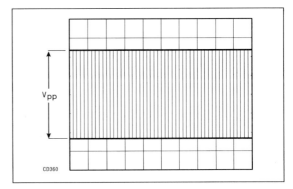

Fig 6.6.1. Oscilloscope display for carrier only

As with the RF voltmeter, the most straightforward measurement is of carrier power which is obtained from the key-down condition for CW operation or the constant amplitude of a frequency-modulated signal. Connect an oscilloscope instead of a voltmeter (Fig 6.5.1), bearing in mind any frequency or voltage limitations of the oscilloscope and probe. Measure the peak-to-peak amplitude V_{pp} (Fig 6.6.1) across the known dummy load R. The average power is then calculated from:

$$P_{avg} = \frac{V_{pp}^2}{8R} \text{ watts}$$

The same physical connections are made across the dummy load with the oscilloscope for PEP measurements, but the transmitter should be driven by a two-tone oscillator – see Fig 6.6.2. The output of the oscillator should be fed into the microphone socket and be of amplitude equivalent to that from the microphone. Set the timebase on the oscilloscope to be in the audio range and a waveform similar to that shown in Fig 6.6.3 will be obtained. Measure the peak-to-peak voltage V_{pp} at the peak of the envelope (as shown); the power is given by the same formula as above.

The input capacitance of an oscilloscope can start to have an appreciable effect at 30MHz – the reactance of 25pF is 212Ω at 30MHz and obviously affects the readings. It may then be better to use a divide-by-10 probe (see Chapter 3) that will decrease the parallel capacitive loading to about 12pF. This still represents a capacitive reactance of 442Ω at 30MHz and the voltage read from the screen will be lower than the real value.

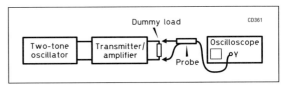

Fig 6.6.2. RF measurement for SSB work

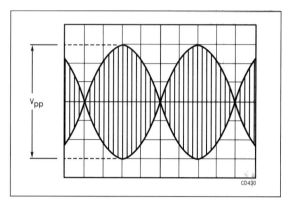

Fig 6.6.3. Two-tone test display

If the same oscilloscope is continually used to monitor output power on SSB, then note should be made on the graticule or display of the positions corresponding to various power levels. The peak of the speech modulated waveform should then never exceed the maximum permitted level – see Fig 6.6.4.

If it is possible to feed the Y-signal directly to the plates, then the capacitive loading is much smaller and the readings are therefore more accurate. It will then be possible to use the oscilloscope at higher frequencies – see Chapter 11.

6.7   The SWR meter

Reflectometers designed as VSWR indicators have normally used sampling loops capacitively coupled to a length of transmission line. This results in a meter deflection that is roughly proportional to frequency, and they are therefore unsuitable for power measurement unless calibrated for use over a narrow band.

By the use of lumped components this shortcoming can be largely eliminated and the following design may be regarded as independent of frequency up to about

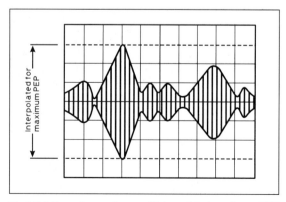

Fig 6.6.4. Speech waveform and interpolated maximum PEP level

70MHz [3]. This design has been around for quite some time.

Reflectometers can also be used for transmission-line measurements – see Chapter 7.

6.7.1   Circuit description

The circuit is shown in Fig 6.7.1 and uses a current transformer T1 in which the low resistance at the secondary is split into two equal parts R3 and R4. The centre section is taken to the voltage-sampling network (R1, R2, RV1) so that the sum and difference voltages are available at the ends of the transformer secondary winding.

Layout of the sampling circuit is fairly critical. The input and output sockets should be a few inches apart and connected together with a short length of coaxial cable. The coaxial cable outer (braid) must be earthed at one end only so that it acts as an electrostatic screen between the primary and secondary of the toroidal transformer. The layout of the sensing circuits in a similar instrument is shown in Fig 6.7.2.

The primary of the toroidal transformer is formed by threading a ferrite ring on to the coaxial cable. The secondary winding is 12 turns of 24swg (0.56mm) enamelled copper wire, equally spaced around the entire circumference of the ring. The ferrite material should maintain a high permeability over the frequency range to be used: the original used a Mullard FX1596 which is no longer available; suggested alternatives are Philips FX3852 or 432202097180 and Fair-rite 5961000301.

Other components in the sampling circuits should have the shortest possible leads; R1 and R2 should be non-inductive carbon types. For powers above about 100W, R1 can consist of several 2W carbon resistors in parallel. RV1 should be a miniature skeleton potentiometer in order to keep stray reactance to a minimum. The detector diodes, D1 and D2, should be matched point-contact germanium types (see note below) with a PIV rating of about 50V; OA91 diodes are suitable (with OA79 an alternative if available). The resistors R3 and R4 should be matched to 5% or better.

The ratio of the sampling resistors R1 and R2 is determined by the sensitivity of the current sensing circuit. As the two sampling voltages must be equal in magnitude under matched conditions, RV1 provides a fine adjustment of the ratio.

Note that diodes with low forward voltage drop are essential if an instrument is to be used at low power levels, and this dictates the use of germanium diodes or Schottky diodes such as the BAT85. Otherwise, silicon diodes such as the 1N914 may be substituted. To increase the sensitivity at low power levels, eg 1W, the feed line could be looped through the toroid. It may be necessary to use a large toroid or smaller coaxial cable (this will not cope with high powers!).

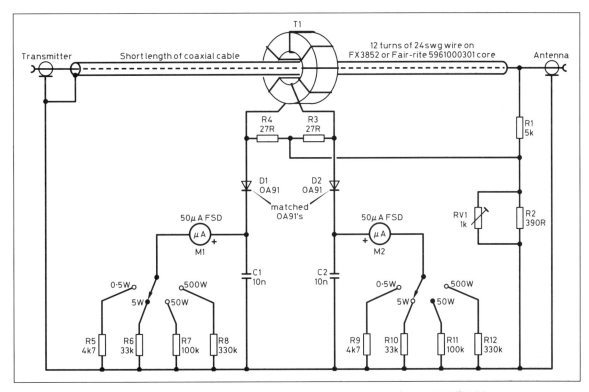

Fig 6.7.1. Circuit of frequency-independent directional wattmeter with four ranges, corresponding to FSDs of 0.5, 5, 50 and 500W in 50Ω lines. The outer of the coaxial cable acts as an electrostatic screen between the centre conductor and the secondary winding of the transformer; the cable length is unimportant

6.7.2   Calibration

Accurate calibration requires a transmitter and a power meter, RF voltmeter or possibly an oscilloscope. The wattmeter is calibrated by feeding power through the meter into a dummy load of 50Ω. RV1 is adjusted for minimum reflected power indication and the power scale calibrated according to the power being dissipated in the load. The reflected power meter is calibrated by reversing the connections to the coaxial line.

The instrument has full-scale deflections of 0.5, 5, 50

Table 6.7.1. Components list for the SWR meter

R1	5k carbon (see text)	C1, 2	10n ceramic
R2	390R carbon	T1	Philips FX3852,
R3, 4	27R, 2W carbon		4332202097180
R5, 9	4k7		Fair-rite 5961000301
R6, 10	33k		with 12t 24swg ECW
R7, 11	100k	D1, 2	OA91 matched (see text)
R8, 12	330k	M1, 2	50μA FSD meters
RV1	1k skeleton pot, 0.5W	S1, 2	1-pole, 4-way rotary switch

Resistors are 0.25W/0.5W, 5% unless specified otherwise.

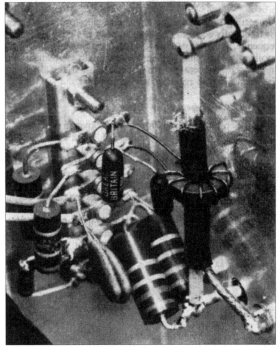

Fig 6.7.2. View of the sensing circuits of the frequency-independent directional wattmeter

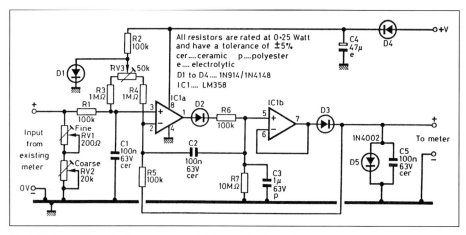

Fig 6.8.1. Circuit for adapting a commercial SWR meter to read PEP

advance in the feedback loop to prevent overshoot on rapid transients. The small voltage drop of approximately 0.6V across D1 is used to balance out voltage and current offsets in the op-amps via RV3, R3 and R4. The LM358 dual op-amp was chosen because it can operate down to zero output on a single DC supply of 4–25V. D4 protects against supply reversal and C4 provides a low supply impedance. D5 and C5 protect the meter from overload and RF respectively.

and 500W which is selected by the range switch. These should not normally be ganged since the reverse power will normally be much less than the forward power.

6.8 Adapting a commercial SWR meter to read PEP

6.8.1 General

This project shows how to convert a standard average-reading VSWR meter to reading PEP as well. It uses the existing meters which are already scaled and means that the RF sensing is already done. It will also mean that all the existing features, characteristics and faults of the existing meter still exist. As the additional circuit only affects the DC side, the original frequency range is still valid. The circuit was first described by GW4NAH [4].

The typical moving-coil instrument is incapable of responding fast enough to record PEP without some assistance. The method used here is to store the value across a capacitor and use an IC op-amp as a buffer amplifier to drive the meter circuit. The circuit is shown in Fig 6.8.1.

6.8.2 Circuit description

The variable resistors RV1 and RV2 replace the meter of an existing VSWR instrument. The voltage developed across this resistor combination is fed via R1/C1 to the non-inverting input of IC1a. The output of this charges C3 via D2 and R6, with a rise time constant of 0.1s. C3 can only discharge via R7 and the input resistance of IC1b, and this gives a decay time constant of about 10s. The voltage across C3 is buffered by voltage follower IC1b and fed to the existing VSWR moving-coil meter and to R5 as 100% feedback to the inverting input of IC1a. The overall circuit has unity gain, causing the output voltage to rise quickly to the exact peak of the input voltage which is held for a short period. C2 provides a slight phase

6.8.3 Construction

The module can be constructed from readily available components on a small PCB. This can be mounted inside an existing RF power/VSWR instrument. It may be fixed by any suitable means but this must be done after calibration. Placement is not critical, except where the VSWR meter is combined with an antenna tuner, and in this case the module should be kept well away from, and shielded from, the strong RF fields which exist around tuner coils, capacitors and their connecting leads.

6.8.4 Interconnections

Undo both leads from the moving-coil meter (only from the forward power meter if there are two). Check that the negative lead is grounded (in most instruments it is but the odd one can be found where the positive lead is earthed and this will have consequences when supplying power to the module). Ascertain that the meter resistance falls in the range of RV1 + RV2, ie between 0 and 2200Ω. All commercial meters encountered so far do but some homebrew models using meters with 100μA FSD or less may not – in this case increase RV2 to 5 or 10kΩ.

Table 6.8.1. Components list for adapting a commercial meter to read PEP

R1, 2,		C1, 2, 5	100n, 63V ceramic
5, 6	100k	C3	1μ, 63V ceramic
R3, 4	1M	C4	47μ electrolytic
R7	10M	D1–4	1N914, 1N4148
RV1	200R preset pot	D5	1N4002
RV2	2k preset pot	IC1	LM358
RV3	50k preset pot		

Resistors are 0.25W/0.5W, 5% unless specified otherwise.

Next, connect the former meter leads to the input terminals of the module and the module's output leads to the meter, carefully preserving polarities. A DPDT switch or PTT-operated relay can be inserted to switch the PEP module in or out for SSB and other modes. An alternative method of reducing the peak-holding feature of the module is to reduce R7 by switching, say, a 220kΩ resistor across it.

A DC voltage supply anywhere between 4 and 25V can be used, and the current required is a minimal 1mA. If the negative meter earth was found to be earthed, a suitable voltage source (9 or 13.8V) that is 'on' when transmitting can be found on the back of most transceivers. Use a single wire to connect that voltage, preferably through a 2.7kΩ current-limiting resistor to the positive terminal on the module. The coaxial braid will provide the negative supply.

In the rare case where the positive meter terminal is found to be earthed, a floating power supply must be used, ie neither terminal connected to earth. As an alternative to either of these, three penlight cells or a PP3 battery could be used.

6.8.5 Calibration

First, the op-amp offsets must be balanced out using RV3. Next, a calibration level must be established. With the PEP module out of circuit, the transmitter in a constant-carrier condition (eg tune, CW or FM) and the VSWR meter between the transmitter and dummy load, apply some RF power to provide at least half-scale deflection. Make careful note of the power reading and *do not change the transmitter power setting until calibration is complete*. Reconnect the PEP module, set RV1 and RV2 to zero (fully counter-clockwise) and apply the DC power to it. Switch the transmitter back on at the previously set power output, adjust RV2 to a setting just below the present output and then use the FINE potentiometer RV1 to obtain an exact reading – it is best to have it at about mid-range position.

This calibration procedure ensures that the combination of the preset potentiometers presents the same load to the VSWR instrument as does the moving-coil meter. As the overall gain is unity, the readings should be the same. Turn the gain setting down quickly and it should be noted that the reading is held for a while on the meter. Switch off the transmitter, revert to SSB and then try transmitting into the dummy load using speech – it should be noted that the peaks are again held for a short period so that the value can be read.

6.8.6 Results

The results will probably be surprising. Without the module normal speech will show peak meter readings of, say, 30% of what an oscilloscope would indicate. With the module it may be of the order of 100%. A whistle without the module will show only some 80–90%. Tapping the microphone without the module will probably give no meter flicker at all; with the module, just see what it reads!

6.9 An in-line wattmeter showing PEP and carrier power

6.9.1 General

Reflectometers designed as VSWR indicators normally use sampling loops capacitively coupled to a length of transmission line. Such instruments give a meter deflection which is approximately proportional to frequency and are therefore unsuitable for power measurement unless calibrated for use over a narrow band.

This shortcoming can be avoided in the HF bands by the use of a toroid transformer as a current detector and a voltage detector consisting of either two resistors or two capacitors connected as a potentiometer across the line. A capacitive divider is used in this design. The complete instrument gives simultaneous indication of forward and reflected power and will indicate either carrier power or, by switching in a long-time-constant circuit, will indicate peak envelope power. This is an alternative to the oscilloscope method. The calibration of this instrument should be checked against the oscilloscope method or other known method of suitable accuracy.

The circuit diagram is shown in Fig 6.9.1. A short length of coaxial cable connected between input and output sockets passes through the toroidal transformer, which consists of a dust-iron core, the coaxial cable acting as the single-turn primary and the secondary consisting of 36 turns of enamelled copper wire. The coaxial outer is earthed at one end only and acts as an electrostatic screen between primary and secondary. If the open-circuit outer is disliked, an alternative is to earth the outer at both ends and to break it for a very short section where the toroid is located, bridging the screen connection outside the toroid. The current transformer secondary is terminated in a pair of series-connected, low-value resistors (R1 and R2) to provide a centre tap. The ends of the winding produce voltages in anti-phase so that addition and subtraction can be performed with the voltage derived from the capacitive divider. Under matched conditions, the voltage divider is set up to produce a voltage equal to that from one half of the current transformer and is fed in at the centre point. This doubles the voltage shown by the meter connected to the forward-indicating diode and nulls the voltage shown by the reverse-indicating diode.

6.9.2 Construction

The prototype was constructed in a die-cast box, the size being mainly determined by the choice of meter size.

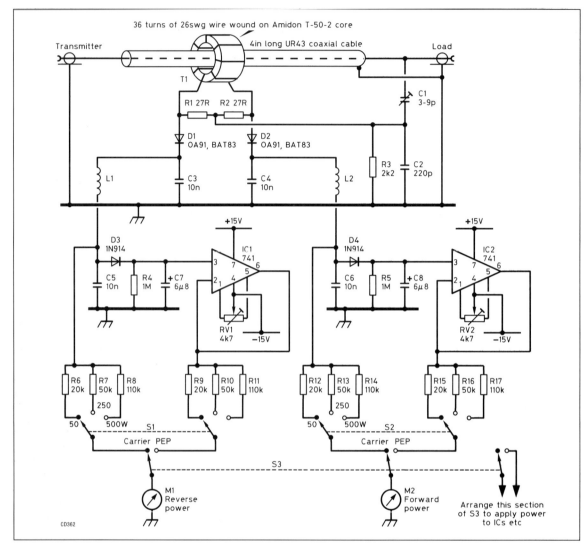

Fig 6.9.1. Circuit of in-line carrier/PEP wattmeter

The input and output connectors are mounted across the short side of the box so that the discontinuity caused by the break in the coaxial outer is minimised – see Fig 6.9.2. The capacitive divider, consisting of a 3–9pF trimmer (note the original used a piston trimmer which may now be hard to find) in series with a 220pF silver mica capacitor, is mounted directly across the coaxial socket with the minimum of lead inductance. The thin wires normally provided on silver mica capacitors are too inductive and should be backed up or replaced by copper foils (5mm wide in the prototype). A very small amount of inductance in this area will make the power indication frequency dependent. The bypass capacitors C3 and C4 should be earthed to the same point as the 220pF capacitor.

Table 6.9.1. In-line meter for carrier and PEP power

R1, 2	27R, 1W (see text)	L1, 2	1mH
R3	2k2 (see text)	T1	Amidon T50-2 core
R4, 5	1M		Secondary 36t, 26swg
R6, 9,		C1	3–9p trimmer, high
12, 15	20k (see text)		voltage
R7, 10,		C2	220p silver mica
13, 15	50k (see text)	C3–6	10n ceramic disc
R8, 11,		C7, 8	6m8 tantalum, 25V
14, 17	110k (see text)	S1, 2	2-pole, 3-way switch
RV1, 2	4k7 preset pot	S3	SPCO to suit
IC1, 2	741		construction
D1, 2	OA91, BAT83	M1, 2	50μA FSD meter
D3, 4	1N914		

Resistors are 0.25W/0.5W, 5% unless specified otherwise.

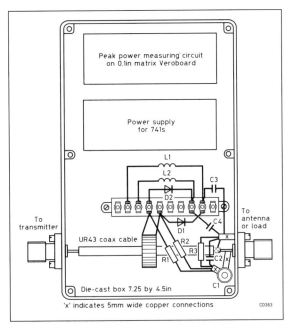

Peak power measuring circuit
on 0.1in matrix Veroboard

Power supply
for 741s

L1
L2
C3
D2
To
transmitter
C4
D1
UR43 coax cable
R2
R3
R1
C2
To
antenna
or load
C1
Die-cast box 7.25 by 4.5in
'x' indicates 5mm wide copper connections
CD363

Fig 6.9.2. Component layout for the in-line wattmeter. Note: the lead lengths around C1 and C2 have been exaggerated for clarity

The winding specified for the toroidal secondary almost fills the inner circumference but allows a spacing of about one wire diameter at the outer circumference. The winding may be varied if necessary, too few turns resulting in reduced sensitivity at low frequency, too many turns having a similar effect at high frequency due to self-capacitance.

The transformer is wound on an Amidon dust-iron core type T50-2 and is wound with 36 turns of 26swg enamelled copper wire. This core will just pass over a length of UR43 coaxial cable which should be adequate for powers up to about 400W PEP. Larger diameter cores are available if it is desired to use a heavier coaxial cable but the required winding must be found experimentally. Ferrite cores may also be used and will generally need a reduced number of turns. This will tend to increase the upper frequency limit due to the reduced self-capacitance of the winding.

The detector diodes should preferably be matched point-contact germanium types or Schottky types (for low capacitance and good HF performance) such as the OA91 or BAT83 which have a minimum PIV rating of 50V. The current transformer resistors should be matched to 5% or better and be of 1W rating.

Separate range switches are provided for forward and reverse power (S1 and S2) since the reverse power will normally be much smaller (the fact that half-power is indicated at about 70% of FSD gives a useful expansion

in the low-power region). The meter resistors (R6–R17) are selected experimentally as described later, and the values given in the component list are typical only. Raising the value of R3 will increase the sensitivity at low frequencies.

The potentiometers RV1 and RV2 serve to null out any offset voltage at the output of the op-amps, which act as voltage followers to drive the meter circuits and prevent loading of the long-time-constant (6.8µF/1MΩ) circuits. It may be possible to omit the potentiometers altogether. The bypass capacitors C5 and C6 should be mounted close to the op-amps.

The op-amps which are used only during PEP measurements require a symmetrical supply of ±12–15V, and this can be obtained from a power supply shown in Chapter 12.

6.9.3   Calibration

Transmitter power should be fed through the instrument into a matched dummy load, with temporary resistors being placed *in situ* for the meter resistors. Both meters will deflect and the trimmer C1 should be adjusted until one meter (REVERSE POWER) indicates zero. If some fictitious reflected power is still shown, balance may be slightly improved by changing one of the 27Ω resistors by a few percent. Sometimes the effect is caused by stray couplings, and slight movement of the coaxial cable may give an improvement, especially if the fictitious reading occurs at the higher frequencies. Steps should be taken to ensure that any adjustment of this type is physically permanent. Once these adjustments are optimised, the forward power meter may be calibrated by adjusting the temporary variable resistors at full-scale deflection for selected powers and then replacing by fixed resistors of equal value. Calibration curves can be drawn for the various ranges – a typical curve is given in Fig 6.9.3. The reverse power meter may be calibrated in a similar way by reversing the direction of power flow. The meter resistors will be similar but not necessarily equal for the two directions. The power being measured can be determined by measuring the voltage across the dummy load and then making the appropriate calculation.

The meter resistors for the PEP part of the meter can then be found in a similar manner. Single-tone drive should be used throughout the calibration process. If a two-tone drive is used, the PEP reading should indicate twice the power shown as for carrier only. The power ranges will be chosen according to individual requirements but it is probably unnecessary to provide a range of less than 50W FSD as the scale shape will give a useful indication down to 1W on this range (10% of full scale). Should a 5W full-scale range be provided, the scale shape is likely to be significantly different to the higher power ranges, due to the diode characteristics. When using the instrument to show peak transmitted power, it is helpful to have both forward and reflected power meters on the same range so that the two readings may be mentally subtracted.

The 1MΩ and 6.8μF time-constant components result in a steady meter reading during continuous speech, but they can be reduced in value if a more rapid response is required.

The prototype instrument showed a variation of indicated power with frequency of about ±5% between 3.5MHz and 28MHz, and showed a fictitious reflected power reading corresponding to 2μA meter deflection on the 50W range at 28MHz only after the adjustments described had been made.

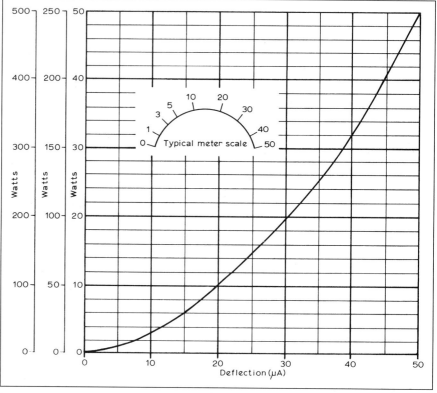

Fig 6.9.3. Typical calibration curve for the in-line wattmeter

6.10 Simple in-line RF power indicator for 1296MHz

A simple and reliable RF power indicator for insertion in the output line of a 1296MHz transmitter can be readily constructed taking advantage of the microstrip technique. For this purpose, good-quality glassfibre double-sided board is needed. Leave one side as an earth plane and etch the other side as shown in Fig 6.10.1.

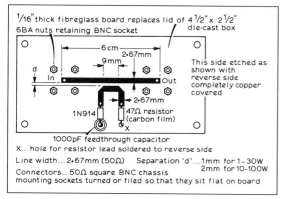

Fig 6.10.1. A simple forward power indicator for a 50Ω line

The insertion loss of this type of indicator is of the order of 0.5dB and it may therefore be permanently connected in circuit. The spacing between the line and the coupling loop will need to be decided on the basis of the power expected to be normally used (ie voltage on the line). The whole assembly should be enclosed in a metal box.

Although the device is defined as a forward indicator, if the connections are reversed it may alternatively be used for indicating reflected power.

6.11 QRP wattmeter

6.11.1 General

The wattmeter described here will read up to a maximum of 3W and a frequency of 30MHz. It is in essence a peak-reading voltmeter with internal 50Ω dummy load and is not designed to read standing wave ratios. Sufficient information is given for the design to cope with varying meters and full-scale power levels.

6.11.2 Circuit description

The circuit of the complete unit is given in Fig 6.11.1. R1 forms the dummy load, D1 provides rectification, C1

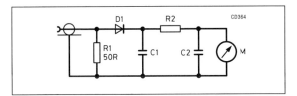

Fig 6.11.1. Circuit diagram of QRP wattmeter

smoothing, R2 is to limit the current through the meter M and C2 provides RF decoupling.

The dummy load should be made from carbon resistors and be able to dissipate 5W. As a minimum, use 1W resistors: three 270Ω and two 220Ω resistors will give a load of 49.5Ω. Another arrangement would be four 330Ω and three 390Ω resistors, giving an equivalent resistance of 50.5Ω. Other arrangements are of course possible.

The diode needs a little consideration as it must be capable of high-speed working, have a minimum PIV of 23V and as low a forward drop as possible in order to minimise errors at the low-power end. Although the ubiquitous 1N914/1N4148 is more than adequate, a lower forward voltage drop can be obtained from a Schottky diode such as the BAT85. For higher power levels use the 1N914. Both capacitors should be of the ceramic type with at least a 30V rating.

The value of resistor R2 can be calculated for use with meters of various sensitivity (use a meter of between 50μA and 1mA sensitivity). Neglecting the meter resistance, R2 is given by:

$$R_2 = \frac{V}{I_{FSD}}$$

where V is the peak value of the rectified sine wave and I_{FSD} is the sensitivity of the meter.

V is calculated from:

$$V = \sqrt{(100P)}$$

where P is the power being measured.

Thus, for a 100μA meter and full-scale deflection for 5W, $R = 223.61\text{k}\Omega$ (220kΩ + 3.6kΩ) – the meter resistance of about 1kΩ is negligible compared to this. Assuming the meter has a linear scale, then the current corresponding to a given power is:

Power (W)	Current reading (μA)
0.1	14
0.5	32
1.0	45
2.5	71
5.0	100

Below 0.1W the forward voltage drop of the diode becomes significant.

6.11.3 Construction

It is suggested that the whole unit is mounted in a metal box with some ventilation for the dummy load. The circuit from diode to meter should be kept as far away as possible from any circuits carrying RF, and shielded if at all possible. Use a BNC or SO239 socket for connection.

6.12 RF ammeters

At frequencies below about 30MHz, it is possible to use thermocouple ammeters to measure the RF current in a load instead of incorporating the thermocouple in the load – such ammeters are known as *RF ammeters*. This is of some convenience when the meter is normally used as an output indicator in series with the antenna feeder/load. These units are still in production (Anders) but are not cheap; they may occasionally be found at various radio rallies. The principal limitations are:

1. The non-linear meter scale makes readings below 25% of FSD of little value.
2. Any standing waves on the feeder will result in fictitious current readings, although for a given load maximum current readings will correspond to maximum output.
3. Shunt capacitance may reduce the meter reading as frequency is increased. Mounting the meter free of metal panels will help but will not overcome the built-in limitations of the instrument.
4. The product of the current squared and load resistance will only give an indication of average power.

6.13 References

[1] *Amateur Radio Licence (A) or (B): Terms, Provisions and Limitations Booklet BR68*, Radiocommunications Agency.

[2] *ARRL Handbook for the Radio Amateur* (any edition after 1986, typically Chapters 25 and 34).

[3] *HF Antennas for all Locations*, 2nd edn, L A Moxon, G6XN, RSGB, 1993.

[4] 'Keeping an eye on your sideband PEP', J Fielden, GW4NAH, *Radio Communication* January 1989.

Chapter 7

Antenna and transmission line measurements

7.1 Introduction

Some knowledge of antenna tuning and matching conditions may be obtained by measuring forward and reflected power or voltage on a transmission line by means of directional wattmeters or reflectometers. If the forward voltage V_f and reflected voltage V_r can be measured, then the VSWR is given by:

$$VSWR = \frac{V_f + V_r}{V_f - V_r}$$

Knowing the voltages, these can be related to the forward and reflected powers P_f and P_r respectively.

The VSWR can also be calculated using the formula shown on the graph of Fig 7.1.1, which also shows the relationship between forward and reflected power and VSWR. The graph of Fig 7.1.2 shows the percentage reflected power versus VSWR. The following computer program will also produce the VSWR and percentage reflected power if the forward and reverse power levels are known:

```
10  REM SWR calculation from forward and
    reflected powers
20  CLS
30  INPUT "Forward power (W) ",PF
40  INPUT "Reflected power (W) ",PR
50  S=SQR(PR/PF)
60  SWR=(1+S)/(1-S)
70  PRP=100*PR/PF
```

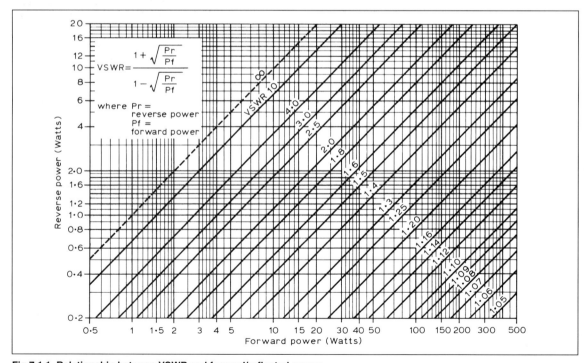

Fig 7.1.1. Relationship between VSWR and forward/reflected power

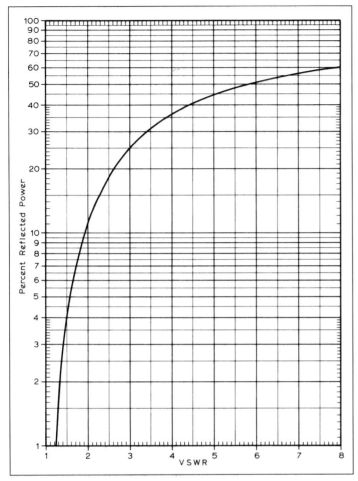

Fig 7.1.2. Reflected power as a percentage vs SWR

```
80 PRINT "SWR is ";SWR;" and % reflected
   power is ";PRP
90 END
```

The VSWR can also be defined by knowing the impedance of the feed line and the terminating impedance: the
equation has two forms:

$$\text{For } Z_L > Z_0, \text{ then VSWR } = \frac{Z_L}{Z_0}$$

$$\text{For } Z_L < Z_0, \text{ then VSWR } = \frac{Z_0}{Z_L}$$

In theory a 1:1 VSWR is desirable but this is a condition
that is often impossible to achieve. Looking at the problem from a practical viewpoint, it is worth trying to get a
VSWR of better than 2:1 (equivalent to 11% reflected
power – see Fig 7.1.2). The guidelines in Table 7.1.1 are
suggested practical conditions and the actions that should
be taken.

The effectiveness of an antenna system
may be investigated by means of a simple
receiver used as a field strength meter. The
measurement should be made ideally at
several wavelengths from the transmitting
antenna and with a receiver having an antenna with the same polarisation. A short
non-resonant dipole is usually adequate.

More complete knowledge of the properties of an antenna may be obtained by
measuring its resistive and reactive components at the desired working frequencies – these are especially required when
trying to provide drive equipment such as
amplifiers and transmitters, designing
matching networks and considering which
coaxial cables to use. These parameters can
be measured by means of RF bridges. Such
bridges may either use a broad-band signal source (eg a noise diode) and a selective detector (ie a receiver) or a signal
source at a specific frequency, in which
case the detector need not be selective. It
is not easy to construct RF bridges for use
over a reasonably wide frequency range
due to the necessity to keep stray cap-
acitances and residual inductances to an
insignificant level. In general, it becomes
necessary to adopt VHF techniques to
make a bridge satisfactory at HF.

Two bridges are discussed. One is the
noise bridge, and here the receiver is tuned
to find the frequency for the measurement
and the signal nulled to find the impedance. The second version also allows impedance to be measured, the measurement
being made at any selected frequency; however, this requires a signal source at the frequency of measurement
and it is more often termed an *RF impedance bridge*.

The reader is also referred to Chapter 6 for RF power
measurements where there may be other suitable equipment.

Table 7.1.1. Guidelines for various VSWRs

VSWR	% reflected power	Comment
0–2.5	0–18	Solid-state transmitter SWR protection starts to operate, try looking for an improvement at the higher SWR value
2.5–5.0	18–45	Valve equipment probably OK, start looking for a problem or improve the VSWR to get closer to 2:1
5.0–∞	45–100	Check the feed/antenna system: there is a problem!

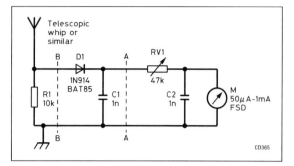

Fig 7.2.1. Simple untuned field strength meter

7.2   Field strength meters

Field strength meters employed by amateurs are normally used as indicators to maximise the radiated power and not to make an actual field strength measurement at a receiving site. The absorption wavemeter or dip oscillator (in absorption mode) can be used for this purpose and suitable units are described in Chapter 5. These units may need some form of external telescopic antenna to be fitted. However, the use of a tuned circuit is sometimes inconvenient as no attempt is being made to differentiate between wanted and unwanted transmitted signals (this should already have been dealt with in the transmitter!).

The alternative is to use a simple type of system such as that shown in Fig 7.2.1. A signal is picked up by the antenna, rectified and smoothed by D1/C1, and the resulting DC signal is then indicated on the meter M1, with RV1 acting as a sensitivity control. C2 provides an AC short across the meter for any unwanted RF signals.

Construct the unit in a box, using either a telescopic whip or a loop of wire. The unit can be used for relative field strength measurements at a given frequency. It should not be used for relative measurements between different frequencies as the efficiency of the antenna and rectifier will affect readings. It should be a useful device for tuning a transmitter to obtain maximum radiated power or adjusting an antenna for maximum radiated power. By splitting the circuit at AA, the antenna/rectifier combination could be used as a remote reading head, with the meter/sensitivity control being in the shack.

7.3   Higher-sensitivity, broad-band field strength meter

7.3.1   General

The concept here is to amplify the received signal first and then to detect it to drive a meter. This can be accomplished by using one of the relatively inexpensive broad-band RF amplifiers. Typical of these are SL560, SL1612, OM335/361 and the MAR series from Mini Circuits amongst others. An alternative would be to use the 10116 IC as used in the 600MHz frequency counter (see Chapter 4).

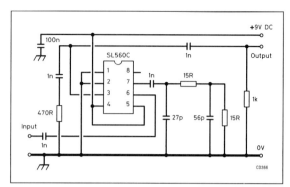

Fig 7.3.1. Broad-band amplifier based on SL560C

The reader is also referred to Section 10.7 of reference [1]. These amplifiers would be placed in the circuit of Fig 7.2.1 at position BB. They should be constructed on circuit board with a good ground plane. All components should have short leads to minimise lead inductance and the capacitors carefully chosen for the frequency range envisaged. These devices generally have outputs of the order of +10dBm, and it is therefore imperative that diode D1 is of a type with low forward volt drop such as Schottky type BAT85. If the field strengths being measured are very low, then it may be possible to cascade two or more such amplifiers.

Constructional details should follow the guidelines as given in Section 7.2.

7.3.2   Circuit description

Fig 7.3.1 shows a circuit based on an SL560C. This operates from a +9V DC supply and is quoted as having a gain of 13dB with the −1dB points at 6MHz and 300MHz. This Plessey IC is available from several suppliers.

Fig 7.3.2 shows a circuit based around a MAR8 monolithic amplifier produced by Mini Circuits – similar devices are available by Avantek. The circuit has a response from DC to 1GHz with a quoted gain at 100MHz of 33dB and 23dB at 1GHz; the maximum output is about +10dBm. The device requires 7.5V at 36mA, and the circuit shows a series resistor for operation from a 9V DC supply.

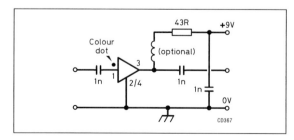

Fig 7.3.2. Broad-band amplifier based around a MAR8

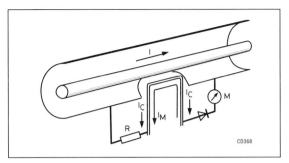

Fig 7.4.1. Coupling between inner conductor and sampling loop

7.4 Reflectometers

7.4.1 General

The measurement of forward and reverse power at HF is covered in Chapter 6. Although similar concepts apply at VHF and UHF, the introduction of the sampling section can create discontinuities and thus itself affect the VSWR on the transmission line. It is for this reason that more care is taken in making the sampling section.

For VHF no practical design is readily available for the home constructor in which the power indication is independent of frequency, although commercial instruments are available covering significant bandwidths.

7.4.2 Reflectometer for VHF and UHF

This instrument will indicate effective forward and reflected power from which the VSWR can be obtained. However, the meter deflections are roughly proportional to the frequency so that it is only useful for power measurement if calibrated against another power meter for each frequency band. The instrument described is intended for use on the 2m and 70cm bands – the meter deflection may be inconveniently small at lower frequencies.

The principle of operation may be seen from Fig 7.4.1, which represents a section along a coaxial line through which a current I is flowing in the direction indicated on the inner conductor. A loop is inserted through the outer wall into the field inside. One end of this loop is terminated by a resistor R and the other by an indicator which is usually a diode and microammeter (M). Current I_M is induced into the loop flowing in the opposite direction to that in the inner conductor. In addition, since there is capacitance between the loop and the inner conductor, a current I_C flows in each leg of the loop.

The currents in the resistance arm are in the same direction, whereas those in the metering arm are in opposite directions and tend to cancel. By adjustment of the mutual inductance and capacitance, complete cancellation may be obtained and the meter will read zero. If the current I in the inner conductor is reversed, I_M reverses

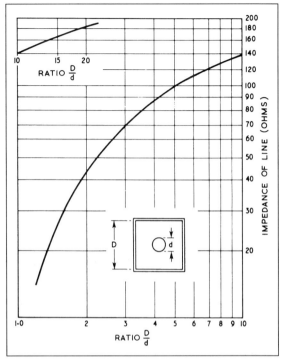

Fig 7.4.2. Graph showing variation of Z_0 with D/d for round conductor in square cavity

and the meter will read $I_M + I_C$, from which the VSWR can be found. It is convenient to use two coupling loops or to reverse one, so as to read current in the two directions without having to reverse the current flow in the coaxial section.

7.4.3 Construction of the line

In order to make the coupling to the inner conductor, it is necessary to have a section of the transmission line enlarged so that the directional couplers can be inserted. The enlarged section may be of either round or square cross-section but the latter is easier to construct unless access to a lathe is possible. The impedance of the new section of the line must, of course, be the same as that of the normal feeder line. The graph of Fig 7.4.2 shows the relationship between the inner and outer dimensions for any impedance between 20 and 200Ω of a square section. The formula for a circular coaxial section is:

$$Z_0 = 138 \log_{10} \frac{1.178D}{d}$$

Fig 7.4.3 shows a suitable general arrangement. In this, the bottom is closed by a suitable plate and the ends by plates fixed to all four sides of the square section. In order to preserve the impedance at each end of the enlarged

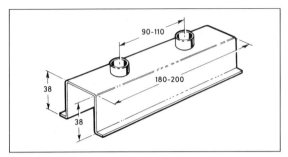

Fig 7.4.3. Square section of line showing positions of coupler sockets. All dimensions are in millimetres

line, tapers of constant D/d must be provided as shown in Fig 7.4.4.

Note that the inner conductor may be shaped by turning or fitting a thin copper cone rolled and soldered to the inner conductor; the outer taper can be made by either fitting blocks in the ends or folding thin sheets into the correct shape. If this latter method is used, overlap should be allowed for adequate contact to the outer.

7.4.4   Detector head mounting

The detector heads and sockets are made from telescopic tubes of about 24 and 25mm diameter, the sockets being 6.5mm long and spaced as shown in Fig 7.4.3. The sockets are soldered into holes cut to fit them and are slotted so that they may be clamped tightly to the detector heads. The clamps can be made from 6.5mm wide brass strip bent round and held together with a 6BA nut and bolt.

7.4.5   The detector heads

The circuit for each detector head is given in Fig 7.4.5 and the general constructional details in Fig 7.4.6. The signal received on the loop (L) is rectified by D1, smoothed by C2 and passed to a meter via the coaxial lead.

The heads are constructed on small rectangular frames made of 6.5mm wide thin brass strip, bent into rectangles which fit snugly into the tubes. It is upon this chassis that all the components are mounted. The upper end of each head is closed by a brass disc and the bottom end is made from a disc of insulating material. These end plates are held in position by 8BA screws which are also used for fixing the chassis inside the tube. It is important

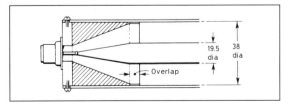

Fig 7.4.4. End taper of both inner and outer of the section (50Ω line). All dimensions are in millimetres

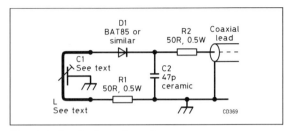

Fig 7.4.5. Circuit of coupler unit

that the heads should be a good fit in their respective tubes so that the whole assembly can be easily pushed together.

The small trimmer capacitor C1 is made by screwing a piece of 6BA studding right through the rectangle end plates. A 9–10mm diameter disc is then soldered to one end, the other slotted to take a screwdriver. The assembly is used to adjust the capacitance between the loop and ground. The coupling loop is made from 1mm (approx 20swg) wire, is 12.5mm wide and about 10mm above the insulated disc on which it is mounted. It is fixed through pairs of small holes 12.5mm apart, each end of the loop being passed through one hole, folded back through its neighbour and then pinched to make a firm anchorage for each leg.

The mounting of the head in the line is shown in Fig 7.4.7.

7.4.6   Terminating resistance

The initial setting-up process requires that a terminating resistance is used at one end. It must look like a resistance, even at 432MHz, which means that must be coaxial and of similar value to the line. This can be either a commercial unit of suitable frequency range or else it can be constructed as shown in Fig 7.4.8. The resistor should have the same DC value as the required terminating

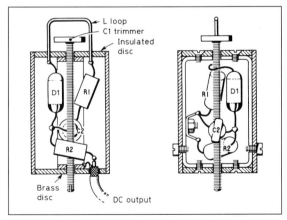

Fig 7.4.6. Two cross-sectional views of detector heads

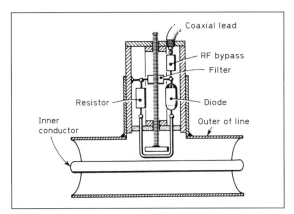

Fig 7.4.7. Mounting of the detector head in the line

resistor and be a carbon type (about 1W). It is used as the inner conductor of a coaxial line. The diameter of the outer conductor should be somewhat smaller than that given by the usual formula for the characteristic impedance of coaxial lines in order to compensate for the reactive nature of the inner – a ratio of diameters of 1.5:1 would be suitable for a 50Ω line.

7.4.7   Setting-up procedure

A low-power oscillator/transmitter modulated with a continuous note should be fed into the reflectometer with the terminating resistor at the other end. Note: use only low power because the terminating resistor may only be 1W. After this setting-up procedure the unit can of course be used at full power.

The detector heads should be inserted so that the loops are about halfway between the inner and outer conductors of the line, using the clamps as depth controls. Plug a set of headphones into the circuit of Fig 7.4.9, which will be connected to the detector heads. Select the head nearest the terminating resistor.

A signal will be heard in the headphones; the detector head should now be rotated in its mounting and the trimmer adjusted until a sharp null is heard – clamp the detector head. The input and output connections to the line should now be reversed and the headphones switched to the opposite head – the same procedure should be followed. This procedure can be carried out on 144MHz but may need slight adjustment for 432MHz.

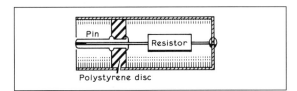

Fig 7.4.8. Construction of the terminating resistance

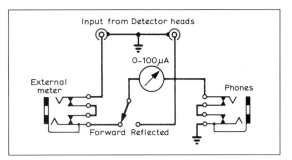

Fig 7.4.9. Circuit diagram of the meter switching for a mounted reflectometer

The unit is now ready for use, and if required it can now be calibrated against a commercial power meter so that the microammeter scale can be read directly in watts.

7.5   Antenna current probe

This fairly simple item of equipment [2] enables estimates of current flowing in antenna/feeder systems to be carried out. Fig 7.5.1(a) shows this in its simplest form, coupled to a wire carrying an RF current. Part of the field

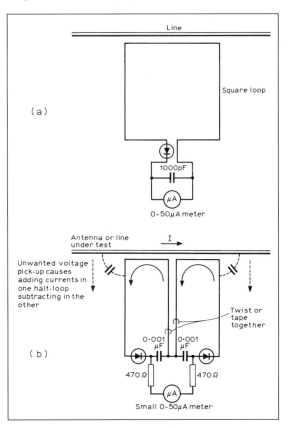

Fig 7.5.1. Two forms of current probe

Fig 7.5.2. Photograph of two-loop current probe

surrounding the antenna wire links with the probe as shown so that an induced voltage given by $V = j\omega MI$ is applied to the diode detector and meter (M being the mutual inductance).

For calibration, in the absence of other access to the transmitter output, a spare plug and socket joined by a small loop of, say, 25mm diameter may be arranged for insertion in the output lead or adjacent to the SWR meter, and this will also allow connection to an oscilloscope. The probe, or other device to be calibrated, is coupled into the small loop to obtain a full-scale reading and the power level reduced in steps.

In use, the loop is held close to the wire or some suitable distance from it, depending on the sensitivity required. Usually a rough estimate of current is sufficient and, having settled on a measuring distance (eg 15mm) as judged by the eye, the repeatability of readings is adequate.

Sometimes, for example when making observations on an open-wire line having a high SWR, readings may be affected by capacitance to ground via the user, a typical symptom of this being dependence of the reading on which way round the probe is held. This effect can be minimised by the balanced diode circuit shown in Fig 7.5.1(b) and as a further measure the meter should be as small as possible – see the photo of Fig 7.5.2. A long insulated handle may also help.

7.6   Representation of an antenna using circuit components

An antenna represents an impedance at the feedpoint to whatever is driving it. This can either be considered as a

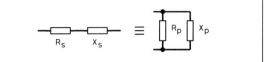

Fig 7.6.1. Series and parallel equivalence

series circuit or a parallel circuit as shown in Fig 7.6.1. It is possible to convert between these circuits, the equations being given below. Please note that these values are only true at one particular frequency.

$$R_p = \frac{R_s^2 + X_s^2}{R_s} \qquad X_p = \frac{R_s^2 + X_s^2}{X_s}$$

$$R_s = R_p \times \frac{X_p^2}{R_p^2 + X_p^2} \qquad X_s = X_p \times \frac{R_p^2}{R_p^2 + X_p^2}$$

For optimum power transfer, the resistive part should equal the source resistance and the reactive part should cancel with the source reactance – in effect the condition for resonance. Thus it is important to be able to make these measurements at the frequency of concern. Remember also, that power can only be dissipated in a resistive element.

Thus, if serious work is to be undertaken on antennas, it is important to determine feedpoint impedances. Commercial equipment to perform this function is quite expensive but the following two circuits will give a good indication of conditions.

Also, do not forget that what the transmitter 'sees' is an impedance represented by the antenna and the associated transmission line. If, and only if, the transmission line is a multiple of half-wavelengths (taking into account the cable velocity factor) will the feedpoint impedance be that of the antenna. Ideally measurements should be made directly at the antenna terminals if at all possible.

7.7   Noise bridge for measuring R and X

7.7.1   General

The circuit described here is an adaptation of that described in the second edition of this book. It allows a modulated signal to be obtained, if desired, by pulsing the supply to the noise generator [3]. Such modulation may aid detection of the balance point, especially if an AM receiver is used. The circuit consists of a wide-band noise generator followed by a bridge for making the measurements. The bridge allows the measurement of the parallel components of an unknown impedance to be measured. The circuit requires 9V DC at about 25mA.

7.7.2   Circuit description

The circuit is shown in Fig 7.7.1. The white noise is generated by the zener diode D1 operating at low current,

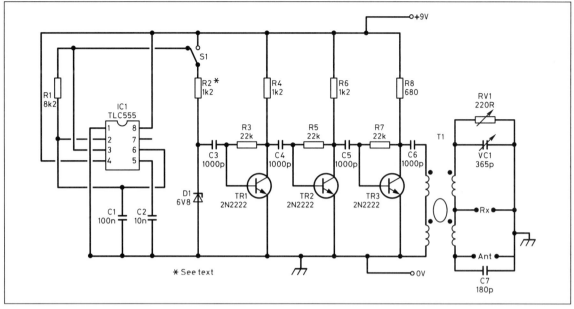

Fig 7.7.1. Circuit diagram of modulated RF noise bridge

and it may be possible to maximise the noise by suitable choice of the zener diode and R2. The frequency range of this noise should extend up to at least 200MHz. The noise source is followed by a three-stage wide-band amplifier to raise the noise level to the order of 100μV, and this enables a receiver to be used as a null indicator.

The noise output from the amplifier is applied to a quadrifilar-wound toroid which forms the transformer T1. This provides two arms of a bridge circuit which has a variable resistor and capacitor in the third arm to obtain a balance against the antenna in the fourth arm. The bridge circuit is shown diagrammatically in Fig 7.7.2.

When the noise across the RV1/VC1 arm equals the noise across the antenna/capacitor combination, the bridge is said to be 'balanced', and this occurs when the received noise signal is at a minimum. The values can be obtained from the settings of RV1 and VC1. The inclusion of C7 allows an offset to be used so that inductive reactance can be measured. The mid-point setting of VC1 is equal to zero reactance. If a noise bridge is only required to measure the resistive part of the antenna impedance, omit C7 and VC1.

Timer IC1 is in astable mode and runs at about 850Hz with 50% duty cycle, and this can be used to provide current for the zener circuit via S1, so modulating the noise source. The zener diode can be alternatively fed from the constant-voltage power supply line.

7.7.3 Construction

The toroid transformer consists of a dust-iron core, type T50-6, which is wound as follows. Cut four lengths of 26swg enamelled copper wire about 120mm long, twist

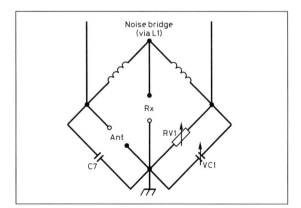

Fig 7.7.2. Diagrammatic representation of noise bridge

Table 7.7.1. Components list for the RF noise bridge

R1	8k2	C2	10n, 50V ceramic
R2, 4, 6	1k2	C3–6	1000p, 50V ceramic
R3, 5, 7	22k	C7	180p silver mica
R8	680R	VC1	365p Jackson type 01 Gang
RV1	220R carbon pot	S1	SPCO switch
TR1–3	2N2222	T1	FT50-6 dust iron core,
D1	6V8 zener,		4 windings, each 14t, or
	400mW		596100001 ferrite core,
IC1	TLC555		4 windings, 6t each
C1	100n, 50V ceramic		

Resistors are 0.25W/0.5W, 5% unless specified otherwise.

them together and then thread them through the toroid to give five or six turns evenly spaced to cover the circumference. Divide the turns into two pairs, each pair consisting of two windings connected in series, the end of one winding connecting to the start of the other – be careful. Check that the two pairs are insulated from each other. Endeavour to keep the lead lengths in the bridge as short as possible and symmetrical. The variable resistor RV1 should be of high quality and with a carbon track – *not wirewound!*

When constructing the circuits, ensure that the noise generator and amplifiers are well away or screened from the bridge transformer and measuring circuit. The potentiometer case should not be earthed and, if it has a metal spindle, this should be isolated from the user and should not contact ground.

The complete circuit should be mounted in a screened box such as a dic-cast type with appropriate connectors – eg UHF type or BNC. In order to avoid noise coupling into the measuring circuit by way of currents in earth loops, the earthed side of the noise source should not be joined to the general chassis earth of the bridge but should be taken by an insulated lead to the frame of the variable capacitor.

As in all high-frequency measuring circuits, lead inductances should be kept to an absolute minimum and, where any lead length more than a few millimetres is unavoidable, copper foil at least 6mm wide should be used. All earth returns should be taken to the capacitor frame. Capacitor C7, which should be silver mica, can be soldered directly across the UNKNOWN socket.

A suitable PCB pattern and component layout are given in Appendix 2.

7.7.4   Calibration

Connect a test resistor (of a carbon type) across the unknown socket with the receiver tuned to 3.5MHz. Adjust RV1 and VC1 to give a null. The value of RV1 is at the position equal to the test resistor, and the capacitor should be at approximately the mid-mesh position or the zero reactance condition – mark these positions. Repeat with different values of test resistor up to 220Ω in order to provide a calibration scale for RV1. Repeat this operation with known values of capacitance in parallel with the test resistor up to a maximum value of 180pF. Mark the corresponding null positions on the VC1 scale with the value of this capacitance. Repeat this procedure at 28MHz to check the accuracy of the bridge. If the layout has been carefully attended to there should be little difference in the null positions.

To calibrate VC1 for negative capacitance values (ie inductance) it is necessary to temporarily place given values of capacitance in parallel with VC1. Gradually decrease the value of these capacitors (CT) from 150pF

towards zero, obtaining null positions and marking the VC1 scale with the value of $-(180 - CT)$ pF, ie if 100pF is substituted then the negative C value is 80pF.

7.8   Using the noise bridge

For work on an antenna, a noise bridge should ideally be connected across the antenna terminals. This is usually not practical, in which case a noise bridge should be connected to the antenna by a length of line which is a multiple of a half-wavelength at the frequency of interest (taking into account the velocity factor of the cable).

Connect the impedance to be measured to the 'unknown' socket, switch on the noise generator and tune the receiver to the frequency at which the test is to be made. Use RV1 and VC1 to obtain a minimum noise reading on the receiver S-meter. The values must now be converted to circuit components. The value recorded from RV1 is the resistive part of the impedance. The value from VC1 is the parallel reactive component of the impedance and, depending on the sign, is either inductive or capacitive. If it is positive, then the value of shunt capacitance is read directly from the VC1 scale. If it is negative, the VC1 reading represents the value of the shunt inductance and must be calculated as below.

If a negative value of capacitance C is obtained, this can be converted to an inductance value using the formula:

$$L = \frac{1}{4\pi^2 f^2 (180 - C)} \quad \mu H$$

where f is in megahertz and C in picofarads. This can be accomplished with the following BASIC program:

```
10   REM Noise bridge inductance calculation
20   CLS
30   C=180
40   INPUT "Negative C value in pF ",CV:
     CV=ABS(CV)
50   INPUT "Working frequency in MHz ",F:
     F=F*1000000
60   K=1/(4*3.14159^2*F^2)
70   L=K*1/((C-CV)*1E-12)
80   L=L*1000000
90   PRINT "Inductance in uH is ",L
100  END
```

7.9   An RF impedance bridge

7.9.1   General

The need for an instrument which will measure impedance is felt at some time or other by every experimenting amateur. The instrument normally used is the full RF bridge, but commercial RF bridges are elaborate and expensive. On the other hand, it is possible to build a simple RF bridge which, provided the limitations are appreciated, can be inexpensive and a most useful adjunct in

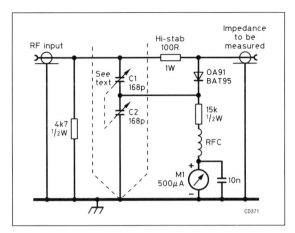

Fig 7.9.1. Simple RF bridge

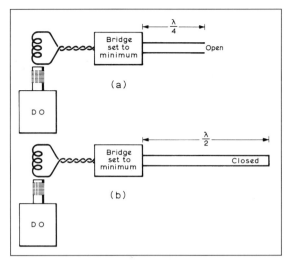

Fig 7.9.2. Use of the RF bridge with a dip oscillator

the amateur workshop. In fact it is essential if experiments with antennas are undertaken.

The instrument described here will measure impedances from 0–400Ω at frequencies up to 30MHz. It does not measure reactance or indicate if the impedance is capacitive or inductive. A good indication of the reactance present can be obtained from the fact that any reactance will mean a higher minimum meter reading, ie not a true null.

7.9.2   Circuit description

There are many possible circuits, some using potentiometers as the variable arm and others variable capacitors, but a typical circuit is shown in Fig 7.9.1. The capacitors have to be differential in action, mounted in such a way that as the capacitance of one decreases the capacitance of the other increases. The capacitors should be the type which has a spindle protruding at either end so that they can be connected together by a shaft coupler. To avoid hand-capacitance effects, the control knob on the outside of the instrument should be connected to the nearest capacitor by a short length of plastic coupling rod. These capacitors form two arms of the bridge, the third arm being the 100Ω non-inductive resistor and the fourth arm the impedance to be measured. Balance of the bridge is indicated by a minimum reading on the meter M1.

7.9.3   Construction

Construction is straightforward, but keep all leads as short as possible. The unit should be built into a metal box and screening provided as shown in Fig 7.9.1.

7.9.4   Signal source and calibration

The instrument can be calibrated by placing across the load terminals various non-reactive resistors (ie not

wire-wound) of known value. The calibration should preferably be made at a low frequency where stray capacitance effects are at a minimum, but calibration holds good throughout the frequency range. In using the instrument, it should be remembered that an exact null will only be obtained on the meter when the instrument has a purely resistive load. When reactance is present, however, it becomes obvious from the behaviour of the meter; adjusting the control knob will give a minimum reading but a complete null cannot be obtained.

The RF input to drive the bridge can be obtained from a dip oscillator, signal generator or low-power transmitter capable of giving up to about 1W of signal power. The signal source can be coupled to the bridge by a short length of coaxial cable directly or via a link coil of about four turns as shown in Fig 7.9.2.

If using a dip oscillator, care should be exercised in order to not overcouple with it as it may pull the frequency or in the worst circumstances stop oscillating. As the coupling is increased it will be seen that the meter reading of the bridge increases up to a certain point, after which further increase in coupling causes the meter reading to fall. A little less coupling than that which gives the maximum bridge meter reading is the best to use. The bridge can be used to find antenna impedance and also used for many other purposes, for example to find the input impedance of a receiver at a particular frequency.

7.9.5   Some practical uses

One useful application of this type of simple bridge is to find the frequency at which a length of transmission line is an electrical quarter-wave or half-wave. If it is desired to find the frequency at which the transmission line is a quarter-wavelength, the line is connected to the bridge and the far end of it is left open-circuit. The bridge control is set to zero ohms. The dip oscillator is then adjusted until the lowest frequency is found at which the bridge shows a sharp null. This is the frequency at which the piece of transmission line is one quarter-wavelength. Odd multiples of this frequency can be checked in the same manner. In a similar way the frequency at which a piece of transmission line is a half-wavelength can also be found but in this case the remote end should be a short-circuit.

The bridge can also be used to check the characteristic impedance of a transmission line. This is often a worthwhile exercise, since appearances can be misleading. The procedure is as follows:

1. Find the frequency at which the length of transmission line under test is a quarter-wavelength long. Once this has been found, leave the oscillator set to this frequency.
2. Select a carbon resistor of approximately the same value as the probable characteristic impedance of the transmission line. Replace the transmission line by this resistor and measure the value of this resistor at the preset frequency. (Note that this will not necessarily be identical with its DC value.)
3. Disconnect the resistor and reconnect the transmission line. Connect the resistor across the remote end of the transmission line.
4. Measure the impedance now presented by the transmission line at the preset frequency. The characteristic impedance (Z_0) is then given by:

$$Z_0 = \sqrt{(Z_s \times Z_r)}$$

where Z_s is the impedance presented by the line plus load and Z_r is the resistor value.

7.10 References

[1] *Microwave Handbook*, Vol 2, ed M W Dixon, G3PFR, RSGB, 1991.
[2] *HF Antennas for all Locations*, 2nd edn, L A Moxon, G6XN, RSGB, 1993.
[3] *The ARRL Handbook for the Radio Amateur*, ARRL, post-1988, Chapter 25.

Chapter 8

Noise measurements

8.1 Introduction

Noise can be defined as any unwanted disturbance that is superimposed on a wanted signal. It will interfere with the information contained within the wanted signal and in the limit will prevent it being decoded. In TV reception it can result in a grainy picture with possible white and black spots and, in the limit, the loss of the picture. In radio reception it can produce crackling or hissing which, in the limit, will mask the speech or music. In data transmission it will affect the reliability with which the data is decoded, a poor signal with a high noise level providing a much higher error rate.

Noise comes from various sources. It can be generated external to any equipment and can be classified as *man-made* (ie from electric motors, ignition systems etc) or *natural* (such as that from lightning discharges or stellar sources). In addition to these, there is what is known as *thermal noise*. At frequencies up to around 21MHz, the external noise is generally greater than any noise generated in a receiver. Above this frequency and up into microwaves the receiver-generated noise is generally dominant, especially at 144MHz and above.

Thermal noise is generated within components by the random agitation of atoms and results in a random voltage. At absolute zero this voltage is zero, increasing as temperature rises. It consists of frequencies that start virtually at DC and rise well into the gigahertz region. Some components generate more noise than others and, if the semiconductor literature is scanned, devices classified as 'low noise' will be noticed.

If a group of components in the front-end of a receiver generate noise in the microvolt region then this can well mask received signals of the same order. It is therefore important that receiver front-ends are well designed and set up in order to minimise the effect of noise. It is the purpose of this chapter to examine noise measurements of receivers.

8.2 Noise figures

In any amplifier, noise is added to the signal so that the signal/noise ratio at the output of the amplifier is worse than at the input, even though the signal has been amplified. This is especially important in receiver RF amplifiers which deal with low-level signals. The ratio

$$\frac{\text{signal/noise in}}{\text{signal/noise out}}$$

is defined as the *noise factor* but, as this ratio can have a wide range of values, it is convenient to express it in decibels (dB). The above ratio then becomes:

$$\text{Noise factor} = 10 \log_{10} \frac{\text{s/n in}}{\text{s/n out}} \quad \text{dB}$$

In a receiver, there are a number of cascaded stages which will each contribute noise but the effect of the noise contribution of each successive stage is reduced by the power gain of the preceding stage. Thus if F_1, F_2 and F_3 are the respective noise figures of each successive stage and P_1, P_2 and P_3 are the stage gains, then the overall receiver noise factor F will be given by:

$$F = F_1 + \frac{F_2 - 1}{P_1} + \frac{F_3 - 1}{P_1 \times P_2}$$

In most cases only the first and second terms are significant.

Noise performance is measured by noting the noise output of the receiver when its input terminals are terminated with the value of source resistance for which it is designed and then adding a known amount of noise at the input such that the value of output noise is doubled. It is then obvious that the added noise is equal to the noise generated by the receiver, although two assumptions are made for this to be true:

(a) all of the known output from the noise source is, in fact, coupled into the receiver; and
(b) the receiver output doubles when the effective input is doubled (ie the receiver is linear over this range of inputs).

The first point will be met provided that:

(a) none of the noise is shunted;
(b) transit time effects are negligible; and

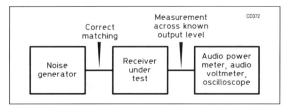

Fig 8.3.1. Arrangement for performing noise measurements

(c) that the output of the noise source is coupled into the receiver by a very short length of low-loss cable of the correct characteristic impedance.

The linearity of the receiver can be established by providing two identical noise sources and shunting the output of the receiver by a 3dB attenuator when the second source is switched on, but for amateur use this is scarcely worthwhile.

8.3   Noise figure measurements [1]

If the radio amateur can get hold of a calibrated noise source then it is possible to obtain accurate noise figures for a piece of equipment. Fig 8.3.1 shows a typical arrangement of equipment. The noise source should be matched to the receiver and the impedance across which the audio output power is measured must be known.

The first reading is taken with the noise generator turned off. The receiver audio gain is adjusted for a convenient noise reading in decibels as observed on the audio power meter.

The noise generator is next turned on and its output is increased until a convenient power ratio, expressed by N_2/N_1 is observed. The ratio N_2/N_1 is referred to as the *Y factor*, and this noise figure measurement is commonly called the *Y-factor method*. The noise figure can be calculated from the *Y* factor and output power of the noise generator, ie:

$$NF = ENR - 10 \log_{10} (Y - 1)$$

where NF is the noise figure in decibels, ENR is the excess noise ratio of the noise generator in decibels and *Y* is the output noise ratio N_2/N_1.

The excess noise ratio of the generator is:

$$ENR = 10 \log_{10} (P_2/P_1 - 1)$$

where P_2 is the noise power of the generator and P_1 is the noise power from a resistor at 290K.

Most manufacturers of amateur communication receivers rate the noise characteristics with respect to signal input, and a common expression is:

$$\frac{signal + noise}{noise}$$

or the *signal-to-noise ratio*. Usually the sensitivity is

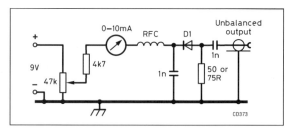

Fig 8.4.1. Noise generator using reverse-biased diode

given as the number of microvolts for a signal-to-noise ratio of 10dB.

Typically, the noise figure for a good receiver operating below 30MHz is about 5 to 10dB. Lower noise figures can be obtained but they are of no real value because of the external noise arriving from the antenna. It is important to remember also that optimum noise figure in an RF amplifier does not always coincide with maximum stage gain, especially at VHF and higher. This is why actual noise measurements must be used to peak for best noise performance.

8.4   Noise sources

In the past, various devices have been used as noise generators such as saturated thermionic diodes or argon-filled fluorescent discharge tubes. However, these devices have now become obsolete and one must look at semiconductor devices.

One noise source that has been used is the reverse-biased germanium diode. Unfortunately, the law relating noise with diode current varies for each diode and cases have been observed where the noise actually decreases for an increase of current over a limited range. Although individual diodes whose characteristics have been determined can be useful to optimise the noise performance of a receiver, they cannot be regarded as a measuring instrument. Fig 8.4.1 shows a typical circuit.

Silicon diodes in the avalanche region often produce wide-band noise. Zener diodes (especially those exhibiting avalanche breakdown) also provide a simple source of consistent noise over a wide frequency range. The noise output is not completely dependent on the current and they are not suitable as adjustable noise sources. A simple reference noise source may be made using the circuit of Fig 8.4.2 – it is possible to mount the components all within a coaxial plug.

8.5   A zener/transistor noise source

This design is taken from reference [2] and the circuit diagram shown in Fig 8.5.1. The major noise source is zener diode D1 which is used to bias the first amplifier TR1. As there is no bypassing of the zener diode at the base of the transistor and the current in the diode is small,

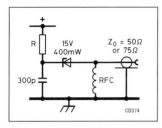

Fig 8.4.2. Zener diode reference noise source. Note that R should be selected for 5mA diode current from a supply of somewhat more than 15V; the components may conveniently be built into a coaxial plug

Table 8.5.1. Components list for the zener/transistor noise source

R1, 2, 5	330R	C1–4	10n ceramic
R3	51R	D1, 2	6V2, 400mW zener, 1N753A
R4	100R	TR1, 2	2N5179

Resistors are 0.25W/0.5W, 5% unless specified otherwise.

the excessive noise currents in the diode will flow through the base of the transistor. The resulting amplified output is applied to a second stage of gain, TR2. The second amplifier has a 51Ω resistor (R3) in the collector in order to provide a controlled output impedance.

The noise output of this circuit has been measured on a spectrum analyser. The detailed distribution of noise with frequency will not be presented since it will vary considerably with zener diode and transistor characteristics. Generally noise in the HF region was quite robust, reaching levels of 80dB higher than the noise output from a room temperature resistor. The noise output is still 20dB above a 290K resistor at 432MHz.

The constructor should not attempt to estimate noise figure with a device as crude as this. It may be used, however, as a source for tuning receivers or amplifiers. If one were to build a free-running multivibrator using a 555 timer, with a total period of one to two seconds, it could be used to automatically turn the generator on and off. The system could then be used in conjunction with a step attenuator to adjust a VHF preamplifier for low noise figure. The output detector would be the constructor's ears, although refined circuitry could be built for this purpose.

8.6 A gated noise source

8.6.1 General

The circuit [3] described in this section may be used to construct a simple low-cost device to optimise a

converter/receiver for best noise figure. The simplicity of this system makes effective alignment possible without a lot of test equipment.

8.6.2 Circuit description

The circuit diagram is given in Fig 8.6.1. TR1 and TR2 form an astable multivibrator operating at about 700Hz. The value of C1 is chosen to be greater than C2 so that the duty cycle is deliberately not 50%. The output from TR2 is capacitively coupled via C3 to the base of TR3, which acts as the current source for D1 via R7 and R8.

The diode generates broad-band noise which is output to a socket via R9. R7, C4 and C5 form a low-pass filter to prevent high-order harmonics of the switching pulses from appearing at the output. It should be noted that an absolute value of noise figure is not obtainable with this unit.

8.6.3 Construction

The circuit uses readily available components and may be easily duplicated. The lead placement in and around the diode should follow good VHF practice with short leads and direct placement. The influence of stray RF signals entering the device under test through the generator may be minimised by shielding the components shown. The unit can be housed in a metal box or one made from PCB scraps.

For best match, this source should be connected directly to the input of the equipment under test; therefore the unit should be equipped with a male connector. This matching becomes a greater consideration as the frequency of interest increases.

8.6.4 Operation

The gated noise source does not require a special detector, or any detector other than the ear. By turning the noise source on and off at an audio rate, the ratio of noise contributed by the system to noise of the system plus excess noise appears as an audio note. The louder the note, the greater the differential in levels. Hence, the greater the influence of the excess noise, the better the noise figure.

If greater precision is desired than that obtained by subjectively listening to the signal, an oscilloscope may be used. Connect the vertical (Y) input to any point in the audio system of the receiver, eg loudspeaker terminals. Adjust the oscilloscope for a display of several

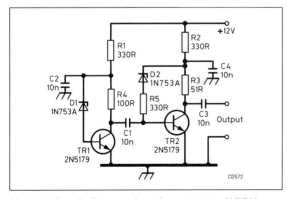

Fig 8.5.1. Circuit diagram of a noise generator (ARRL)

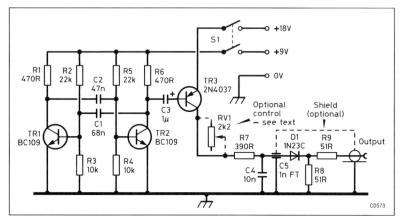

Fig 8.6.1. Circuit diagram of gated noise source (ARRL)

multiples of the train of rectangular pulses. Proceed by adjusting the device being tested for greatest vertical deflection.

In some cases the available noise generated by this unit may be too great. The output may be reduced by inserting attenuators between the generator output and the equipment under test. Alternatively a potentiometer (RV1) may be added as indicated in Fig 8.6.1. The use of an attenuator is preferred because it reduces the apparent output VSWR of the generator by increasing the return loss. If a control is used, it must be returned to its minimum insertion loss position when starting a test, or else no signal may be heard.

Some contemporary receivers and transceivers cannot be operated in the AM mode and consequently the noise source seems unusable. The detection of noise is the process by which the noise source operates; therefore it will not work through an FM detector, nor will it work through a product detector since one of the terms of the detection (the noise) is not coherent.

The oscilloscope jack on many receivers is loosely coupled to the IF amplifier preceding the detector. A wide-band oscilloscope connected to this point will show the train of pulses and eliminate the need for aural detection. The alignment of the later IF stages of a system

Table 8.6.1. Components list for the gated noise source

R1, 6	470R	C2	47n
R2, 5	22k	C3	1μ, 50V
R3, 4	10k	C4	10n
R7	390R	C5	1n feedthrough
R8, 9	51R	TR1, 2	BC109 or equivalent
RV1	2k2 pot (see text)	TR3	2N4037 or equivalent
S1	DPDT switch	D1	1N23C or equivalent
C1	68n		

Resistors are 0.25W/0.5W, 5% unless specified otherwise.

should have the least impact on the noise performance, and maximum signal response will always occur at the same setting. Therefore the simple detector of Fig 8.6.2 will generally work for aural AM detection. Connect point A to the last IF amplifier anode, collector or drain. Connect point B to the audio amplifier at or near the volume control and ground point C. With this arrangement, the normal output detector is turned down with the volume control and the temporary detector provides AM detection.

The gated noise source has been used for literally hundreds of applications and has proved to be a powerful yet simple addition to the test bench. While no guarantee of duplication may be made, these units develop approximately 18dB of excess noise in the region 50–300MHz. This unit was originally described by Hartsen in *QST* January 1977.

8.7   A receiver alignment aid

8.7.1   General

By far the most common method of aligning amateur low-noise receivers relies upon listening to a weak signal from a distant station, such as a beacon, and adjusting the matching components of the receiver input stage for maximum signal to noise ratio [4].

Signals from distant sources are notoriously unreliable, varying rapidly in strength over a range of many decibels. This makes it necessary to repeatedly check the strength of the beacon to ensure that an improvement in signal-to-noise ratio has been achieved.

A locally generated signal which can be adjusted in level down to barely detectable would appear to be ideal, since it would not suffer from the vagaries of propagation. In practice it can be very difficult to attenuate the test signal to the required level because of the amount of screening needed.

A second, and not often considered, problem with this approach is matching between the source and the receiver.

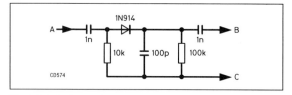

Fig 8.6.2. A simple detector that can be used when aligning SSB and FM receivers (ARRL)

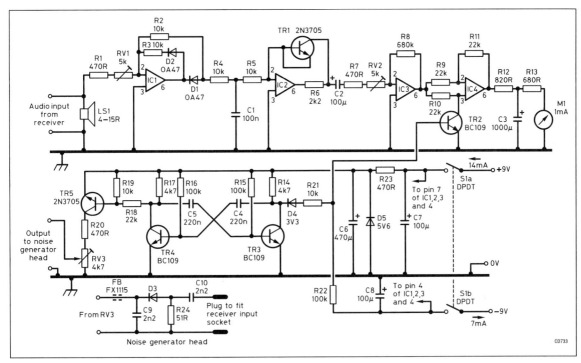

Fig 8.7.1. Circuit diagram of the alignment aid

A well-attenuated signal generator output will provide a good 50Ω match, whereas the antenna may not provide the same degree of matching. The result can be less than optimum.

A better approach to aligning low-noise receivers is to use a noise generator in place of the signal generator [5]. With this technique, broad-band noise is injected into the receiver input. The noise source is turned on and off and the receiver matching adjusted until the ratio of *noise on* to *noise off* at the receiver output is at a maximum. It can be very difficult to judge aurally when the ratio is maximum, so that some form of visual indicator becomes desirable.

Such an instrument is known as an *automatic noise figure* meter when it indicates directly the true noise figure of the item under test. It is, however, necessary to use a source with an accurately known noise output in order to make an accurate measurement. If the noise output of the source is not accurately known the instrument can still be used to adjust the receiver for best signal-to-noise performance, although the actual noise figure will not be known.

The instrument described in the following sections can be used to adjust receivers operating at any frequency for optimum sensitivity. The instrument provides a continuous readout of the difference between the audio output of a receiver with no RF input and the output when a

wide-band noise generator is connected to the receiver's antenna socket. The meter indicates the ratio between the outputs under these two conditions.

By design, the meter reading is not affected by changes in audio level over a wide range of volume settings. The circuit has a logarithmic response so that the meter scale can be linearly calibrated in signal-to-noise ratio in

Table 8.7.1. Components list for the receiver alignment aid

R1, 7	470R	C4, C5	220n polyester
R2–5,		C6	470µ, 16V elec
19, 21	10k	C7, 8	100µ, 16V elec
R6	2k2	C9, 10	2n2 ceramic disc
R8	680k	D1, 2	OA47, OA79,
R9–11,			OA90, BAT85
18	22k	D3	See text
R12	820R	D4	3V3, 400mW zener
R13	680R	D5	5V6, 400mW zener
R14, 17	4k7	TR1, 5	2N3705, 2N3703,
R15, 16,			2N4126
22	100k	TR2–4	BC109, 2N2926
R20, 23	470R	IC1–4	741, 8-pin
R24	51R or 75R	FB	FX1115 or
RV1, 2	5k skel preset, 0.1W		equivalent
RV3	4k7 lin carbon pot	LS1	4–15R miniature
C1	100n polyester		speaker
C2	100µ, 6V3 tantalum	S1	DPDT switch
C3	1000µ, 10V elec	M1	1mA FSD meter

Resistors are 0.25W/0.5W, 5% unless specified otherwise.

decibels. Unless the absolute level of noise output from the noise source is known, the scale cannot be marked in noise figure.

The unit uses a reverse-biased diode as a noise source.

8.7.2   Circuit description

The circuit diagram is shown in Fig 8.7.1. Audio input from the loudspeaker socket of the receiver under test is connected to a small speaker (LS1) at the instrument input. This speaker provides a means of monitoring the receiver output which would otherwise be inaudible due to the muting action of most loudspeaker external connection sockets. The AC across the speaker is rectified by the precision rectifier formed around IC1. This arrangement effectively overcomes the forward voltage diode drop of a rectifier and thus AC signals at very low levels can be accommodated. The voltage gain of this circuit is given by:

$$\frac{R2}{R1 + RV1}$$

while D2 and R3 prevent the operational amplifier saturating on the negative half-cycles of the input. R4 and C1 act as a low-pass filter to the input of IC2.

IC2 is formed into a logarithmic amplifier by the use of TR1 in the feedback loop. Note that the voltage across the base/emitter junction of a transistor with its base connected to its collector is proportional to the logarithm of the current through the transistor.

Because the receiver is fed with two signals then IC1 and hence IC2 are also fed with these signals. The difference (in the millivolt range) between the output voltages under these two conditions is a function of the ratio between the two input voltages, and this ratio is independent of the average input level. Provided that the various stages of the receiver and the circuit around IC1 are working within their linear range, the AC output from the circuit formed around IC2 at the pulse frequency used will be dependent only on the overall signal-to-noise ratio. As the output from IC2 is only a fraction of a volt peak-to-peak, it is amplified by the following stage formed around IC3 which has a voltage gain given by:

$$\frac{R8}{R7 + RV2}$$

The output of IC3 is fed to a unity-gain, phase-sensitive detector (PSD) based on IC4. The reference signal is fed via TR2 from the pulse generator (or multivibrator) TR3 and TR4.

A PSD is ideally suited to applications such as this, where an indication is required of the magnitude of an AC signal which has a known frequency and phase but a high accompanying noise level. In this application the PSD gives a usable output when the signal is accompanied by so much noise that it is undetectable by ear.

IC4, which has a relatively low output impedance, can drive a 1mA meter, and the FSD of the meter in the prototype was set at approximately 10dB signal-to-noise with the scale reading linearly in decibels. R12 and R13 limit the current through the meter, with C3 providing smoothing of the detected signal, otherwise the meter would show an erratic response due to the nature of the noise inputs.

The pulse generator is formed from a conventional astable multivibrator (TR3 and TR4) operating at about 30Hz, the output of this being fed to amplifier TR5 which is used to pulse the noise source.

The noise generator uses a reverse-biased diode mounted in a separate enclosure with matching and decoupling components. An ideal arrangement would be to mount this within a coaxial plug. The diode D3 used in the prototype was a CV364 microwave mixer, but alternatives are 1N21, 1N23, 1N25 and 1N32. A possible, but not tried, alternative is a BAT31 silicon avalanche device which is intended as a noise source from 10Hz to 18GHz.

8.7.3   Construction

Construction of the receiver alignment aid is not critical and audio techniques can be used with the exception of the noise head, which must be built using VHF techniques if it is to operate reliably at the highest frequencies. The circuit requires a symmetrical ±9V DC supply at about 20mA – see Chapter 12 for a suitable circuit.

8.7.4   Alignment

The unit requires little alignment and no test equipment is needed.

Plug the noise head into a receiver and gradually increase the diode current until an audible 'purring' sound is heard in the receiver loudspeaker. Connect the audio output of the receiver to the input of the unit. The 'purring' should now transfer to the unit's loudspeaker and the meter should show a fairly steady reading which can be varied by adjusting the noise diode current (using RV3). Set RV1 so that the meter reading is constant over a wide range of receiver volume settings. Set RV2 to give an FSD of the meter at maximum diode current on the highest frequency band of interest. The unit is now ready for use.

8.7.5   Operation

Connect the unit and noise head to the receiver under test and adjust RV3 for about half-scale deflection on the meter. Any adjustment to the receiver that results in an improved signal gain with no change in the noise figure, or a reduced noise figure with no change in signal gain, or both simultaneously, will result in an increased meter reading. By noting the reading of the meter before and after any circuit adjustments, improvements in performance can readily be seen.

Although the unit is not especially sensitive to small temperature changes, it is best to switch the unit on at least 10min before use and to ensure that the ambient temperature is reasonably constant.

8.7.6   Additional notes on use

Use of the receiver alignment aid assumes reasonable linearity of the receiver, and therefore care must be taken when aligning FM receivers to ensure that the receiver does not limit with the noise source on. With most receivers this will mean that the level of noise injected must be as small as possible, consistent with still exceeding the FM threshold. With AM/SSB receivers the noise blanker and AGC must be disabled if meaningful results are to be obtained.

Care must be taken if the alignment aid is to be used for initial alignment of a converter or receiver. Noise output from the unit is constant over a wide range and it is therefore possible to inadvertently align on a spurious or image frequency, especially if the receiver has a low intermediate frequency. A signal generator or similar should therefore be used for initial alignment to avoid the problem.

Some receivers have been encountered that have a small DC voltage appearing at the loudspeaker socket. When connected to the alignment aid this voltage can bias IC1 beyond its linear range, thus resulting in false readings on the meter. Connecting an electrolytic capacitor of about 47μF in series with the input overcomes this problem. The negative terminal of this capacitor should be connected to the junction of R1 and the monitor loudspeaker.

8.7.7   Further improvements

Considerable development work has been carried out to the receiver alignment aid since it was first published and this has resulted in several very useful improvements – see references [6] and [7].

The original noise head was designed primarily for VHF operation. An alternative design that can be used throughout the HF range and up to at least 1.3GHz is shown in Fig 8.7.2. Useful output may still be available at 2.3GHz when a suitable transistor is used for TR1. It is best to select a transistor with a high f_T for TR1. It may be necessary to try several transistors before one with enough output is found.

Better phase detector performance is achieved at low levels with an FET (eg 2N3819) in place of the bipolar transistor TR2.

Sometimes difficulties have been encountered with the meter reading not being independent of audio drive level. This can be just a matter of incorrect use or it can arise

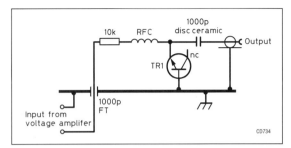

Fig 8.7.2. HF-to-UHF noise head. TR1: 2N2369, BFY90 etc – see text; RFC: 3t of the 10kΩ resistor lead, 2mm inside dia

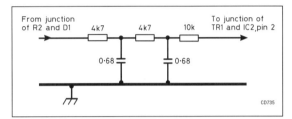

Fig 8.7.3. An improved interstage coupling network between IC1 and IC2

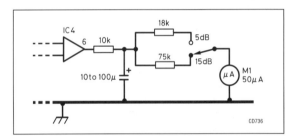

Fig 8.7.4. Modified meter circuitry

when the comparator is used in conjunction with receivers possessing an odd audio frequency response. This can be cured by replacing the components R4, C1 and R5 by the circuit shown in Fig 8.7.3.

A slight improvement to the performance of the logarithmic amplifier may be obtained by replacing R6 with a shorting link and increasing the value of C2 to 22 or 33μF.

Fluctuating meter readings can also be a problem at times. Changing the meter to one of 50μA FSD and altering the time constant of the meter circuit can noticeably improve matters. Fig 8.7.4 incorporates these modifications as well as including a switch to give different full-scale readings of signal to noise ratio.

8.8   References

[1] 'Noise figure measurements', *The ARRL Handbook for the Radio Amateur*, ARRL, Chapter 12.

[2] 'Noise generator', *Solid State Design for the Radio Amateur*, ARRL, pp167, 168.

[3] 'A gated noise source', *The ARRL Handbook for the Radio Amateur*, ARRL, Chapter 25.

[4] *Microwave Handbook*, Vol 2, ed M W Dixon, G3PFR, RSGB, 1991.

[5] 'An alignment aid for VHF receivers', J R Compton, G4COM, *Radio Communication* January 1976.

[6] 'Microwaves', C Suckling, G3WDG, *Radio Communication* October 1979.

[7] 'Microwaves', C Suckling, G3WDG, *Radio Communication* March 1980.

Chapter 9

Component measurements

9.1 Introduction

The individual items which make up radio equipment can be divided into passive and active components. Passive components consist largely of resistors, capacitors, inductors and transformers. All of these components can be readily purchased with chosen values but occasionally it is required to check something, especially if the colour coding has been worn or burnt off or if it is desired to make, for example, a coil of specific value.

Resistors can most easily be checked with the ubiquitous multimeter or digital voltmeter. However, this should not preclude using home-made equipment for this purpose. For resistance measurements, this chapter includes a digital resistance meter and LCR bridge and, for higher accuracy, the old favourite: the Wheatstone bridge. For capacitance, two methods are provided: the capacitance meter and the LCR bridge. Inductance measurements are catered for by the inductance meter and the LCR bridge.

The testing of semiconductor devices is not so easy to establish. Some characteristics such as diode properties are fairly easy to ascertain, but the inner functions of an IC are virtually impossible. For this reason only simple circuits for transistor and diode testing are included.

To aid with checking the operation of digital ICs, *in-circuit* logic probes are included for TTL and CMOS. To otherwise test ICs it is necessary to set up a test circuit and check the functions of the device.

9.2 Resistance

The most basic method for measuring resistance is to set up the circuit shown in Fig 9.2.1, measure *V* and *I* and then to use Ohm's Law. The easiest way is to use the ubiquitous multimeter, whether it be analogue or digital. This chapter provides three additional methods for resistance measurement.

9.3 The Wheatstone bridge

Another basic method for measuring resistance is the Wheatstone bridge as shown on Fig 9.3.1, and most other types of bridge derive from this. It relies on the voltages

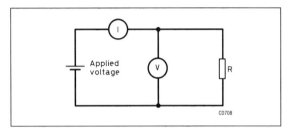

Fig 9.2.1. Basic resistance measurement

at A and B being equal and therefore no current flowing through the meter. Alternatively a voltage-indicating item of equipment (eg an oscilloscope) will show zero volts difference. It does not matter if the supply voltage varies or is AC or DC, provided that the detecting instrument responds to the frequency used and is sensitive enough. If R1 and R2 are two reasonably good resistors, eg ±1%, and R_s is a standard calibrated resistor and R_u is the unknown value, then at balance:

$$R_u = R_s \frac{R_2}{R_1}$$

In a practical arrangement, if R1 is fixed at 1kΩ, then R2 can be made switchable in decades and acts as a range multiplier while R_s is arranged as a decade unit; this is shown on Fig 9.3.2. This circuit can be powered from an oscillator or, say, a 12V DC source. A PCB layout is shown in Appendix 2 with a component overlay.

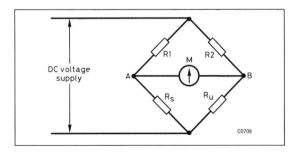

Fig 9.3.1. Basic Wheatstone bridge circuit

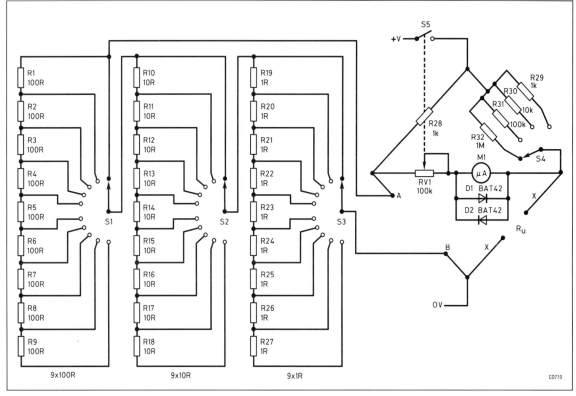

Fig 9.3.2. Practical implementation of Wheatstone bridge

Terminals are provided for the unknown resistor, meter/instrument connection and the power source. The sensitivity potentiometer is wired so that when the bridge is first switched on it is in its least sensitive state – a precaution for protecting the meter.

Please note that the meter will only cope with a DC supply.

To use the bridge, apply power and adjust the range and decade controls to try and centre the meter, increase the sensitivity and keep centring the meter until no further improvement can be made. If an oscilloscope is used, start with the sensitivity controls high and keep reducing, minimising the signal all of the time until no further improvement can be made. When the null position is

Table 9.3.1. Components list for the Wheatstone bridge

R1–9	100R	R32	1M
R10–18	10R	RV1	100k lin pot with switch (S5)
R19–27	1R	S1–3	1-pole, 10-way rotary, PCB mounting
R28, 29	1k	S4	1-pole, 4-way rotary, PCB mounting
R30	10k	M1	25μA-0-25μA
R31	100k	D1, 2	BAT42 or similar

Resistors are metal film type MRS25, 1% unless specified otherwise.

reached, read off the values from the decade box and multiplier and substitute in the above formula.

For better sensitivity at high resistance values, increase the supply voltage to, say, 24V DC.

9.4   Digital resistance meter

9.4.1   General

This uses the panel meter which was discussed in Chapter 2 for measuring voltage and current. The meter is used in a circuit in which a known current is passed through an unknown resistor and the voltage is measured. Using Ohm's Law ($V = IR$) and a fixed value of I, V is then a measure of the resistance. If I is made a multiple of 10, then the display will indicate the resistance up to the scale display of 1999, and all that needs to be fixed is the decimal point and the multiplier.

9.4.2   Circuit description

The circuit diagram is given on Fig 9.4.1. The meter reads from zero to 199.9kΩ in four switched ranges. The known current is set up by IC1, switch S1a and the resistors R1–R4. The unknown resistance is connected between terminals X and Y. IC1 is a constant-current source whose

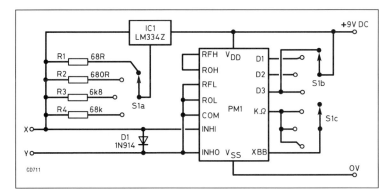

Fig 9.4.1. Digital resistance meter

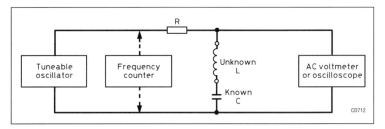

Fig 9.5.1. Basic arrangement for measurement of L or C

value can be set up by one external resistor. Parts of S1 set up the decimal point position and the legend. Note: if no legend displays then the units are ohms. Diode D1 limits the maximum input to the meter with no resistance connected to 600mV.

To measure the resistances, the constant current set up by IC1 for the various ranges and the ranges are:

Switch position	Current (μA)	Max resistance to be measured (kΩ)
1	1000	0.1999
2	100	1.999
3	10	19.99
4	1	199.99

9.4.3   Construction and calibration

Some care should be given in handling and soldering to the panel meter. The layout of the circuit is not critical. There is no setting up procedure but the reading should be checked against some resistors of known accuracy.

Table 9.4.1. Components list for the digital resistance meter

R1	68R	PM1	OEM22 panel meter
R2	680R	IC1	LM334Z
R3	6k8	S1	3-pole, 4-way rotary switch, PCB mounting
R4	68k	D1	1N914

Resistors are metal film type MRS25, 1%, 0.6W or similar.

Do not forget to cut the link to the BP line on the panel meter.

9.5   Basic capacitance and inductance measurements

In Sections 9.6, 9.7 and 9.8, equipment is described for measurement of capacitance and inductance. Capacitors and inductors can both be bought in standard values and with known tolerances, and their values can be determined in various ways.

One method to use is that of resonance, and Fig 9.5.1 shows a basic arrangement using series resonance. In the case shown it is the inductance that is unknown but the converse could also be used. The frequency of the tuneable oscillator is varied until a minimum deflection is shown on the AC voltmeter or oscilloscope, then the frequency is noted. The unknown component can then be calculated from:

$$L_{\text{unknown}} = \frac{1}{4\pi^2 f^2 C} \qquad C_{\text{unknown}} = \frac{1}{4\pi^2 f^2 L}$$

where C is in farads, L in henrys and f in hertz.

A similar method can be used with a dip oscillator, and the reader is referred to Chapter 5 where this is covered in detail.

9.6   A linear-scale capacitance meter
9.6.1   General

This instrument is based on the familiar 555 timer. The circuit is shown in Fig 9.6.1 and is an adaptation of that described in references [1] and [2]. It has five basic ranges with a ×10 multiplier. This gives the equivalent of six ranges of full-scale values 100pF, 1nF, 10nF, 100nF, 1μF and 10μF.

The meter works by charging the unknown capacitor Cx to a fixed voltage and then discharging it into a meter circuit. The average current is proportional to the capacitance and hence gives a direct reading on the meter. Please observe the polarity if measuring electrolytic or tantalum capacitors. The unit requires a low-current 9V DC supply, so it can be powered from a PP3 battery or equivalent adapter.

9.6.2   Construction

The layout of components is not critical; a PCB/component layout is given in Appendix 2, together with component placings. One can either make a box or, as is more usual, purchase one of the cheaper plastic types.

9.6.3   Calibration

Calibration may be carried out on any range; if possible obtain 100pF, 1nF and 10nF capacitors with ±1% tolerance. With the range switch (S1) set to position 2, and multiplier switch S2 in the ×1 position, connect the 1nF capacitor. Adjust RV1 for full-scale deflection. Switch to the ×10 position of S2 and adjust RV2 for a meter reading of 0.1.

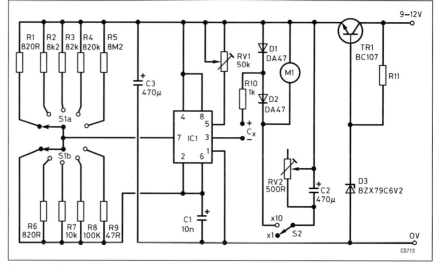

Fig 9.6.1. Circuit diagram of linear-scale capacitance meter

Use the other capacitors to check the different ranges. Calibration is now complete.

Warning – if an attempt is made to measure a large-value capacitor, the meter will be overloaded.

9.7   Inductance meter

9.7.1   General

This design was originally described by W6HPH [3] but was subsequently modified by G3FDG [4].

Small values of inductance are commonly measured on a Q meter or LCR bridge. Inductance can also be determined by resonating with a known value of capacitor if a variable-frequency sine-wave source is available. One advantage of an inductance meter over the traditional measurements is speed: with an inductance meter it is not necessary to search for a peak or a null as the coil is simply connected to the meter, the correct range selected

Table 9.6.1. Components list for the linear scale capacitance meter

R1, 6	820R	C1	10n polystyrene, 1%
R2	8k2	C2	470µ, 16V electrolytic
R3	82k	D1, 2	OA47 or BAT85
R4	820k	D3	BZX79C6V2 or similar
R5	8M2	TR1	BC107 or similar
R7	10k	IC1	555 timer
R8	100k	S1	2-pole, 6-way rotary, PCB mounting
R9	47R, 5%, 0.5W	S2	SPST min toggle, PCB mounting
R10	1k, 5%, 0.5W	M1	50µA FSD moving-coil
RV1	50k single-turn cermet trimmer, 0.5W		
RV2	500R single-turn cermet trimmer, 0.5W		

Resistors are metal film type, MRS25, 1% unless specified otherwise.

and the inductance value read. The advantage becomes particularly apparent when sorting through a large number of unknown inductances.

A properly designed inductance meter can achieve a measurement accuracy at least equal to the more traditional measurements. The principle of a differentiator type of inductance meter can be understood by referring to Fig 9.7.1. If $R \gg X_L$, the RF voltmeter reading will be proportional to inductance and the meter scale can be made to read directly in micro- or millihenrys through proper selection of generator frequency and amplitude, the value of R and the voltmeter sensitivity.

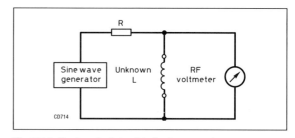

Fig 9.7.1. Basic principle of inductance meter

If R exceeds $10X_L$, the two principal sources of error usually result from the coil distributed capacitance and the finite coil Q. Unfortunately these two sources of error cannot be expected to cancel one another because they both add to the inductance reading. The effect of capacitance can be minimised by making the measurement at the lowest possible frequency, but if the frequency is too low the coil Q will be insufficient. Fortunately the effect

Table 9.7.1. Oscillator frequencies and inductive reactances

Range	Oscillator frequency (kHz)	Inductive reactance at full scale (Ω)
0–1µH	1000	6.28
0–3µH	1000	18.84
0–10µH	300	18.85
0–30µH	300	56.5
0–100µH	100	62.8
0–300µH	100	188.5
0–1mH	30	188.5
0–3mH	30	565
0–10mH	10	628
0–30mH	3	565
0–100mH	3	1885

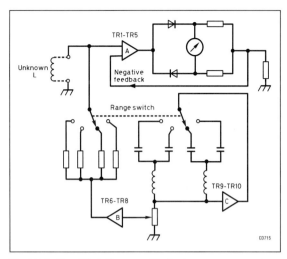

Fig 9.7.2. Simplified diagram of inductance meter

of finite Q is negligible until quite low values are approached. A Q as low as 5 gives rise to only a 2% error, while a Q of 10 results in a minuscule error of 0.5%.

For each inductance range there will normally be an optimum generator frequency which will lie somewhere between a lower frequency where Q is inadequate and an upper frequency where distributed capacitance effects begin to introduce significant error.

9.7.2 Ranges

The oscillator frequencies were chosen to minimise the effects of coil distributed capacitance and series resistance and are shown in Table 9.7.1.

Typically, both wire resistance and shunt capacitance increase with increasing inductance. Because of distributed capacitance the optimum measurement frequency will be lower for larger inductors but not so much lower as to prevent reactance from rising. Reactance must gradually rise in step with inductance so that it remains large compared with series resistance.

This particular meter was designed around a 1mA FSD meter with scales marked 0–3 and 0–10. As the table indicates, the inductance meter covers 0–100mH in 11 ranges, with a lowest range of 1µH full scale.

A DC output is taken from the meter/rectifier via R15/R16 and RV14; this makes possible the connection of a digital voltmeter for inductance display. However, the inductance meter does not have the accuracy of a digital voltmeter.

9.7.3 Circuit description

Fig 9.7.2 shows a block diagram of the system and uses three blocks of amplification labelled A, B and C. A simplified circuit of the oscillator is shown in Fig 9.7.3 and the full circuit diagram in Fig 9.7.4.

Amplifier A requires a high input impedance which is formed by a junction FET TR1. This stage has source degeneration for gain stability with a resulting gain of

about two. This is followed by TR2/TR3 and then the totem-pole output stage TR4/TR5. This drives the meter circuit which is also in the feedback loop to ensure linearity.

Amplifier B is formed by TR6, 7 and 8 and is used to amplify the oscillator output which is only about 0.35V RMS. This amplifier provides about a 26dB gain and is sufficient to overcome the loss of the RL differentiator; the level is such that it can drive the meter/rectifier into its linear range. The amplifier provides undistorted sine-wave output of approximately 3.5V RMS with an output impedance of about 6Ω. This sine wave is fed to the range potentiometers RV1–RV11 and is also an output signal for other uses. RV15 allows the amplitude to be adjusted for the maximum attainable without distortion.

The oscillator is formed by TR9 and TR10 and Fig 9.7.3 is a simplified diagram of this with all switching removed.

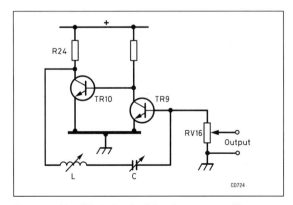

Fig 9.7.3. Simplified circuit of the sine-wave oscillator

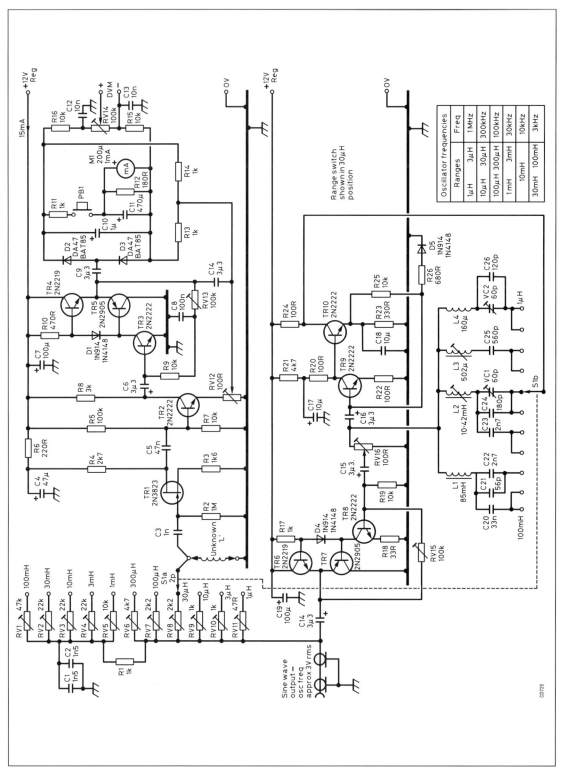

Oscillator frequencies		
Ranges		Freq
1µH	3µH	1MHz
10µH	30µH	300kHz
100µH	300µH	100kHz
1mH	3mH	30kHz
10mH		10kHz
30mH	100mH	3kHz

Fig 9.7.4. Modified circuit diagram of the inductance meter

The range switch S1 performs two functions. S1a selects the correct differentiator resistance from the 11 potentiometers. These pots are set during the calibration of the instrument and will normally have values of about 20 times the full-scale inductive reactance on each range. S1b selects the resonating components for the oscillator – it has one more inductance than the original circuit [3].

The resistor R11 in series with the meter M1 is chosen so that clipping occurs in amplifier A at a level about 20% beyond full-scale deflection. In the original design, with no coil being measured, the meter would normally have gone to full scale and beyond – thus putting some strain on it. To overcome this, a pushbutton has been included so that there is zero reading until the button is depressed.

9.7.4 Construction

Construction is not especially critical. The original was built on a panel but strip board or similar is satisfactory. Note in Fig 9.7.4 how connections are made to the upper inductance terminal to avoid error from lead inductance. Likewise, the lower terminal should be earthed with the shortest possible lead or with multiple short leads.

9.7.5 Setting up

Before calibration can be attempted various items need setting up.

1. Turn the inductance range switch to the OFF position to disconnect the amplifier input from the range of preset potentiometers selected by S1a. The input will still be connected to the unknown 'L' terminals. Check the DC voltage at the emitter junction of TR4 and TR5 relative to ground; this should be half the supply voltage but it can be adjusted by RV13.
2. To set the overall gain of the meter amplifier circuit, apply a 300mV signal at 100kHz to the 'L' terminals and adjust RV12 to give a meter reading on M1 of 3 (assuming full scale is 10). With the signal still applied, connect a digital voltmeter to the DVM output terminals and adjust RV14 so that the DVM reads '0.300V'. Reduce the input signal to 100mV and check that the meter M1 and DVM now read '1' and '0.100' respectively.
3. Set the emitter potential at the TR6/TR7 junction to half the supply voltage by RV15.
4. Check the frequency of operation of the oscillator at various range settings. For 30kHz, adjust L2, then adjust VC1 for 100kHz. For 300kHz, adjust L3 and at 1MHz adjust VC2.
5. Set RV16 to give an output voltage of about 3V RMS.

9.7.6 Calibration

For calibration, a known value of inductance should be used for each range. Ideally these coils should have a

Table 9.7.2. Inductance meter

R1, 11, 13		C6, 9,	
14, 17	1k	14–16	3µ3, 16V elec
R2	1M	C7, 19	100µ, 16V, elec
R3	1k6	C8	100n ceramic
R4	2k7	C10	1µ, 16V elec
R5	100k	C11	470µ, 6.3V elec
R6	220R	C12, 13	10n ceramic
R7, 9,		C17, 18	10µ, 16V elec
15, 16,		C20	33n polystyrene
19, 25	10k	C21	56p polystyrene
R8	3k	C22, 23	2n7 polystyrene
R10	470R	C24	180p polystyrene
R12	180R	C25	560p polystyrene
R18	33R	C26	120p polystyrene
R20, 22,		VC1, 2	60p trimmer
24	100R	D1, 4, 5	1N914, 1N4148
R21	4k7	D2, 3	OA47, BAT85
R23	330R	TR1	2N3823
R26	680R	TR2, 3,	
RV1	47k skeleton pot	8–10	2N2222
RV2–4	22k skeleton pot	TR4, 6	2N2219
RV5	10k skeleton pot	TR5, 7	2N2905
RV6	4k7 skeleton pot	L1	85mH
RV7, 8	2k2 skeleton pot	L2	10.42mH
RV9, 10	1k skeleton pot	L3	502µH
RV11	470R skeleton pot	L4	160µH
RV12, 16	100R skeleton pot	S1	2-pole, 11-way
RV13–15	100k skeleton pot	M1	200µA with R12
C1, 2	1n5 ceramic		1mA no shunt R12
C3	1n ceramic	PB1	Momentary
C4	47µ, 16V elec		pushbutton switch
C5	47n polyester		

Resistors are 0.25W, 5% unless specified otherwise.

high Q, low distributed capacitance and an inductance value that falls somewhere in the upper half of the meter scale. Connect the inductor across the inductor across the unknown terminals, select the correct range and then adjust the appropriate preset potentiometer (RV1–RV11) to obtain the correct meter reading.

9.8 LCR bridge

9.8.1 Introduction

This bridge design was originally published in 1968 [5] with modifications in 1969 [6]. Although these articles appear somewhat ancient, the basic principles of bridges have not changed, and the version in this book includes modifications so that more modern components can be used. In most cases measurement is made at 1kHz but provision is also made to measure resistance in a DC bridge so that components having significant reactance, such as chokes and transformers with iron cores, may be accurately measured. The bridge also enables the Q of a coil to be measured. The ranges provided are given in Table 9.8.1.

It should be noted that the oscillator and detector amplifier are bypassed for any DC measurement and hence

Table 9.8.1. LCR bridge ranges (switch S3)

Position	R	L	C
1	0.1Ω	1μH	100μF
2	1.0Ω	10μH	10μF
3	10Ω	100μH	1μF
4	100Ω	1mH	100nF
5	1kΩ	10mH	10nF
6	10kΩ	100mH	1nF
7	100kΩ	1H	100pF
8	1MΩ	10H	10pF
9	10MΩ	100H	1pF

Table 9.8.2. Switch positions

Switch position	Function switch S1	1–1000Ω decade switch S2
1	Off	0
2	Capacitance	100
3	Inductance	200
4	Resistance AC	300
5	Resistance DC	400
6		500
7		600
8		700
9		800
10		900
11		1000

the meter needs to be a centre-zero type. For all AC measurements, the oscillator and detector/amplifier are in use and the meter will only deflect one way from its zero position.

9.8.2   Circuit description

The circuit of the bridge used in this instrument derives from the Wheatstone bridge for resistance measurement and the Hays and Maxwell bridges for reactance. The derivation is explained more fully in [5] or any suitable textbook. The circuits split into three basic units: the bridge and switching circuits (Fig 9.8.1), the oscillator circuit (Fig 9.8.2) and the detector (Fig 9.8.4).

The bridge and main switching layout is given in Fig 9.8.1(a) with interconnection details. The coarse balance decade (1–1000Ω) is shown in Fig 9.8.1(b) and provides 11 switched steps, the fine balance control RV3 providing the intermediate values. RV3 should be a good-quality linear wirewound component, ideally a multi-turn helical potentiometer with counter dial. Use good-quality potentiometers in all cases. R7 has a value of 600Ω, and it is possible to buy one or else to use two 300Ω in series or two 1.2kΩ in parallel.

C1 is required to be a low-loss, high-stability type. It may not be possible to buy one of this value with 1% tolerance. The alternatives are to make it up from three or four units in parallel, each of 1% tolerance or, if one has the access to measuring equipment, measure a batch and choose one that is within 1% tolerance.

The range resistors, shown in Fig 9.8.1(c), consist of nine switched positions. On positions 1 and 2 the low values of resistance required (R8 and R9) must take into account the switch contact and wiring resistances. (Note: several switch wafers could be connected in parallel in order to reduce contact resistance). The input and output switches, S3a and S3b, should have a screening plate between them; it is an advantage if the unused range resistors are connected to earth by a shorting-type switch.

The oscillator (Fig 9.8.2) is a standard Hartley circuit with the output taken from a secondary winding on top of the main tapped coil. The output is at 1kHz with good sine-wave shape. The transistor now used is an NPN

silicon device: a 2N697 or equivalent. A certain amount of negative feedback is introduced into the oscillator by leaving the emitter circuit unbypassed – this helps the oscillator to maintain a good sine-wave output even into the wide range of load impedances caused by variations in bridge input impedance due to range changes.

The transformer is constructed as shown in Fig 9.8.3. The ferrite now used is an LA4345 (4322-022-71280) which has the same inductance factor as the original LA1, meaning that the winding details are unaltered. The bobbin is supplied with PCB connecting pins, and it is left to the constructor as to which pins are used.

The amplifier/detector proposed in reference [6] and used in the second edition of this book has been revised. It is no longer possible (or only with difficulty) to obtain the IC (CA3020). Fig 9.8.4 shows a suggested replacement.

IC1 is a common dual operational amplifier with JFET inputs which have a resistance of the order of $10^{12}\Omega$. IC1a is a unity gain buffer and, with bias components R23, R24 and R25, has an input resistance of about 10MΩ. This is followed by an inverting amplifier, IC1b, with a voltage gain of about 47 (R28/R26). The components following IC1b provide rectification and smoothing of the AC signal, and drive meter M1. Full meter deflection is obtained with an input signal of about 40mV peak to peak.

When out of balance, the meter can be heavily deflected; it is protected by a series resistance R2 and shunt diodes D1 and D2. The sensitivity can be increased near balance by shorting out R2 with the momentary push-button PB1.

The position of switches not specified are shown in Table 9.8.2.

Position 1 of the PHASE BALANCE switch S4 gives a Q range from 6 to ∞ and is suitable for high-Q coils and low-loss capacitors. Position 2 gives a Q range from 0 to 6 and is suitable for RF coils of modest Q, transformers and electrolytic capacitors. Position 3 is suitable for coils of low Q in the range 0 to 0.16.

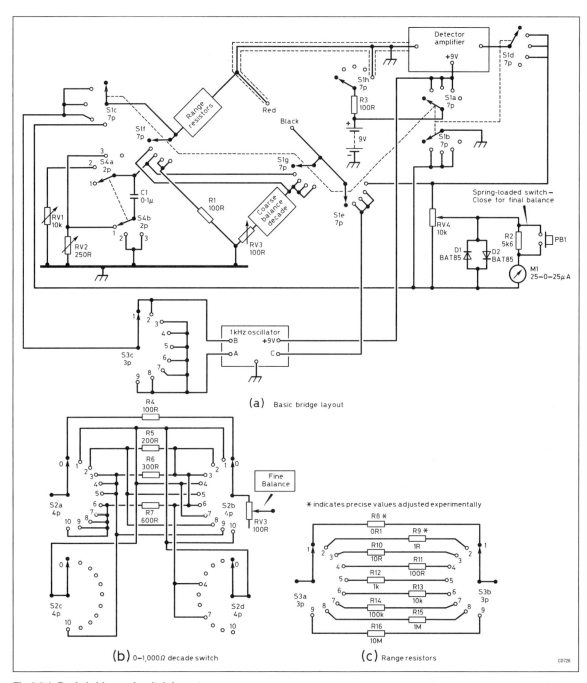

Fig 9.8.1. Basic bridge and switch layout

9.8.3   Construction and alignment

The layouts of the oscillator and amplifier/detector are not critical: they can be constructed on strip board but should be well screened in their own metal boxes with adequate power supply decoupling. The screened leads between the range resistors and the amplifier should be as short as possible. If the oscillator is not quite at 1kHz then either an adjuster can be used in the core or C4 can be changed (or have additional capacitors soldered across it).

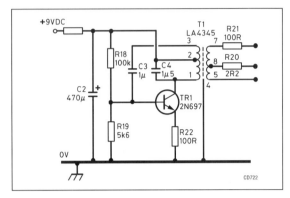

Fig 9.8.2. Oscillator circuit

Once the bridge is in virtual working order, the 0.1Ω and 1Ω range resistors should be constructed as follows. (Note: Section 9.8.4 describes how the bridge is used.)

Use a high-value resistor (eg 1 or 2W, 100kΩ) as a former for the 1Ω resistor R9. A 180mm length of 0.3mm (30swg) resistance wire should be bent double to give a twin wire of length 90mm. The doubled wire should be wound on the resistor former with the uncut end first, and then finally the two free ends tacked with solder to the connecting wires of the former resistor. This is known as a *non-inductive winding*. Some form of adhesive such as shellac, varnish or nail varnish etc should be applied to most of the wound resistor but the free ends must be available for adjustment *in situ*. An alternative to this approach, if a good range of metal film resistors is available, is to place various resistors in parallel with a metal film 1Ω resistor and use the same procedure as described below for calibration.

Connect a 10Ω, 1% resistor across the measuring terminals. The 1Ω resistor as described above should now be adjusted by either trimming the wire ends equally or changing the parallel resistor until the bridge readout gives 10Ω. If the wire-wound method is used, put some more varnish on the coil and ensure the soldered connections are good.

The 0.1Ω resistor (R8) should have a value nearer to 0.09Ω. This can be constructed either by using a 0.1Ω commercial resistor and placing a resistor across it or else from resistance wire as described next. Take 64mm of 0.5-mm (24/25swg) eureka resistance wire, bend into

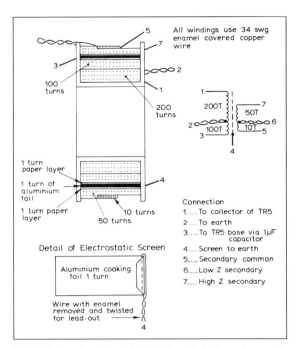

Fig 9.8.3. Constructional details of oscillator transformer T1. The foil ends should be insulated from each other by paper or polythene so as not to form a shorted turn

a hairpin and solder *in situ*. Take a 1Ω, 1% resistor and measure, then adjust the '0.1Ω' resistor in similar manner as for the 1Ω resistor described above. Allow any soldering to cool before attempting calibration.

9.8.4 Using the bridge

In order to measure resistance, the RANGE switch and COARSE BALANCE controls are rotated with the GAIN control at minimum while searching for a null in the meter indication. As this is approached, the gain should be

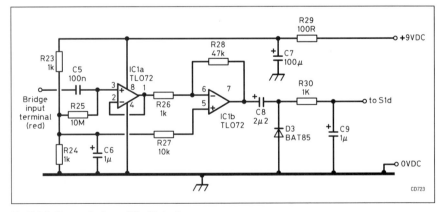

Fig 9.8.4. Suggested amplifier/detector

Table 9.8.3. Components list for the LCR bridge

R1, 4, 11	100R, 1%	RV1	10k, lin
R2, 19	5k6, 5%	RV2	250R lin
R3, 21,		RV3	100R multi-turn ww
22, 29	100R, 5%	RV4	10k lin, twin ganged
R5	200R, 1%	C1	0.1μ, 1% (see text)
R6	300R, 1%	C2	470μ, 16V electrolytic
R7	600R, 1% (see	C3	1μ
	text)	C4	1μ5
R8	0R1 (see text)	C5	100n ceramic
R9	1R (see text)	C6, 9	1μ, 50V electrolytic
R10	10R, 1%	C7	100μ, 16V electrolytic
R12	1k, 1%	C8	2μ2, 50V electrolytic
R13	10k, 1%	D1–3	BAT85, OA91 or similar
R14	100k, 1%	TR1	2N697 or similar PNP
R15	1M, 1%	IC1	TLO72
R16	10M, 1%	T1	LA4345 transformer
R17	47R, 5%		(see text)
R18	100k, 5%	M1	25-0-25μA moving-coil
R20	2R2, 5%,		meter
R23, 24,		S1	7-pole, 5-way
26, 30	1k, 5%	S2	4-pole, 11-way
R25	10M, 5%	S3	3-pole, 9-way
R27	10k, 5%	S4	2-pole, 3-way
R28	47k, 5%	PB1	Momentary pushbutton

increased and the FINE BALANCE control used to obtain a complete null, pressing PB1 in the final stage. The resistance value can then be read from the decade switch and the calibrated scale of the FINE BALANCE control. If a three-digit counter dial is fitted to the latter, the value will be indicated to four significant figures; the last figure would only be meaningful if the range resistors were of 0.1% accuracy.

Measurement of capacitance and inductance requires the use of the phase-balance controls as well as the decade and fine balance resistors. An accurate reading will be obtained only if an almost perfect null is obtained.

9.9 Transformer tests

The purpose of the testing in this section is to determine the turns ratio of the transformer and the phasing relationship of the windings. It cannot determine the voltages or currents at which the transformer is designed to operate, nor can it determine the number of turns of a winding. However, for a mains transformer the primary winding voltage rating is often known.

Rather than build a transformer tester, it is simpler to use equipment already described in this book. The tests are all carried out at low voltage.

Set the oscillator to the test frequency and connect to the primary of the transformer under test so that there is 1V on the AC voltmeter or oscilloscope (Fig

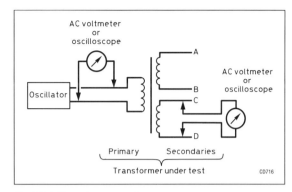

Fig 9.9.1. Transformer testing

9.9.1). Connect, for example, the AC voltmeter or oscilloscope to CD and read the voltage. The value read is the turns ratio. It can then be repeated for winding AB.

To check phase relationships of the secondary windings, link BC and measure the voltage across AD. If this equals the sum of the voltages in the turns ratio test, then A and C can be considered as the start of the windings. If not, connect C to A and measure across BD, which should then equal the sum of the voltages taken in the turns ratio test – B and C can then be considered as the start of the windings. If the phasing of more windings is required continue in a similar manner.

9.10 A crystal tester

The purpose of this unit is to check if a crystal will oscillate. It is a fairly basic item of equipment, and the circuit is shown in Fig 9.10.1. TR1 forms the oscillator, the crystal being plugged in across XY. The emitter from the output is rectified by C3 and D1, C3 also providing DC blocking. The resulting unidirectional waveform is applied to the meter circuit R4 and M1. R5 is optional but provides an output for a frequency counter.

If a crystal forms an oscillator then there will be a deflection on the meter. Please note that this is an untuned

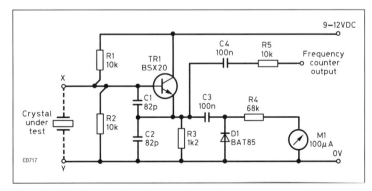

Fig 9.10.1. Basic crystal tester

Table 9.10.1. Components list for the crystal tester

R1, 2, 5	10k		C1, 2	82p ceramic
R3	1k2		C3, 4	100n ceramic
R4	68k		TR1	BSX20 or similar NPN
M1	100μA FSD		D1	BAT85 or similar

Resistors are 0.5W, 5%.

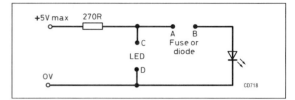

Fig 9.11.1. Simple diode, LED and fuse tester

circuit so that a crystal will resonate at its fundamental and not at an overtone as may be stamped on it. This circuit works up to between 15MHz and 20MHz, depending on the crystal. The output of the meter is not absolute and comparing two crystals of differing frequency means little. However, if crystals of exactly the same frequency are checked, then the deflection will give an indication of the differing activity of each device.

A PCB and component layout are given in Appendix 2.

9.11 A diode, LED or fuse tester

This is a very simple circuit and is shown in Fig 9.11.1. It consists of a 5V or 6V source feeding via a current-limiting resistor (270R). For the fuse or diode it will give a 'go/no go' indication.

Connect the fuse or diode across AB and see if the LED lights. If it does, then the fuse is intact and the diode is conducting. If the LED does not light with the fuse, put the fuse in the bin. For the diode, reverse its connections and see if the LED illuminates. Providing the LED lights with the diode only one way round, then the device shows diode properties. If the LED never lights then the diode is open-circuit, and if it lights both ways round then the diode is short-circuit – in either case put the diode in the bin.

Connect the unknown LED between CD: if it lights, then the anode is the side connected to C. If it does not light, reverse the LED connections and it should light – if not, discard it. The supply voltage of 5 or 6V should not be exceeded as it may damage the LED under test.

As this is a very simple circuit it is left to the constructor to house the unit.

9.12 A transistor and diode tester

9.12.1 General

The circuit of Fig 9.12.1 shows a simple tester which will identify the polarity and measure the leakage and small-signal gain of transistors plus the forward resistance of diodes.

9.12.2 Testing transistors

To check the DC current gain h_{FE} (which approximates to the small-signal current gain h_{fe} or β) the transistor is connected to the collector, base and emitter terminals and S2 switched for the transistor type. Moving switch S3 to

the GAIN position applies 10μA of base current and meter M1 will show the emitter current. With S3 at the LEAK position, any common-emitter leakage current is shown, which for silicon transistors should be barely perceptible. The difference between the two values of current divided by 10μA gives the approximate value of $h_{FE} + 1$ which is close to h_{fe} for most practical purposes.

A high value of leakage current probably indicates a short-circuited transistor, while absence of current in the GAIN position indicates either an open-circuited transistor or one of reversed polarity. No damage is done by reverse connection and PNP and NPN transistors may be identified by finding the polarity which gives normal gain.

With S3 in the V_{be} position, the base-emitter voltage is controlled by RV1 which should be near the negative end for NPN and near the positive end for PNP. V_{be} may be measured by a voltmeter connected between the terminal marked 'V_{be}' and either the positive or negative rail, depending on the polarity of the device. This test position may be used for FETs but only positive or zero bias is possible.

9.12.3 Testing diodes

The forward voltage drop across a diode may be measured by connecting it across the terminals marked '+' and 'V_{be}' with a voltmeter in parallel. The forward current is set by RV1. Diodes may be matched for forward resistance and, by reversing the diode, the reverse leakage can be seen (which for silicon diodes should be barely

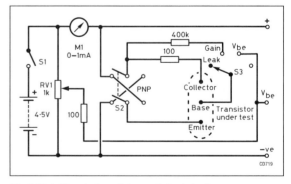

Fig 9.12.1. Simple transistor and diode tester

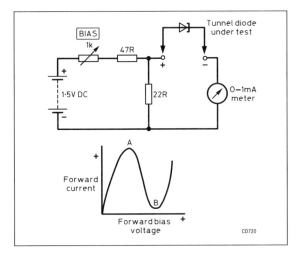

Fig 9.13.1. Tunnel diode test circuit and typical characteristic

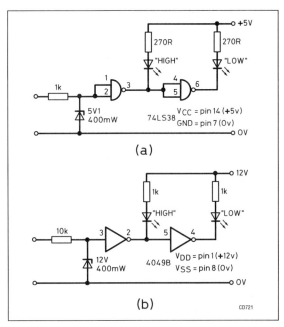

Fig 9.14.1. Logic probes

perceptible). The value of forward voltage drop can be used to differentiate between germanium and silicon diodes. The unit can also be used to check the polarity of LEDs as the maximum reverse voltage of 4.5V is hardly likely to damage the device (note: the reverse voltage applied to an LED should not exceed 5V). For this test RV1 should be set to about mid-position.

9.13 A tunnel diode tester

In order to test a tunnel diode, one must be able to increase the forward bias and observe the change in forward current while the diode is supplied from a low-impedance source. A suitable test circuit is shown in Fig 9.13.1 and typical forward-biased conduction characteristics are plotted on the same figure.

The bias resistor should initially be at maximum resistance; as the value is reduced, the characteristics as indicated should be seen on the current meter. The peak current (point A) will be typically 0.9mA and the valley current (point B) 0.15mA. A shunt on the meter to give a second range of 0–10mA may be needed for some tunnel diodes.

9.14 A logic tester/probe

Because of the differing voltage levels of TTL and CMOS (3–18V) it is easiest to cope with them using two probes of very similar design. TTL circuits are 5V, with the decision level between a logic 0 and 1 at about 2V, but with CMOS it is at about 65% of the supply voltage.

The circuits for the simple logic probes are shown in Fig 9.14.1. They both incorporate a zener diode as overvoltage input protection. If the circuit under examination is either at a logic 0 or 1 then one of the LEDs will illuminate, and if the circuit under test is alternating then both LEDs will illuminate but not at full brightness. If there is a very low or high mark-to-space ratio, then one LED may be difficult to distinguish as illuminating at all.

9.15 References

[1] 'Direct reading capacitance meter', A Wilcox, *Television* May 1976.
[2] 'Technical Topics', *Radio Communication* January 1977.
[3] 'An RF inductance meter', F Brown, W6HPH, *Radio Communication* December 1984.
[4] 'W6HPH inductance meter revisited', R Morris, G3FDG, *Radio Communication* June 1989.
[5] 'G3LUB R, C and L bridge', D R Bowman, G3LUB, *Radio Communication* December 1968.
[6] 'Some notes on the G3LUB bridge', R Thornton, G3PKV, *Radio Communication* September 1969.

Chapter 10

Signal sources and attenuators

10.1 Introduction

Signal sources of controlled frequency and amplitude are necessary for setting up both transmitters and receivers. Ideally, for receiver adjustment, it is desirable to have an RF source covering from a few hundred kilohertz up to the highest frequency used at the station. The amplitude should be known from a fraction of a microvolt up to tens of millivolts. In a good signal generator both frequency and amplitude are accurately known, but such instruments are costly and certainly difficult to make and calibrate in an amateur workshop.

Fortunately many good instruments appear on the surplus market, although the frequency calibration is sometimes not too accurate. This is not really important as the amateur almost always has means of checking frequency. Therefore, the quality of the attenuator and the effectiveness of the screening are all-important in selecting an instrument. At very low levels, a poorly screened oscillator will emit sufficient to bypass the attenuator and prevent low-microvolt output levels being attained.

For less-onerous requirements, simple oscillators can be constructed for tuning over a limited range, and several examples are given in this chapter. The dip oscillator (Chapter 5) is a simple form of signal source but suffers from the defect that the frequency is easily pulled with changes in coupling and it has no attenuator. However, a dip oscillator placed remotely from the receiver under test is often useful. It should be borne in mind that the output may have significant harmonic power and the possibility of interference with domestic receivers, including televisions, should be considered.

An audio frequency generator is useful for testing audio amplifiers and for checking the performance of transmitters. The design given in this chapter provides a sine-wave output and a frequency range well in excess of the audio range.

When testing sideband transmitters for linearity and intermodulation products, an audio source consisting of two fixed and non-harmonically related frequencies is required. Since some transmitters employ output devices

Table 10.2.1. Components list for the square-wave generator

R1	10k	C1	10µ, 25V
R2	1k	C2	100n ceramic
R3, 5	2k2	C3	47p polystyrene, 2.5%
R4	560R	C4	680p polystyrene, 2.5%
R6	330R	C5	6n8 polystyrene, 2.5%
R7, 8	47R	C6	68n polyester, 7.5mm pitch, 5%
RV1	100k log pot	C7	680n polyester, 7.5mm pitch, 5%
TR1, 2	2N3904 or	IC1	TLC555M or equivalent
	similar NPN	IC2	78L05, 100mA, 5V regulator
		S1	6-pole, 2-way rotary switch

Resistors are 0.25W/0.5W, 5% unless specified otherwise.

whose dissipation ratings are exceeded if the full peak envelope power is repetitively produced, it is sometimes necessary to pulse the two sources so that the mean dissipation is reduced, while the performance at peak output can still be observed.

With the increase in digital circuits it is also necessary to occasionally require a square-wave source, usually of fixed amplitude (5V or 12V) but of varying frequency. A unit for home construction is also included in this chapter.

10.2 Square-wave generator for 10Hz–1MHz

10.2.1 General

This oscillator provides a square-wave output at 5V and 12V amplitudes, and this makes it suitable for both TTL and CMOS circuits. The switched ranges produced are approximately those outlined below, but slight variations can be expected due to component tolerances:

Range 1	9Hz–110Hz	Range 4	9kHz–110kHz
Range 2	91Hz–1.1kHz	Range 5	90kHz–1MHz
Range 3	910Hz–11kHz		

10.2.2 Circuit description

The circuit is straightforward and based on a low-power 555 timer, the TLC555M (IC1). The circuit diagram is given in Fig 10.2.1. While it is easy to construct, a PCB

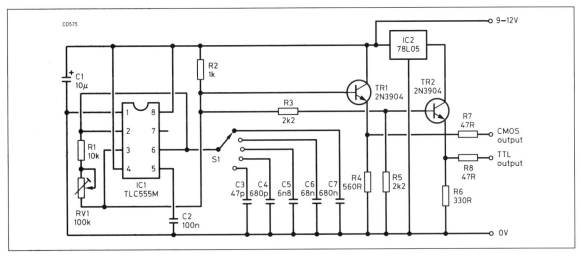

Fig 10.2.1. Square-wave generator

layout and component overlay are given in Appendix 2. R1 and RV1 with C3 to C7 are the frequency-determining components, switch S1 selecting the capacitor for the various ranges. Note that the capacitor for the highest frequency ranges is only 47pF, and this takes into account stray capacitance in the circuit and timing restraints within the IC. The outputs are a fixed 5V or 12V square wave from buffers TR2 and TR1 respectively, and R7 and R8 define the outputs at approximately 50Ω. Voltage regulator IC2 is required to produce the 5V supply for TR2.

10.3   Wide-band signal injector

10.3.1   General

This is a very useful aid for servicing equipment from audio frequencies up to radio frequencies. It enables a signal to be injected at some point via the probe and the response listened for or searched for with an oscilloscope. This unit generates a rectangular wave at about 2.7kHz with a mark-to-space ratio of about 2:1. This generates sufficient harmonics to be useful at RF.

10.3.2   Circuit description

The circuit is based around a low-power 555 timer – a TLC555, see Fig 10.3.1. R1 and R2 in conjunction with C2 determine the frequency of oscillation; R1 and R2 also determine the mark-to-space ratio. The rectangular wave output is via R4 which limits the current, and C4 is for DC isolation.

10.3.3   Construction

Fig 10.3.2 shows a diagrammatic construction of the device, but the exact details are left to the ingenuity of the constructor. The wide-band injector circuit should be housed in a metal container if possible, together with a battery (possibly a PP3) and on/off switch. If an external supply is used then power switching can also be external. The probe should ideally be sleeved so that there is

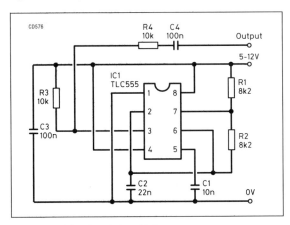

Fig 10.3.1. Wide-band signal injector

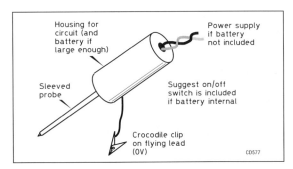

Fig 10.3.2. Typical construction for wide-band signal injector

Table 10.3.1. Components list for the wide-band signal injector

R1, 2	8k2	C2	22n
R3, 4	10k	C3, 4	100n
C1	10n	IC1	TLC555

Resistors are 0.25W/0.5W, 5%.

no inadvertent touching and damaging of circuit components. A flying lead with crocodile clip or similar is required to make the ground connection, although at radio frequencies this may be found to be unnecessary.

10.4 A low-frequency oscillator for 10Hz–100kHz

10.4.1 General

This circuit provides a sine-wave output in the range 10Hz–100kHz. The ranges provided are:

Range 1 10Hz–100Hz   Range 3 1kHz–10kHz
Range 2 100Hz–1kHz   Range 4 10kHz–100kHz

The circuit requires a symmetrical plus and minus supply between 9 and 15V – see Chapter 12.

10.4.2 Circuit description

The circuit diagram for this oscillator is shown in Fig 10.4.1. It is based on a Wien bridge oscillator formed around IC1a and buffered by IC1b.

Table 10.4.1. Components list for the 10Hz–100kHz low-frequency oscillator

R1, 2	4k7	C1, 2	330n
R3	10k	C3, 4	33n
R4	560R	C5, 6	3n3
RV1	1k trimmer	C7, 8	330p
RV2	47k dual gang pot	C9, 10	100µ, 25V
RV3	10k lin pot	C11	47µ bipolar
B1	28V, 40mA bulb	IC1	LM358

Resistors are 0.25W/0.5W, 5% unless specified otherwise.

The main frequency-determining components are R1, R2 and RV2 with C1 to C8. In the configuration shown, stable oscillation can occur only if the loop gain remains at unity at the oscillation frequency. The circuit achieves this control by using the positive temperature coefficient of a small lamp to regulate the gain as the oscillator varies its output.

Potentiometer RV3 forms the output level control with R4 giving a defined output resistance of approximately 600Ω, with C11 providing DC isolation. C9 and C10 provide power supply line decoupling.

10.4.3 Construction

The layout of the circuit is not critical – a PCB layout is given in Appendix 2. If some ranges or the output level control are not required then the layout can be tailored accordingly. The feedback resistor RV1 should be

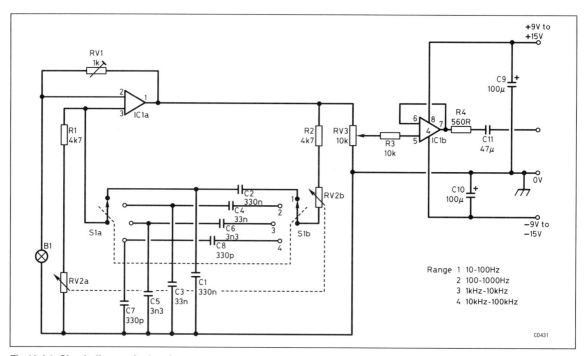

Fig 10.4.1. Circuit diagram for low-frequency oscillator

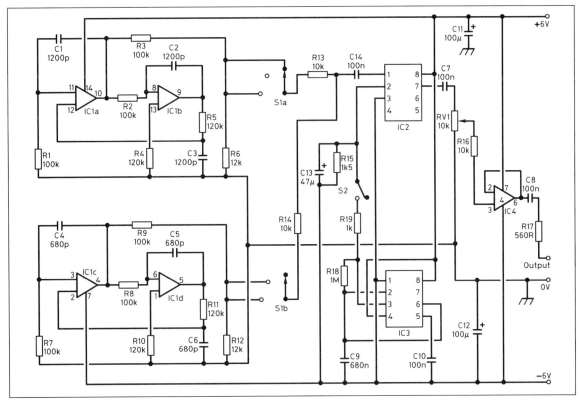

Fig 10.5.1. Circuit diagram of two-tone burst oscillator

adjusted so that the output on all ranges is just below the clipping level.

10.4.4   Testing

No frequency calibration is required of this circuit but it would be wise to check with a frequency counter that the ranges are as suggested. An oscilloscope is required for setting up the adjustment of RV1.

10.5   A two-tone burst oscillator

10.5.1   General

This is a self-contained unit for producing two tones for the testing of sideband transmitters. The frequencies produced are approximately 1.4kHz and 2kHz, ie they are not harmonically related. It is formed around a circuit given in the second edition of this book but has been modified to give a burst output if required of about 1Hz, controlled by S2. Switch S1 allows either tone or both tones to be output.

10.5.2   Circuit description

The two oscillators are formed around quad op-amp IC1 – see Fig 10.5.1. The sine-wave outputs from these are

routed via S1 which allows either tone through or both. The resulting signal is summed by resistors R13 and R14 before being fed into an electronic attenuator IC2. The attenuator gain is controlled by a DC voltage on pin 2. For the condition of continuous output this pin is connected to –6V via R15. For the burst mode the square-wave output from IC3 is fed to the integrating network formed by R15 and C13. This modified signal controls

Table 10.5.1. Components list for the two-tone oscillator

R1–3, 7–9	100k	C4–6	680p polystyrene
R4, 5, 10,		C7, 8	100n
11	120k	C9	680n
R6, 12	12k	C10, 14	100n ceramic
R13, 14,		C11, 12	100μ, 16V
16	10k	C13	47μ, 16V
R15	1k5	IC1	LM3900
R17	560R	IC2	MC3340P
R18	1M	IC3	TLC555M
R19	1k	IC4	741
RV1	10k lin pot	S1	4-pole, 3-way rotary
C1–3	1200p		switch
	polystyrene	S2	SPST PCB mounting

Resistors are 0.25W/0.5W, 5% unless specified otherwise.

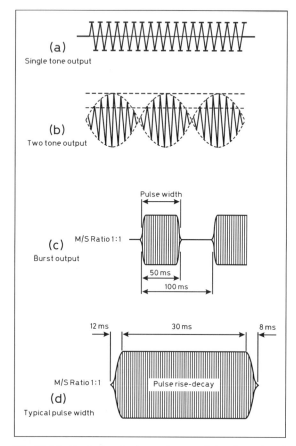

Fig 10.5.2. Typical output waveforms of two-tone burst oscillator

the gain of IC2 and provides a burst output as shown in Fig 10.5.2. The output from the attenuator is buffered by

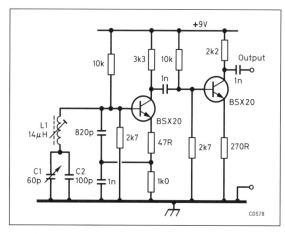

Fig 10.6.1. An HF bands signal source

IC4, the output level control being set by RV1. The output resistance is defined by R17 at approximately 600Ω.

10.5.3   Construction

Construction is straightforward and requires no special techniques. The burst option can be omitted if required but ensure that pin 2 of IC2 is connected to −6V via R15. C13 can be omitted in this case as it only shapes the envelope of the pulsed output. A PCB and component layout are given in Appendix 2.

10.5.4   Testing

No calibration of the circuit is necessary but the operation should be checked. Fig 10.5.2 gives typical outputs for the tone output, continuous or pulsed.

10.6   HF bands signal sources

10.6.1   General

Sometimes it is necessary to inject a signal into an item of equipment in order to check its response, and this signal is usually produced by a signal generator covering at least the HF bands to 30MHz. Signal generators not only produce a variable frequency output but also contain attenuators, so that the input signal can be calibrated right down to the microvolt range and the sensitivity of an item of equipment checked. Various items of such equipment do come up at radio rallies and are not too expensive, especially the valve equipment – see Appendix 1.

The production of the signal source is probably the easier part of the problem, while the most difficult is the signal attenuator. This must be constructed so that there is no signal leakage between the various sections – see Section 10.17.

It is possible to construct other signal sources. One possible item has already been described (Section 10.3, wide-band signal injector), while another item is described later (Section 10.13, crystal-based marker generator). Other items include the dip oscillators as described in Chapter 5. Below is given a simple circuit that can be adapted for various ranges.

10.6.2   Variable-frequency circuit

Using the values shown, the circuit shown in Fig 10.6.1 will tune over in excess of 500kHz in the vicinity of the 80m band. By modifying the values of L1, C1 and C2, the tuning range can be modified to cover a suitable segment of any part of the HF bands, for 9 and 10.7MHz – see Section 10.11.

In general, slug tuning of a suitable coil will set the band centre and the value of the two capacitors will set the tuning range. The capacitive divider which controls the feedback may have to be reduced in effective value for the higher frequencies. By switching several inductance

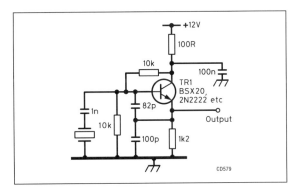

Fig 10.6.2. Crystal oscillator for 1–20MHz

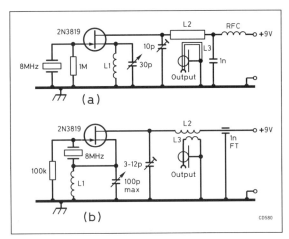

Fig 10.7.1. Two alternative simple VHF signal sources. Inductor details for (a) are: L1, 20t 8mm dia; L2, 120mm long by 3mm dia; L3, output coupling loop, 16swg wire; RFC, 35t 6mm dia. Inductor details for (b) are: L1, 28t 28swg wire, 0.25in dia; L2, 4t 18swg wire, 0.5in dia; L3, output coupling, 1t 18swg wire

values and maybe several values for C2, it would be possible to make a generator covering a number of bands. However, the output which is of the order of tens of millivolts would vary with frequency.

10.6.3 Crystal-controlled circuit

It is possible to use a circuit that will accommodate crystals running in their fundamental mode (usually 1–20MHz). Such a circuit is shown in Fig 10.6.2 with typical circuit values. Some adjustment may be required as the frequency rises. Above about 20MHz, crystals function on their overtones and so the output of the active device must contain a tuned circuit to ensure that the correct overtone is active.

10.7 VHF signal sources

10.7.1 General

Much of what has been said for the HF bands signals sources in Section 10.6.1 is equally true here, but the design of the attenuators is even more important. The construction of VFOs operating at VHF becomes particularly difficult and it is wiser to resort to the use of crystal-controlled units.

10.7.2 Circuit description

Fig 10.7.1 shows two possible crystal oscillators with the appropriate tuned circuit, and both use 8MHz range crystals. The output should be checked with an absorption wavemeter to make sure that the correct harmonic of the crystal frequency has been selected. The possibility of error would be reduced if a higher-frequency crystal were used; this would be particularly desirable if the output circuit were modified to give an output on 432MHz.

10.8 Sweep generators

A *sweep generator* or *wobbulator* is an oscillator whose frequency can be varied by, say, the application of a

suitable voltage – in essence a voltage-controlled oscillator (VCO). If a control voltage is used which varies between two limits (eg a ramp), then the frequency of the generator can be changed or swept between two limits. A wobbulator is a useful instrument for setting up such items as IF strips, bandpass filters and FM discriminators as the response of the circuit can be displayed on an oscilloscope and the effect of tuning adjustments can be seen without recourse to step-by-step methods. The variation in frequency is normally achieved by varying a power supply voltage or using a varicap diode with an LC oscillator.

A prime requirement of a sweep frequency generator is that it should be completely free of any amplitude modulation over the range to be swept and have a linear change of frequency with sweep voltage. While these features can be achieved with careful design, the more simple devices all too frequently have considerable amplitude modulation. If this defect is not minimised, it is possible to produce response curves on the oscilloscope which appear to be ideal while the true response of the equipment being aligned might be quite unsatisfactory.

Section 10.9 details a triangle-wave generator which can be used to drive the sweep generators of Sections 10.10 and 10.11. The practical use of sweep generators is given in Section 10.12.

10.9 A triangle wave generator

This circuit (Fig 10.9.1) provides a triangle output waveform and can be used to drive the following two oscillators. The generator is formed around the NE566 function

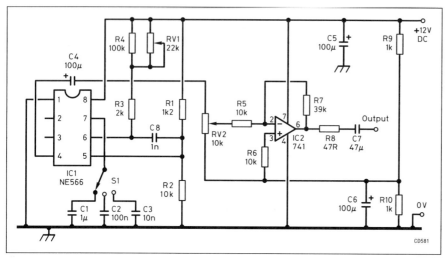

Fig 10.9.1. Circuit diagram of triangle wave generator

Table 10.9.1. Components list for the ramp generator

R1	1k2	C1	1μ
R2, 5, 6	10k	C2	100n
R3	2k	C3	10n
R4	100k	C4–6	100μ, 25V
R7	39k	C7	47μ, 25V, non-polarised
R8	47R	C8	1n
R9, 10	1k	S1	1-pole, 12-way
RV1	22k lin	IC1	NE566
RV2	10k log	IC2	741

Resistors are 0.25W/0.5W, 5% unless specified otherwise.

generator (IC1) which is a voltage-controlled oscillator. The output is a triangle waveform with high linearity and of about 2.5V peak to peak. This is then AC coupled to a 741 amplifier (IC2) with a gain of just under 4. The potentiometer RV2 allows the output to be varied between zero and 10V peak-to-peak. The frequency is controlled by S1 and RV1. There is also a square wave available at pin 3 of IC1.

The ranges are approximately:

Range 1 10Hz–100Hz   Range 3 1kHz–10kHz
Range 2 100Hz–1kHz

The construction of the circuit is not difficult but a PCB and component layout are given in Appendix 2.

10.10 A 440–550kHz sweep generator

10.10.1 General

Usually there is no need for the sweep generator to produce sine waves, and a square-wave generator of suitable repetition frequency is equally effective. The basic multivibrator may be readily modulated in frequency with a linear sweep while giving an output of

constant amplitude, and this is the basis of the design shown in Fig 10.10.1 and described here. The values given are suitable for 440–450kHz, but with suitable component changes can cope with centre sweep frequencies in excess of 20MHz.

10.10.2 Circuit description

The centre frequency (tuning) is adjusted by varying the voltage applied to the base of TR2 by RV2. The amount the frequency is swept (*deviation*) is controlled by varying the amplitude of the input sweep voltage via RV1. The sweep voltage is AC coupled to ensure symmetrical deviation. The transistors used should be of medium current gain (ie 30–50); if high-gain devices such as BC109s are used, both transistors will turn on together and the circuit will not oscillate.

The output voltage is taken from the emitter of TR2 via potentiometer RV3 and the three-position attenuator formed around S1. Provided the output circuit is shielded, the control of output is quite adequate to allow the

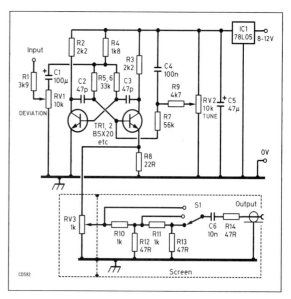

Fig 10.10.1. Circuit diagram of 440–550kHz sweep generator

Table 10.10.1. Components list for the 440–550kHz sweep generator

R1	3k9 (see text)	RV3	1k pot
R2, 3	2k2	C1	100µ, 16V electrolytic
R4	1k8	C2, 3	47p
R5, 6	33k	C4	100n ceramic
R7	56k	C5	47µ, 16V electrolytic
R8	22R	C6	10n ceramic
R9	4k7	TR1, 2	BSX20 or similar (see text)
R10, 11	1k	IC1	78L05
R12–14	47R	S1	1-pole, 3-way rotary switch
RV1, 2	10k pot		

Resistors are 0.25W/0.5W, 5% unless specified othwerwise.

Table 10.11.1. Components list for the 10.7MHz sweep generator

R1	33k (see text)	C1, 4	1n polystyrene
R2	100k	C2	100p polystyrene
R3, 8	10k	C3	820p polystyrene
R4, 10	2k7	C5, 6	100p ceramic
R5	1k	C7	100n ceramic
R6	47R	VC1	60p, eg Jackson C804
R7	3k3	D1	BB809 or similar
R9	2k2	TR1, 2	BSX20 or similar
R11	270R	L1	TOKO 113KN2K1026HM
RV1	4k7 pot		or 12t, 26swg on 7mm
RV2	1k pot		former with iron slug, 1.4µH

Resistors are 0.25W/0.5W, 5% unless specified otherwise.

effects of AGC on change of gain of IF response to be checked. The circuit operates at 5V which is supplied by IC1, which has an input in the range 8–12V.

The layout of the components is not critical but the attenuators should ideally be screened from the rest of the circuit. A PCB and component layout are given in Appendix 2. The tuning controls can be checked by monitoring the output of the unit with a digital frequency counter.

Note that if the sweep signal is obtained from an oscilloscope timebase output, then R1 may need to be included and is estimated at about 40kΩ per 10V peak-to-peak of timebase voltage.

10.11   A 9 or 10.7MHz sweep generator

This design is shown in Fig 10.11.1 and is an adaptation of Fig 10.5.1. It is based on a Clapp oscillator formed around TR1. This is then followed by a buffer amplifier TR2. The centre frequency is set by the variable capacitor VC1 and the slug in the coil. The values given will adjust between 9 and 11MHz but could be modified for other frequency ranges.

The sweep signal is applied to a variable-capacitance diode D1 and the swept frequency adjusted by RV1 in conjunction with R1. If an oscilloscope timebase is used the value for R1 may need to be adjusted.

The deviation can be calibrated by applying DC voltages to the diode and observing the output frequency on a digital frequency meter. The amplitude of the output is controlled by RV2, the maximum output being about 500mV (RMS). A sweep of up to 5% of the centre frequency (about 0.5MHz) can be obtained without significant amplitude change.

A PCB and component layout are given in Appendix 2.

10.12   How to use sweep generators with an oscilloscope

Fig 10.12.1 shows the typical arrangement for displaying the frequency characteristics of a circuit under test. The ramp signal which is used to sweep the RF oscillator is also applied to the oscilloscope X-input (ie internal timebase switched off). The output of the circuit under test is fed to the oscilloscope Y-input. The gain controls on the oscilloscope can then be set to give a typical display as shown.

10.13   A crystal-based frequency marker

10.13.1   General

The purpose of this unit is to produce a comb of output frequencies which are all based on a crystal. The unit described here gives outputs at harmonics of 1MHz, 100kHz, 25kHz, 12.5kHz and 10kHz, with an additional output of a sine wave at 1kHz which may be useful as an accurate modulation signal. The sine-wave output has an output resistance of approximately 600Ω and maximum amplitude of approximately 2.5V peak-to-peak.

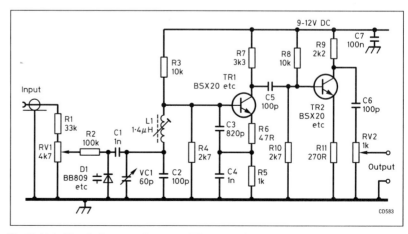

Fig 10.11.1. Circuit diagram of 9 to 10.7MHz sweep generator

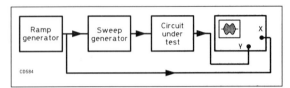

Fig 10.12.1. Connections for oscilloscope display

10.13.2 Circuit description

The circuit diagram is shown in Fig 10.13.1. The signal is derived from a 1MHz crystal-controlled oscillator formed by XL1 and IC1 plus various components. Capacitor VC1 allows a slight variation of the crystal frequency for calibration as described later. The 1MHz signal is divided by 10 by IC2 to give a 100kHz signal. This signal is then passed to IC3 which has a 50kHz output and also a 10kHz output. The 50kHz output is divided by dual flip-flop IC5 to give a 25kHz and 12.5kHz output. The 10kHz signal from IC3 is divided by 10 by IC4 to give a 1kHz square-wave output.

The 1kHz square wave is then filtered by an active low-pass filter formed by IC7a. The variable-amplitude

Table 10.13.1. Components list for the crystal-based frequency marker

R1, 2	1k8	IC1	74LS02
R3, 4	10k	IC2–4	74LS90
R5	560R	IC5	74LS74
VR1	10k lin pot	IC6	78L05
C1	10n ceramic	IC7	LM358
C2	100n ceramic	S1	2-pole, 6-way rotary
C3–6	10n ceramic	XL1	1MHz crystal, HC6U
C7	15n	VC1	30p trimmer
C8	33n	IC sockets	14-pin, 5 off
C9, 11	10μ, 25V tant bead		8-pin, 1 off
C10	2μ2		

Resistors are 0.25W/0.5W, 5% unless specified otherwise.

sine wave output is then buffered by IC7b. R5 forms the output resistance of the buffer.

10.13.3 Construction

The layout for this circuit is not critical but the completed circuit should be housed in a metal box to prevent unwanted radiations. The output should be via a coaxial socket to a small antenna when in use. The circuit

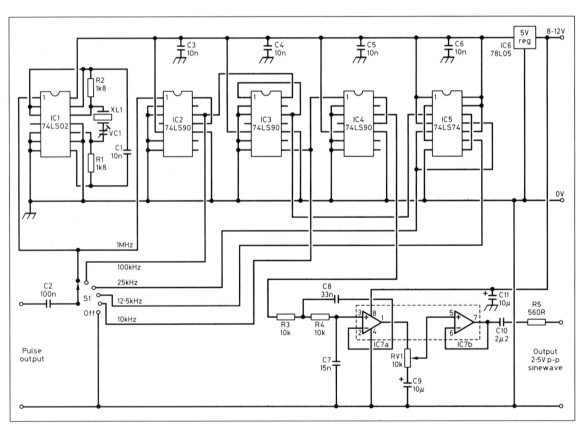

Fig 10.13.1. Circuit diagram for crystal-based frequency marker

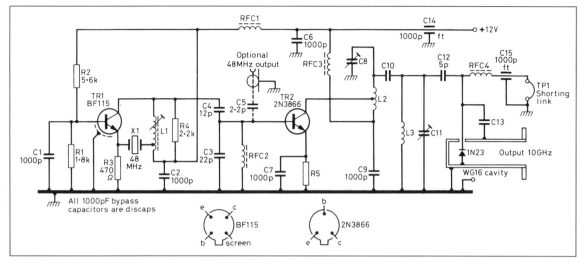

Fig 10.14.1. Circuit of the 10GHz frequency marker

requires a power supply of 8 to 12V DC at about 50mA – if the voltage regulator IC6 is omitted the circuit can be fed straight from a 5V supply but ensure there is a supply to the 1kHz filter IC7. A PCB and component layout are given in Appendix 2.

10.13.4 Calibration
The crystal should be adjusted using the trimmer capacitor VC1 to give a frequency of exactly 1.000000MHz. Alternatively an output should be compared with a standard frequency source.

10.14 Crystal-controlled frequency marker for 10GHz

10.14.1 General
This unit generates a large number of signals at precisely known frequencies which can be used to calibrate wideband receivers and transmitters accurately, thus effectively eliminating uncertainties from this source.

Although the output power of individual harmonics is very low, signals are detectable with efficient receivers even with 40–50dB of attenuation between the unit and the receiver. This means that the unit can provide a rough check on the sensitivity of a receiver; signals should be detectable with even the most insensitive receiver. The output power is more than adequate for use as a frequency reference for an AFC system but insufficient for the unit to be employed as a signal source for tuning antennas. The range of the unit is only about 10m when antennas of 15dB gain are used.

The unit produces relatively strong signals at 96MHz spacing, with signals about 20dB weaker spaced every 48MHz. The choice of 48 and 96MHz as stage

frequencies represents a compromise between generating a reasonable number of signals within the tuning range of most receivers while minimising the risk of confusion due to difficulty in identifying each of the harmonics. Other crystals may, of course, be used but there is an obvious advantage in using 'round number' frequencies and especially such frequencies as 36, 54 and 72MHz which also produce harmonics at other amateur frequencies and are therefore more easily measured.

Note that no provision is made for modulating the output. This is unnecessary if the local oscillator of the receiver can be frequency modulated with a tone which greatly assists finding signals. In calibrating a receiver it is essential that its local oscillator is already calibrated to within 20MHz using a wavemeter.

10.14.2 Circuit description
The circuit diagram of the unit is shown in Fig 10.14.1. TR1 forms an oscillator on 48MHz with XL1. This is followed by a doubler formed by TR2. The resulting output at 96MHz is fed to a mixer diode D1 which is used as the final multiplier. TR2 should be fitted with a small heatsink and its emitter lead kept as short as possible, typically 3–4mm. The output of TR2 is fed via a bandpass filter to the mixer diode in order to reduce 48MHz feedthrough.

10.14.3 Constructional details
The VHF circuitry is mounted on a piece of single-sided PCB which is bolted to the inside of the lid of a 111 × 60 × 31mm die-cast box – Fig 10.14.2.

The final multiplier (Fig 10.14.3) consists of a length of WG16 waveguide at least 60mm long which is closed

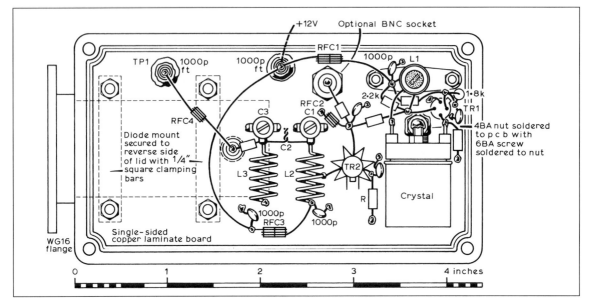

Fig 10.14.2. Component layout of the 10GHz frequency marker

at one end, with the mixer diode D1(1N23) mounted centrally and 7.5mm from the closed end. The waveguide is clamped to the outside of the lid, connection to the diode being made using the inner of a Belling-Lee TV socket which passes through holes drilled in the PCB and the lid as shown in Fig 10.14.2.

10.14.4 Alignment

Remove the link LK1 and replace with a milliammeter (50mA FSD) which will measure the diode current. In aligning the unit, L1 is adjusted to produce the maximum voltage across R5, and C1 and C3 are adjusted and

re-adjusted to maximise the diode current. The value of R5 is then changed as necessary to set the diode current

Table 10.14.1. Components list for the crystal-controlled marker for 10GHz

R1	1k8
R2	5k6
R3	470R
R4	2k2
R5	68–100R (see text)
C1, 2, 6, 7, 9	1n ceramic disc
C3	22p ceramic disc
C4	12p ceramic disc
C5	2p2 ceramic disc
C8, 13	1n feedthrough
C10	Two lengths of thin single strand insulated wire twisted together for 12mm
C11	4p7 ceramic disc
C12	Formed by a 0.005in PTFE or polythene sheet between the end of the 1N23 diode and the waveguide wall
D1	1N23
TR1	BF115
TR2	2N3866
XL1	48MHz third-overtone crystal
L1	10t, 28swg ECW on 8mm former, tapped 1t from C2 end
L2, 3	5t 28swg tinned copper wire 6mm inside dia, 12mm long, L2 is centre-tapped
L4	2.5t 28swg ECW on one FX1115
L5, 6	As L4 but on two FX1115
L7	10t 28swg on one FX1115
WG16	60mm minimum length waveguide-16

Resistors are 0.25W/0.5W, 5% unless specified otherwise.

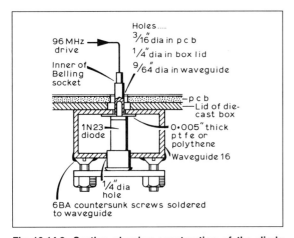

Fig 10.14.3. Section showing construction of the diode multiplier signal source

to 20–25mA. The frequency of the crystal oscillator can be checked on a counter via the optional output connector or using, for example, a 144MHz receiver. Maximum output may not coincide exactly with maximum diode current.

Instability may occur at maximum diode current, so it is worth

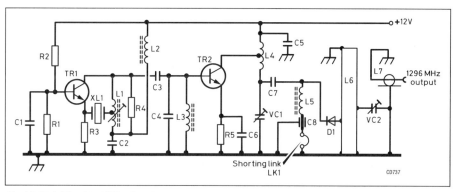

Fig 10.15.1. The 1296MHz signal source

checking with a 144MHz and 10GHz receiver that the unit is working correctly. Some useful performance parameters are given below:

Voltage supply	12V DC
Current required	25–40mA
Frequency pushing	8kHz/V
RF level of 96MHz harmonics 10.0–10.2GHz	−75dBm
RF level of 48MHz harmonics 10.0–10.2GHz	−95dBm

10.14.5 Using the frequency marker

The marker is preferably connected directly to the receiver via a variable attenuator, but alternatively it can be spaced from the receiver input by a few metres. With 20–30dB attenuation, the receiver should detect weak signals which are harmonics of 96MHz only. If the attenuation is reduced to around 10dB, the 48MHz intermediate harmonics should be heard as weak signals with the now-strong 96MHz harmonics.

It is possible that more signals than expected will be heard as a result of the receiver having poor or even no image rejection. Thus a receiver with a 30MHz IF will respond to relatively strong harmonics at 9.984GHz (104 × 96MHz) when its local oscillator is tuned to either 9.954 or 10.014GHz and to signals at 10.080GHz (105 × 96MHz) when tuned to either 10.050 or 10.110GHz. For the same reason, the receiver may also respond to the weaker harmonics at 48MHz spacing. The receiver local oscillator may therefore be calibrated precisely at several points, from which the (two) corresponding signal channels may be determined, provided the IF is known accurately. If a larger number of calibration points is required, then either the IF may be temporarily changed or a different crystal used in the marker.

It is possible to use the unit 'in the field', since it is small enough to be waved about in front of the receiver prior to establishing a contact. Alternatively the unit could be built into the system, coupled to the receiver through a 10dB directional coupler, to provide an instant check on its calibration and, in turn, that of the transmitter.

It is worth noting that the 10GHz multiplier stage can be replaced with one for any of the lower microwave bands, hence producing a unit capable of providing calibration signals on any of the intermediate bands.

10.15 A 1296MHz signal source

10.15.1 General

It is possible using the same basic 48MHz crystal oscillator as described above to make a 1296MHz signal source. Although the output signal level is only of the order of a few microwatts, signals have been received, using high-gain antennas, from a similar unit over a distance of 21km with a report of 569.

10.15.2 Circuit description

The circuit diagram is shown in Fig 10.15.1. As for the 10GHz source, TR1 forms a crystal-controlled 48MHz oscillator. This is followed by TR2 which provides a tripler to 144MHz. This output is fed to D1 which acts as a ×9 multiplier. A $\lambda/2$ line L6 is tuned to the required

Table 10.15.1. Components list for the 1296MHz signal source

R1	1k8	C1, 2,	
R2	5k6	5, 6	1n ceramic disc
R3	470R	C3	10p ceramic disc
R4	2k2	C4	27p ceramic disc
R5	100R	C7	4p7 ceramic disc
L1	10t, 28swg ECW on 8mm	C8	1n feedthrough
	former, tapped 1t from C2	VC1	20p ceramic
	end		tubular trimmer
L2	2.5t, 28swg ECW on two	VC2	6p ceramic
	FX1115 ferrite beads		tubular trimmer
L3	As L2 but only one bead	TR1	BF115
L4	5t, 28swg tinned copper wire,	TR2	BSX20
	6mm inside dia, 12mm long,	D1	1N914, 1N4148
	centre tapped	XL1	48MHz third-
L5	As L2		overtone crystal
L6, 7	See Fig 10.15.2(c)		

Resistors are 0.25W/0.5W, 5% unless specified otherwise.

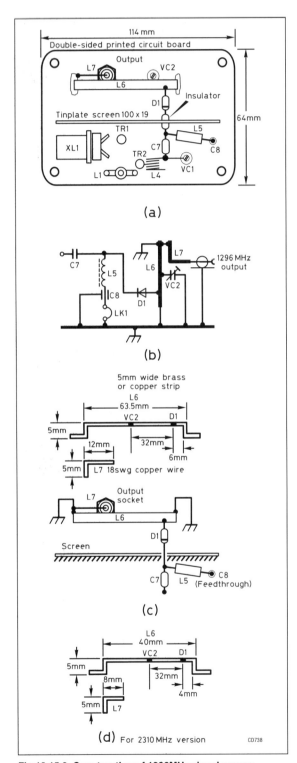

(a)

(b)

(c)

(d) For 2310 MHz version

Fig 10.15.2. Construction of 1296MHz signal source

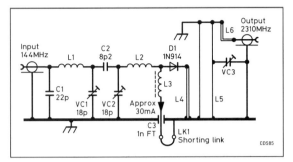

Fig 10.16.1. Circuit of the 144/2310MHz multiplier

harmonic with trimmer VC2. The multiplier diode is tapped onto the line 6mm from the ground end where the impedance is low.

10.15.3 Constructional details

Constructional details are shown in Fig 10.15.2. The unit is built on a piece of double-sided PCB which forms the lid of a standard die-cast box.

10.15.4 Alignment

Alignment is similar to that for the 10GHz multiplier. Remove the shorting link and replace with a milli-ammeter: this measures the diode current. First adjust VC1 for maximum drive, then adjust VC2 for maximum current in the region of 10mA. If possible, monitor the output signal on a 1296MHz receiver to ensure the signal is clean. There may be a tendency for the output spectrum to 'break up' at maximum diode current, in which case it is best to reduce drive slightly by detuning VC1 by a small amount.

10.16   A 2310MHz band signal source

10.16.1 General

It is possible to use the marker described for 1296MHz on 2320MHz by shortening the tuning lines – see Fig 10.15.2(d). Unless the 48MHz crystal is changed, the only useful harmonics will be at 2352, 2400 and 2448MHz. None of these are in the recognised narrow communications section of 2320 to 2322MHz. Changing the basic crystal frequency to 48.333MHz will give an output at 2320MHz which is likely to be much more useful.

An alternative approach for this band can be provided by using a 144MHz exciter into a ×16 multiplier. The drive required at 144MHz is 300–500mW.

10.16.2 Circuit description

The circuit diagram is shown in Fig 10.16.1. Instead of a 1N914/1N4148 diode for D1, slightly improved output may be obtained by using a Schottky barrier device such as the Hewlett Packard HP2800.

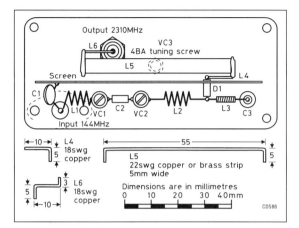

Fig 10.16.2. Layout of multiplier

10.16.3 Construction

The multiplier is built on a double-sided PCB which forms the lid of a $92 \times 38 \times 31$mm die-cast box. Further details are given in Fig 10.16.2.

10.16.4 Alignment

Replace shorting link LK1 with a milliammeter (50mA FSD). Apply sufficient drive to obtain movement on the meter. Tune VC1 and VC2 to peak the diode current at about 30mA. The output line is then tuned by VC3 which is formed by a 4BA screw.

10.17 Attenuators

Attenuators are useful for receiver measurements, especially when testing from signal generators that have minimal or no attenuators within them. The greatest problem is the radiation and leakage of signals from within the unit. Because of this the attenuator should consist of a good RF-tight metal box with high-quality connectors. An attenuator might also be useful between a transmitter and transverter.

Attenuators are normally made from pi-networks or T-networks. For this exercise it is assumed that load and source impedances are equal. Two computer programs

Table 10.16.1. Components list for the 2310MHz band signal source

C1	22p ceramic disc	VC1, 2	18p tubular trimmer
C2	8p2 ceramic disc	VC3	4BA screw in nut
C3	1n feedthrough		soldered to PCB
L1	4t 20swg ECW, 6.5mm inside dia		
L2	5t 20swg ECW, 6.5mm inside dia		
L3	3t 22swg ECW, on FX1115		
L4–6	See Fig 10.16.2		
D1	1N914, HP2800 (see text)		

Resistors are 0.25W/0.5W, 5% unless specified otherwise.

Table 10.17.1. Resistors for 50Ω and 75Ω attenuators based on pi- and T-sections

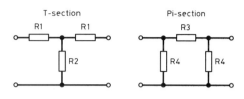

	R1 (Ω)		R3 (Ω)	
dB	**(50)**	**(75)**	**(50)**	**(75)**
1	2.9	4.35	5.7	8.5
2	5.73	8.6	11.6	17.4
4	11.3	17.0	24.0	36.0
8	21.5	32.3	52.9	79.2
16	36.3	54.4	154.0	231.0
32	47.5	71.1	1.0k	1.5k
64	50.0	75.0	39.6k	59.3k

	R2 (Ω)		R4 (Ω)	
dB	**(50)**	**(75)**	**(50)**	**(75)**
1	434.0	650.0	870.0	1.3k
2	215.0	323.0	436.0	653.0
4	104.0	156.0	213.0	320.0
8	47.3	71.0	116.0	174.0
16	16.25	24.4	69.0	103.5
32	2.5	3.75	53.0	79.5
64	0.075	0.113	50.0	75.0

[1] are given below for assistance as the calculation is somewhat tedious but there is also Table 10.17.1 for those who do not want to use a computer.

```
10   PRINT "RESISTIVE PI-ATTENUATOR CIRCUIT"
20   DEF FNA(X)=INT(X*100+.5)
30   DEF FNB(X)=LOG(X)/LOG(10)
40   DIM P(12)
50   FORI=1TO12: READ P(I): NEXT
60   DATA 1.2,1.5,1.8,2.2,2.7,3.3
70   DATA 3.9,4.7,5.6,6.8,8.2,10
100  INPUT "CIRCUIT IMPEDANCE (OHMS) ";Z
110  INPUT "ATTENUATION (DB) ";DB
120  V=10^(-DB/20)
130  A=Z*(1+V)/(1-V)
140  B=Z*(1-V*V)/(2*V)
150  PRINT "OPTIMUM VALUES:"
160  PRINT "SIDES: ";A;" OHMS"
170  PRINT "  TOP: "B;" OHMS"
180  R=Z: GOSUB 500
190  PRINT "NEAREST PREFERRED VALUES: "
200  PRINT " SIDES    TOP      DB      Z"
210  R=A: GOSUB 600: AL=L: AH=H
220  R=B: GOSUB 600: BL=L: BH=H
230  A=AL: B=BL: GOSUB 400
240  A=AL: B=BH: GOSUB 400
250  A=AH: B=BL: GOSUB 400
260  A=AH: B=BH: GOSUB 400
300  INPUT "SIDE RESISTORS ";A
```

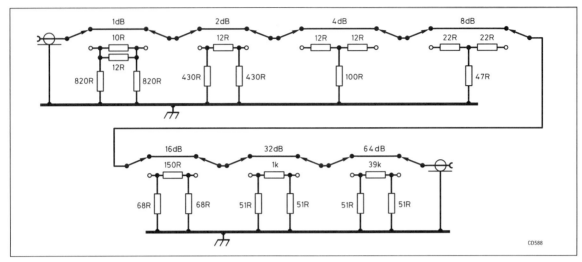

Fig 10.18.1. Circuit diagram of 50Ω attenuator using preferred values of resistor

Fig 10.18.2. Construction of the 50Ω attenuator

```
310  IF A<0 GOTO 100
320  INPUT "TOP RESISTOR ";B
330  GOSUB 400
340  GOSUB 500
350  GOTO 300
400  R=A*Z/(A+Z): V=R/(R+B)
410  R=A*(R+B)/(R+A+B)
420  DB=-20*FNB(V)
430  PRINT A;TAB(8);B;TAB(16);FNA(DB)/100;
     TAB(24);FNA(R)/100
440  RETURN
500  P1=R/A: P2=P1*V*V: PB=R*(1-V)*(1-V)/B
510  PRINT "POWER: INPUT ";FNA(P1);"%"
520  PRINT "TOP ";FNA(PB);"%","OUTPUT ";
     FNA(P2);"%"
530  RETURN
600  I=1: M=10^INT(FNB(R)): L=M
610  H=M*P(I)
620  IF H>R THEN RETURN
630  I=I+1: L=H: GOTO 610
```

For T-attenuator design, replace the appropriate lines in the above program by the following:

```
10   PRINT "RESISTIVE T-ATTENUATOR NETWORK"
130  A=Z*(1-V)/(1+V)
140  B=(Z*Z-A*A)/(2*A)
150  PRINT "OPTIMUM VALUES:"
160  PRINT " ARMS: ";A;" OHMS"
170  PRINT " BASE: ";B;" OHMS"
180  R=Z: GOSUB 500
190  PRINT "NEAREST PREFERRED VALUES:"
200  PRINT "  ARMS   BASE    DB      Z"
300  INPUT "ARM RESISTORS ";A
310  IF A<0 GOTO 100
320  INPUT "BASE RESISTOR ";B
400  R=B*(Z+A)/(B+Z+A)
410  V=Z/(Z+A)*R/(R+A): R=R+A
500  H=V+V*A/Z:P1=R*(1-H)*(1-H)/A:
     P2=R*V*V*A/(Z*Z):PB=R*H*H/B
```

10.18   A 50Ω low-power switched attenuator

The circuit shown in Fig 10.18.1 is a switched attenuator using a combination of pi-networks and T-networks, which enables preferred-value resistors to be used. A 1-2-4-8- . . . dB switching sequence is used so that the maximum attenuation range is obtained for a given number of sections.

The switches used are standard wafer-type, panel-mounting, slide switches, for which the effective transfer capacitance in the circuit used is only 0.8pF. With 5% carbon film resistors the attenuator accuracy is ±0.5dB on the 1, 2, 4 and 8dB positions up to 500MHz. The 16dB position is 1dB low at 500MHz, the 32dB position 1dB low at 30MHz and the 64dB position 1dB low at 750kHz.

The photograph of Fig 10.18.2 shows the construction of the unit.

10.19 Reference

[1] *Amateur Radio Software*, J Morris, GM4ANB, RSGB, 1985.

Chapter 11

Modulation measurements

11.1   Introduction

To be able to measure some of the parameters of the modulation of transmissions is both highly desirable in order to fulfil not only the licence conditions but also to be a good neighbour in what have become very crowded bands, especially from HF to 144MHz. For RF power measurements see Chapter 6.

11.2   Using the oscilloscope for modulation measurements

11.2.1   General

The purpose of this section is to show how the oscilloscope which was described in Chapter 3 can be used for the monitoring of amplitude modulation (including CW and SSB) and taking measurements where appropriate. The methods can also be used with the modulation monitor as described in Section 11.3. The radio frequency range that can be covered depends on the frequency response of the oscilloscope but the principles are independent of this restriction.

It must be possible to obtain a sample of the signal in order to be able to examine a transmitter output. This can be accomplished by direct connection or by isolation methods, eg a transformer. A direct-connection method is shown in Fig 11.2.1, where the potential divider formed by the 9.1kΩ and 1kΩ resistors provides an output voltage which is one tenth of that across the load. Providing carbon resistors are used, this method is

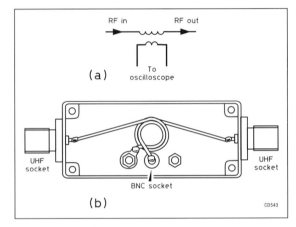

Fig 11.2.2. Inductive coupling: (a) theoretical and (b) practical. The pick-up unit is constructed in an 89× 35× 30mm die-cast box. The UHF sockets are linked by a length of 12swg wire with a single-turn loop at the centre; a two-turn coupling loop is taken to a BNC socket to feed the oscilloscope tuning unit

usable up to the limits of the oscilloscope. The resistors are 5W rated (ie for an RF output of 400W). Fig 11.2.2 shows a method using inductive coupling, ie the oscilloscope is completely isolated from the transmitter. Fig 11.2.3 shows another method whereby an insulated coil connected to the oscilloscope can be positioned somewhere in the vicinity of the amplifier output components.

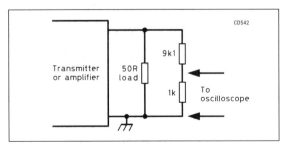

Fig 11.2.1. Direct connection

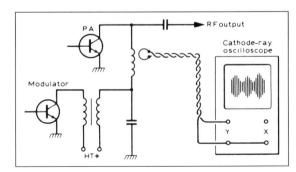

Fig 11.2.3. Arrangement with movable coupling loop

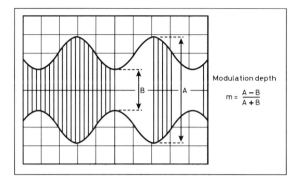

Fig 11.2.4. Modulation depth measurement

11.2.2   Amplitude modulation (A3E) – method 1

This method requires an oscilloscope with a timebase. The oscilloscope is set up with a sample of the modulated RF being applied to the Y-plates, the timebase being adjusted to give a waveform similar to that shown in Fig 11.2.4 for a single-frequency, sine-wave modulation. As it is easiest to measure peak-to-peak values on an oscilloscope, the percentage modulation is given by:

$$\frac{A - B}{A + B} \times 100$$

Fig 11.2.5 shows various conditions of modulation.

11.2.3   Amplitude modulation (A3E) – method 2

This method does not require a timebase, but instead the modulating audio frequency is fed to the X-input and a sample of the modulated output is fed to the Y-input, as shown in Fig 11.2.6. Fig 11.2.7 shows some typical waveforms that can be expected. The modulation depth is given also by the above formula. If more convenient, the audio can be obtained by detecting the modulated output using the circuit as shown in Fig 11.2.8.

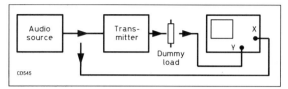

Fig 11.2.6. Amplitude modulation – method 2

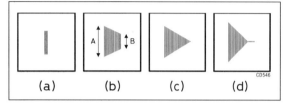

Fig 11.2.7. Typical oscilloscope patterns obtained by method 2. The vertical line at (a) shows the unmodulated carrier amplitude. In (b) the carrier is modulated 50% while in (c) it is modulated 100%. Where the sloping edges of the pattern are flattened, as in (d), the carrier is over-modulated

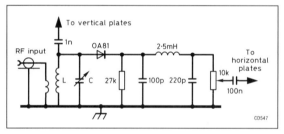

Fig 11.2.8. Alternative method of obtaining modulating signal. LC must tune to the RF signal

11.2.4   Amplifier linearity – general

When a post-transmitter amplifier is used with amplitude modulation, then linearity is of the utmost importance otherwise distortion of the modulation may occur.

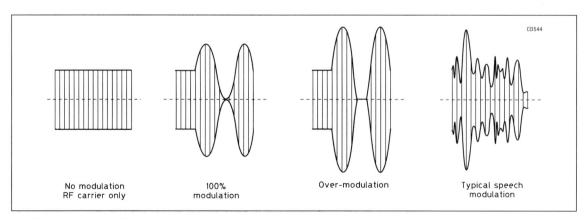

Fig 11.2.5. Various conditions of modulation

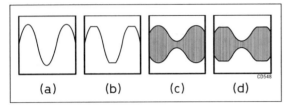

Fig 11.2.9. Possible oscilloscope waveforms: (a), (c) no apparent distortion; (b), (d) amplifier overdriven

This distortion can in turn cause unnecessary interference to other users. A very simple check is to take a sample of the output of the amplifier/transmitter and display it on an oscilloscope with internal timebase. Fig 11.2.9 shows possible oscilloscope waveforms together with an interpretation.

11.2.5 Amplifier linearity – single sideband (J3E)

The linearity of an SSB amplifier may be checked by the 45° method. This is shown in Fig 11.2.10, which also includes a suitable sampling circuit. A sample of a detected signal is taken from before and after the amplifier and applied to the X- and Y-plates respectively. The resistors R1 and R2 of the sampling circuit should be adjusted so that the voltage output from each detector is similar. The ideal display should be a single line at 45°. Fig 11.2.10(c) shows various possible displays with their interpretation.

Using the arrangement as shown in Fig 11.2.11, the modulation pattern can be monitored. Typical two-tone test outputs are also shown on the same diagram. If, on removing the audio modulation, there is still some trace of a carrier shown on the screen, then this indicates that the carrier null may need adjustment. A two-tone test oscillator is described in Chapter 10. The use of the two-tone method for output power measurement is explained in Chapter 6.

11.3   A modulation monitor

The circuit of an oscilloscope that can be used as a dedicated modulation monitor is shown in Fig 11.3.1. This, though deliberately moderate, is adequate for setting up SSB transmitters and monitoring AM transmitters.

Warning: this unit contains high voltages and care should be exercised in constructing, testing and using it.

The CRT used is no longer in production but may be found on stalls at radio rallies and flea markets, otherwise an alternative may be used.

An EHT of 1000/1500V is obtained from a voltage doubler circuit formed from T1, D1–D4 and C4/C5. Brilliance of the display is controlled by RV3 and focus by RV2. It should be noted that a high-intensity spot must not be permitted to remain stationary on the screen for any length of time otherwise it will leave a permanent

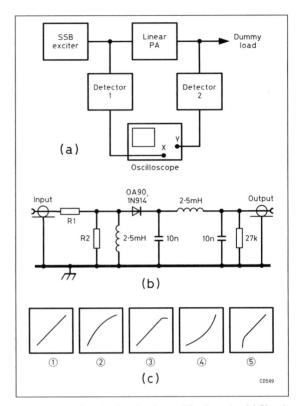

Fig 11.2.10. 45° method to check amplifier linearity. (a) Circuit diagram for checking SSB transmissions by this method. (b) Suggested demodulator unit. Adjust R1 and R2 for equal outputs from the two detectors. (c) Displays using the 45° method: (1) linear condition; (2) incorrect bias; (3) amplifier overloaded; (4) insufficient standing current in amplifier; (5) pattern obtained from speech input to a correctly adjusted amplifier

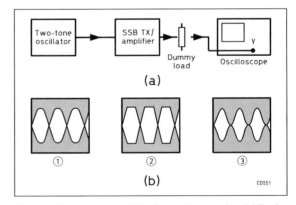

Fig 11.2.11. Two-tone amplifier/transmitter testing. (a) Equipment arrangement for two-tone testing. (b) Oscilloscope patterns at the output of a linear amplifier with two-tone test output: (1) amplifier correctly adjusted; (2) peaks flattened because of insufficient output loading or overdriving; (3) distortion at cross-over points due to incorrect bias

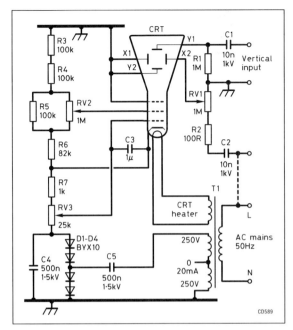

Fig 11.3.1. Oscilloscope display unit for monitoring telephony transmissions. Note: resistor chain R3–7 may need adjustment to suit particular CRTs or power supply voltages

blemish on the fluorescent phosphor. Horizontal sweep is taken from the 50Hz mains, and it is therefore necessary to make sure that C2 is connected to the live side of the mains supply. If no sweep is obtained on switching on, it is clear that C2 is connected to the neutral lead and the fault should be rectified by transferring it to the other side of the T1 primary.

A 50Hz sweep causes some distortion of the display but this may be kept within reasonable limits by using a high sweep amplitude so that only the centre portion of the sweep appears on the screen. The resulting trace is linear enough for most monitoring work. The sweep amplitude may be reduced by RV1 but this control should be set at maximum when monitoring is being carried out.

If a linear sweep is preferred then the circuit of Fig 11.3.2 can be employed. This is a Miller-transitron oscillator which provides a sawtooth waveform and which

Table 11.3.1. Components list for the modulation monitor

R1	1M	C1, 2	10n, 1kV ceramic
R2	100R	C3	1μ, 400V
R3–5	100k	C4, 5	0.5μ, 1.5kV
R6	82k	T1	250-0-250V, 20mA, 6.3V
R7	1k	D1-4	BYX10, BY448 or similar
RV1, 2	1M	CRT	3BP1 or similar
RV3	25k		

Resistors are 0.25W/0.5W, 5% unless specified otherwise.

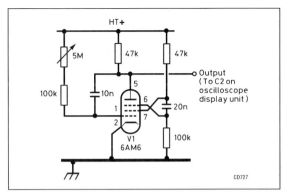

Fig 11.3.2. Miller-transitron sawtooth timebase generator

is used instead of the 50Hz mains for the sweep signal. The HT supply for this can be obtained by rectifying and smoothing the voltage at the centre tap of the transformer T1. Disconnect C2 from the primary of T1 and connect to the anode of the valve.

Fig 11.3.3 shows typical connections to obtain the various displays as already discussed.

11.4   A modulation meter for SSB

11.4.1   General

The modulation meter described below is by G4BTV and appeared in *Radio Communication* in 1985 [1].

The level of modulation of an SSB transmitter is usually judged by the movements of a moving-coil meter. An oscilloscope can be used to determine when the onset of 'flat topping' is observed. Fig 11.2.11(b) shows the traces obtained from an audio two-tone sine wave fed in at the microphone socket.

These observations are under steady-state conditions and show the current which should not be exceeded when speaking into the microphone. A snag immediately arises because the meter, due to its inertia, cannot respond quickly enough to the speech waveform. The modulation will reach a peak level and decay before the meter needle reaches the peak current value.

The advice usually given is to limit the indicated current on speech peaks to half that determined by the

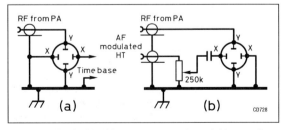

Fig 11.3.3. Typical oscilloscope connections: (a) for envelope patterns and (b) for trapezoidal pattern

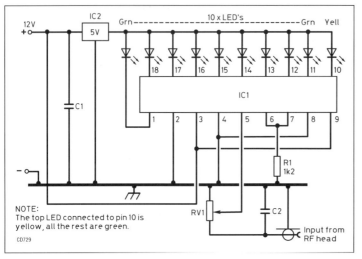

NOTE:
The top LED connected to pin 10 is yellow, all the rest are green.

CD729

Fig 11.4.1. Circuit of the bargraph unit

two-tone test, but this advice may be somewhat difficult to implement. Meters vary in their response to spiky waveforms, some being heavily damped and others extremely responsive. In the latter case, mechanical resonances come into play as well and the needle can dance all over the place and give no real guide as to what is happening. It was decided that an indicator in the form of an LED bargraph would solve the meter response problem. The equipment described consists of an RF detector and a display unit.

11.4.2   Circuit description

The circuit diagram for the display unit is shown in Fig 11.4.1. IC1 is a bargraph driver which also contains comparator circuits (see Chapter 2). Ten individual LEDs are used but it is possible to buy them in one module. The nine LEDs for the lower modulation levels are green and the 10th LED, which gives warning of excess modulation, is yellow. The internal reference level is used for the internal comparator chain and all the LEDs will illuminate for an input of 1.25V or greater (pin 5). The level from the RF detector head is adjusted by RV1 so that for a given transmitter nine LEDs illuminate for maximum

Table 11.4.1. Components list for the SSB modulation meter

R1	1k2	D1	OA91 or similar
R2	12k	IC1	LM3914
R3	10k	IC2	7805, 5V, 500mA
C1	10n, 50V ceramic	LEDs	Separate or module
C2	1n, 50V ceramic	RV1	4M7
C3	47n, 100V ceramic	3.5mm jacks and socket	
C4	2n2, 160V	SO239/PL259 socket and plug	

Resistors are 0.25W/0.5W, 5% unless specified otherwise.

modulation. By providing RV1 with a scale (dial) settings may be determined for other transmitters or linear amplifiers having different power ratings.

The display unit requires a DC supply, and for this application 12V is fed to pins 3 and 9, the LEDs being fed with 5V (maximum current drawn is typically 150mA). This is supplied by IC1. R1 determines the LED currents and C1 provides power supply decoupling. C2 provides additional smoothing for the detected RF. Construction of the display unit is not critical.

The circuit of the detector head is shown in Fig 11.4.2. The unit provides a tapping on the 50Ω coaxial antenna lead from which a sample of the RF is rectified and smoothed for driving the bargraph display. The signal from the potential divider formed by R2 and R3 is detected by diode D1, with C4 providing DC isolation and C3 the smoothing. (Note: some transceivers have DC on the antenna lead for control of linear amplifiers).

The rise time of the circuit for a step input is determined by R2 and R3 in parallel, and C3. Thus the combination of a resistance of 5450Ω and a capacitance of 47nF gives a time constant of 256µs. In order to show up short modulation peaks of a few milliseconds, the fall time needs to be greater than, say, 100ms. This is determined by RV1 and C3 and produces a time constant of the order of 220ms.

11.4.3   Construction

The display unit was mounted in an aluminium case measuring $100 \times 65 \times 50$mm. The PCB can be mounted so that the potentiometer spindle passes through the case and a dial arrangement can be attached. Also provided is a 3.5mm jack socket for the detector head and power supply sockets.

The detector head is an aluminium enclosure $65 \times 30 \times 30$mm, details of which are given in Fig 11.4.3 – this

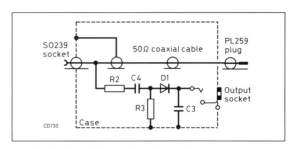

Fig 11.4.2. Circuit of the RF detector head

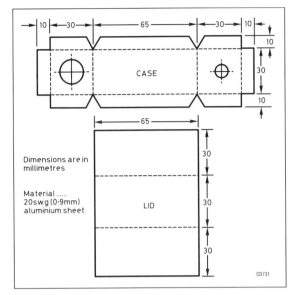

Fig 11.4.3. Details of case for RF detector

could also serve as a pattern for the display unit box with suitable dimensions. The ends of the box need to be just large enough for a SO239 socket on either end. Fig 11.4.4 shows the layout of components in the detector head.

11.4.4　In use

The separate detector head allows the display to be located in any convenient position, while the head can be inserted at any suitable point in the coaxial antenna lead, providing it is monitoring the correct signal.

Calibration of the bargraph input permits the monitoring of different power levels. In the prototype R2 and R3 were adjusted so that 3W PEP from a 144MHz transceiver just lit nine LEDs at a setting of RV1 near 100 on the dial. The lower readings for 25W and 100W PEP outputs were then recorded using an oscilloscope to indicate the onset of flat topping. The component values

are such that the unit should work satisfactorily down to 1.8MHz.

11.4.5　Choosing values for R2 and R3

The unit was designed for a maximum transmitted power of 100W PEP. For higher powers the potential divider R2 and R3 needs to be adjusted to ensure that the OA91 is not subjected to a PIV approaching 115V.

1. Find the RMS voltage on the 50Ω line: $V = \sqrt{50W}$ where W is the transmitter output in watts.
2. If V_2 is the RMS voltage at the diode anode, then:

$$V_2 = \frac{V_1 \times R_3}{R_2 + R_3}$$

3. Calculate PIV for the diode: this is $2.83 \times V_2$. Ensure that it is well within the rating.
4. Check the wattage ratings of R2 and R3.

Power dissipated in R2 $= (V_1 - V_2)^2/R_2$

Power dissipated in R3 $= V_2^2/R_3$

The power rating for each of these resistors is normally limited to about 0.5W each.

11.5　An automatic gain compression meter

11.5.1　General

As has been explained in *Radio Communication* [2] and elsewhere, an amplifier which is driven beyond its linear range and into gain compression will generate intermodulation products around the main signal. A grossly overdriven amplifier will generate high-order intermodulation products which appear across a large portion of the band as 'splatter'.

The meter described here is by G4SHH [3]. It offers a direct readout of gain compression in a linear amplifier when it is amplifying a modulated signal. This is very useful when making adjustments to obtain the highest possible undistorted output power, and also gives peace of mind during routine operation. The meter functions from the 1.8MHz band up to at least 144MHz. The original prototype, built following good VHF/UHF practice, worked perfectly well up to the 70cm band. Although the sensitivity at 432MHz was about 6dB lower than at HF, this does not affect the calibration.

11.5.2　Circuit operation and description

In Fig 11.5.1, the amplifier under test, the input and output

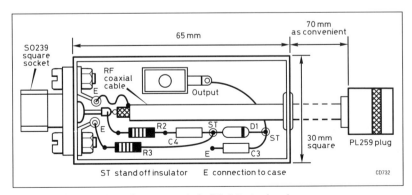

Fig 11.4.4. Arrangement of components in RF detector head

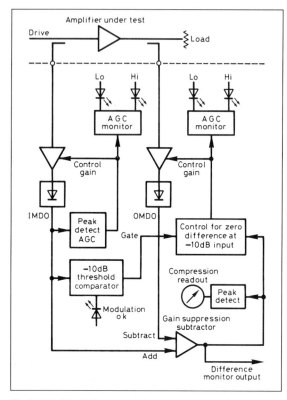

Fig 11.5.1. Block diagram of the gain compression meter

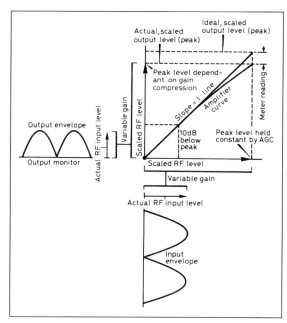

Fig 11.5.2. Operating principle of the gain compression meter

couplers, the drive source and the load are shown above the dotted line. Below the dotted line are the constituent parts of the gain compression meter. The samples of RF from the input and output of the amplifier are passed through identical gain-controlled amplifiers and detectors. The amplifier gains are controlled by systems within the meter and the input samples need only be set to give approximately the correct levels. The gain-control signals to the two amplifiers are monitored by circuits which drive LEDs to indicate if the signals are too high or low for correct operation of the meter.

The peak envelope power (PEP) from the input monitor detected output (IMDO) is held at a constant level by a peak-detecting AGC loop which has a time constant of several seconds, much longer than the syllabic rate of the modulation. The output monitor AGC (described later) has a similarly long time constant and is used to set the output monitor detected output (OMDO) equal to the IMDO at a point in the modulation cycle approximately 10dB below peak output power. The OMDO is subtracted from the IMDO to drive the meter display via a peak detector.

The effect of the two AGC loops is to scale the input and output signals from any amplifier, regardless of level

or gain, onto one common linearity diagram as shown in Fig 11.5.2. When the OMDO is subtracted from the IMDO, the difference signal is proportional to the gain compression percentage at peak power, irrespective of the actual input and output power levels or the gain of the amplifier. Gain compression causes a progressively increasing difference between IMDO and OMDO which reaches a maximum at peak power. This maximum level is detected and displayed on the meter.

The output monitor AGC is derived as follows. Since the IMO has its peak value held at a constant level, the point in the modulation cycle at which the drive is, say, 10dB below the peak power may be detected by comparing the IMDO with a suitable DC level. At this −10dB threshold the control line marked 'gate' in Fig 11.5.1 gives a 'go' signal to the output AGC loop to set the output AGC voltage to a value which gives zero output from the gain compression subtractor. In other words, the meter assumes there is no compression at a drive level 10dB below the peak RF input power to the amplifier, and measures any subsequent compression at higher drive levels.

11.5.3   RF monitors

Each RF monitor in Fig 11.5.3 consists of a dual-gate MOSFET (3SK85) variable-gain amplifier followed by a common-emitter amplifier (BFY90) and detector formed by two BA481 diodes. It should be noted that although the circuits are straightforward the detector operates with a constant-voltage load (temperature-compensated and set by RV3), and the current which the diodes pump into this load is a measure of the RF level. This low-impedance configuration gives a good broad-band frequency response. Mild non-linearity in the detectors will not cause significant readout errors since the non-linearities of the input and output detectors will tend to cancel, provided that the two detectors operate at reasonably similar signal levels. However, linearity in the input amplifiers is very important so they both need to operate at low signal levels.

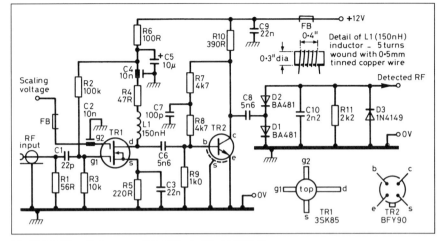

Fig 11.5.3. Circuit diagram of the RF monitor amplifiers

Referring now to the rest of the gain compression meter (Fig 11.5.4), IC1a and IC1b convert the detector output currents into voltages (with a +3.0V bias), ie the IMDO and OMDO. The response speed of these amplifiers is limited by capacitors as filtering against transients generated by the AGC.

11.5.4   Gain compression subtractor

IC1c subtracts the OMDO from the IMDO. The bias at the output of this stage is adjustable by the preset RV1 and the gain compression waveform is available at a monitor output for viewing on an oscilloscope if desired.

11.5.5   Gain compression peak detector

IC1d detects the peak level of the difference between the OMDO and IMDO signals and drives the meter M1. This stage operates with an input bias of half the 5.6V reference voltage, and the other side of the meter is returned to a resistive divider (R42 and R43) providing the same voltage level. Sensitivity is adjusted by RV2, diodes D33 and D34 across RV2 helping to linearise the compression scale.

11.5.6   Input AGC generator

IC2 is a quad voltage comparator (LM339) with open-collector outputs. IC2a produces the required input AGC voltage by discharging C37 if the peak level of the IMDO at one input of IC2a exceeds the reference DC level at the non-inverting input. Capacitor C37 tends to recharge through R49 when IC2a is cut off, leading to a small increase in RF gain. This produces a larger detected signal which turns IC2a on again and discharges the

capacitor. Thus IC2a maintains an AGC voltage which remains essentially constant unless the peak input level changes.

11.5.7   Output AGC generator

The output AGC generator is considerably more complex. R44 and R47 set a DC reference level which is equal to the output of the IMDO at about 10dB below maximum drive power, this voltage being fed to the inputs of IC2b and IC2d. The circuit associated with IC2d provides an LED indication that the depth of modulation is greater than the −10dB threshold, while IC2b provides a signal to IC2c which is equal to half the 5.6V reference voltage – but only when the IMDO is above the −10dB threshold. For IMDO voltages below this threshold, the signal to IC2c is slightly below half the reference voltage and thus the comparator function is disabled; this signal is called 'gate' in Fig 11.5.1.

The detailed operation of the output AGC generator is best understood by considering what happens as the modulation envelope rises past the −10dB threshold (assuming that the AGC loop has stabilised).

As the threshold is approached, the gain subtractor output will be approximately equal to half the 5.6V reference voltage and IC2c will be cut off because the 'gate' signal is low. C38 at the output of IC2c will have been gradually charging through R50 during the previous modulation cycle. Immediately above the threshold, IC2c will discharge the capacitor until the output of IC1c is just equal to half the reference voltage. As gain compression starts to set in and IC1c output begins to rise, IC2c will revert to the cut-off state. Hence the output AGC voltage will remain very close to the level which was set when the modulation waveform crossed the −10dB threshold.

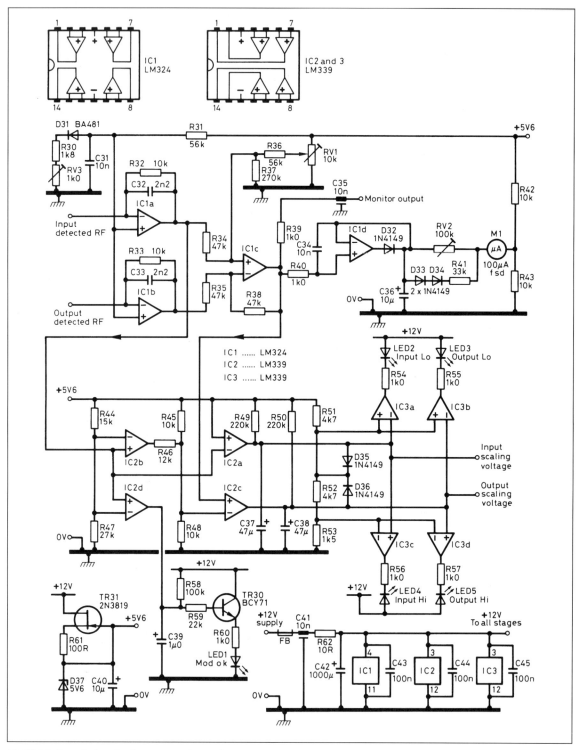

Fig 11.5.4. Remainder of gain compression meter

11.5.8 AGC monitoring

The maximum voltage to which C37 and C38 (on the input and output AGC lines respectively) can charge is limited by D35 and D36 which are connected to a bleeder network between the voltage reference rail and ground. Comparators IC3a to IC3d compare the AGC voltages with levels set by the bleeder network divider (R51, R52, R53) to confirm that the AGC levels are within acceptable limits and that the RF levels are satisfactory.

11.5.9 Construction

Suitable construction is essential for correct operation and, if built as described, the meter should work first time without great effort.

The instrument must be enclosed in a metal box for adequate screening. The RF inputs must pass through bulkhead coaxial connectors mounted on the box and all external low-frequency connections must be via feed-through capacitors with ferrite beads each side in order to remove unwanted RF. A screening plate behind the meter movement was not found necessary but can be added as good screening practice.

The two RF monitor amplifiers should be mounted on a ground plane of copper-clad PCB and built using the shortest possible leads. Fig 11.5.5 shows one method of construction. The components are mounted through holes drilled in a piece of single-sided PCB, with all the components (except TR1) on the copper side and direct point-to-point wiring on the rear as shown. Leads marked with an 'X' are soldered directly to the copper ground plane and all holes are countersunk to avoid short-circuits. Provided that the components are kept close to the board and the two separate amplifiers are kept at least 2in apart, no internal screening will be required. The low-frequency meter/indicator drive circuits may be built on Veroboard or similar.

11.5.10 Couplers

The meter requires input levels of −10dBm ± 10dB on both inputs, ie nominally 0.1mW, but the AGC will cope with anything between 0.01mW and 1mW. To use the meter with a linear amplifier, some form of RF sampling coupler is required at both input and output. Fig 11.5.6 shows some suitable methods of achieving this. Fig 11.5.6(a) shows a low-power resistive coupler with a maximum coupling factor of −26dB. This coupler is not

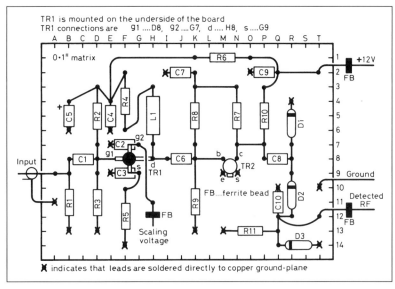

Fig 11.5.5. Layout for the input and output monitors

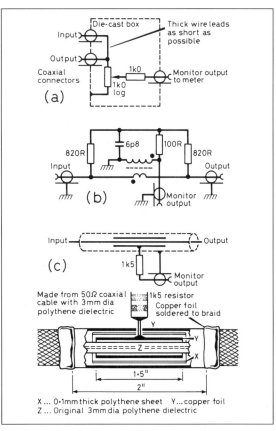

Fig 11.5.6. A selection of wide-band couplers for power monitoring

Table 11.5.1. Components list for the automatic gain compression meter

R1	56R	RV1	10k multi-turn
R2	100k	RV2	100k multi-turn
R3, 32, 33,		RV3	1k multi-turn
42, 43, 45,		C1	22p
48, 58	10k	C2, 4, 31, 34	10n
R4	47R	C3, 9	22n
R5	220R	C5	1μ tantalum bead
R6, 61	100R	C6, 8	5n6
R7, 8, 51,		C7	100p
52	4k7	C10, 32, 33	2n2
R9, 39, 40,		C35, 41	10n feedthrough
54, 55, 56		C36, 40	10μ tantalum bead
57, 60	1k	C37, 38	47μ tantalum bead
R10	390R	C39	1μ tantalum bead
R11	2k2	C42	1000μ electrolytic
R30	1k8	C43–45	0.1μ electrolytic
R31, 36	56k	D1, 2, 31	BA481
R34, 35, 38	47k	D3, 32–36	1N4149
R37	270k	D37	5V6 zener, 400mW
R41	33k	TR1	3SK85
R44	15k	TR2	BFY90
R46	12k	TR30	BCY71
R47	27k	TR31	2N3819
R49, 50	220k	IC1	LM324
R53	1k5	IC2	LM339
R59	22k	LED1–5	Red LED
R62	10R, 0.5W	M1	100μA FSD meter

Die-cast box
Copper-clad board
Ferrite beads, Fair-rite 26-43000101
Veroboard (plain)
BNC bulkhead connectors

Note component numbers greater than 30 are for the meter/ indication circuits. All resistors are 0.25W, 2% unless specified otherwise. Two components are required for each of R1–R11, C1–C10, D1–D3 and TR1, TR2.

very broad-band but can be adjusted as required for any band.

If the input VSWR of the power amplifier is liable to alter with drive level, a more reliable indication of linearity may be obtained by using a directional input coupler which does not respond to the signal being reflected back towards the driver. Fig 11.5.6(b) shows such a coupler which closely resembles a popular type of VSWR bridge and has a coupling factor of −14dB. The toroidal transformer is wound on a Fair-Rite type 26-43000101 core which limits the through power level to about 7W CW or 15W PEP on SSB. The one-turn primary is a wire passing straight through the core. The secondary is 10 turns wound on the core. For wide-band performance all components must be mounted above a ground plane with leads no longer than 4mm. The three flange-type BNC connectors must be bolted directly to the ground plane with no extra leads or tags.

The coupler on the output side must be suitable for carrying high power but it need not necessarily be a directional type. Fig 11.5.6(c) shows a simple −60dB coupler made from a piece of UR67 cable. A short length of the outer braid is replaced by a thin copper coupling sleeve which acts as a capacitive voltage divider between the inner and outer of the coaxial cable. The thickness of the 0.1mm polyethylene outer insulation controls the division ratio. If the coupler is carefully constructed with no gaps between the layers of copper foil and polyethylene, it will introduce no significant VSWR up to the 70cm band. Alternatives to this type of coupler would be a high-power version of Fig 11.5.6(b) with a larger toroid or, at VHF and UHF, a stripline directional coupler. Almost any type of VSWR meter can be adapted for use with the gain compression meter providing it is suitable for the power and frequency range in use.

Note that the coupler on the input side of the power amplifier may abstract a noticeable fraction of the input power, causing some reduction in drive. The high-power couplers take negligible power.

11.5.11 Setting up

If the meter works without any troubleshooting, no test equipment beyond a multimeter is required for setting up as detailed below:

1. Set RV2 to maximum resistance and switch on power. Check for correct supply voltage to each transistor and IC, and check for approximately 5.6V on the reference voltage rail. Adjust RV3 for 3.0V at the outputs of IC1a and IC1b – the two voltages should be almost equal.

2. Adjust RV1 to zero meter M1. The MOD OK and both of the RF LO LEDs should be illuminated. Short the input AGC line to ground and check that the INPUT LO LED extinguishes and the INPUT HI LED illuminates. Repeat the test for the output AGC line.

3. Connect the input monitor line to the low-power sampler and apply a little RF (eg CW on any band) to extinguish the INPUT LO LED. Adjust RV2 to give full scale on M1. The RF level should now be adjustable between the INPUT LO and INPUT HI limits without any significant change in meter indication. The MOD OK indicator should not illuminate.

4. Connect both the input and output RF monitor lines to the same sampler and apply CW RF as before. Vary the level and confirm that the input and output LEDs behave the same. M1 should be reading close to zero. If it is not exactly zero then note the reading, switch off the RF and adjust RV1 to give the same reading. Apply RF again and use the adjusting screw on M1 to set the reading exactly to zero. Apply RF to the input monitor only and re-adjust RV2 for full-scale meter deflection.

If the circuit is working correctly, the meter is now set

Table 11.5.2. Indicated compression at different frequencies compared with the actual compression

Frequency	Actual compression		
(MHz)	Zero	9.5%	18%
10	<1%	8%	16%
30	<1%	8%	16%
70	<1.5%	9%	20%
150	<1.5%	12%	22%
435	<1.5%	13%	24%

up. This must be confirmed by testing with a modulated carrier or multi-tone SSB signal but with input and output connected together, ie monitoring the same signal level with no possibility of gain compression. The source of modulation on SSB can be either a two-tone generator (see Chapter 10) or simply a 'waaloh' into the microphone. The MOD OK indicator should illuminate when the instrument detects a modulated signal but for inputs between the HI and LO limits the indicated gain compression should be no more than 2% of full scale.

Tests on the prototype showed the relationship between actual and indicated compression given in Table 11.5.2.

Although the meter tends to over-indicate, it is far more important that it continues to read close to zero when the amplifier is behaving in a linear manner. It is actually measuring the voltage gain compression percentage compared with a reference point about 10dB down from the peak drive power. A lower reference point would increase errors due to the way the meter operates, while a higher reference might itself fall in the region of gain compression.

11.5.12 Using the meter

When the meter is used with a linear amplifier, it should become quite clear when the amplifier is being driven into gain compression. Always aim to keep the meter at zero, because even a little flick upwards may be very noticeable to fellow amateurs on the bands. For a clean signal the indicated gain compression should not exceed 5% and more than 10% is *definitely* unacceptable. A nasty shock may be in store when one examines the linearity (or non-linearity!) of one's amplifier(s). It may be necessary to turn down the drive to achieve a clean signal – other people may already have been trying to tell you this!

To get the best out of the meter, it is important to realise what the indication means. Intermodulation products are caused by changes in gain (non-linearity) or in the phase of the output signal as the input drive level varies. Of the two, the gain changes are the more important since any phase change is usually accompanied by a change in gain. Hence this instrument can give useful indications of intermodulation by looking only at changes in gain.

Some tests were carried out on various valve and transistor power amplifiers to explore the relationship between gain compression and the resulting levels of intermodulation products (IPs). The levels of close-in, third-order IPs can be fairly accurately predicted and are largely independent of the sharpness of the onset of gain compression (sometimes referred to as *saturation*). However, the levels of 5th and higher-order IPs depend very much on how sharply the amplifier saturates. The smoother the passage into saturation, the better the higher-order intermodulation performance.

The meter will not measure distortion present in the driving signal or distortion in the final amplifier that is not accompanied by gain compression – so it will not detect that the bias was left switched to Class C! Any harmonics in either the drive or the output signal will be detected along with the fundamental and will cause errors, so harmonics should be at least 40dB down. For accurate measurements, distortion and harmonics arising from a poor input VSWR to the final amplifier should be considered.

It is not essential to use a directional coupler to monitor the drive power but this is a good idea unless one is certain that the input VSWR does not change with drive level – this is frequently the case with transistor power amplifiers and with poorly adjusted Class AB1 valve amplifiers.

11.6   Deviation measurements

11.6.1   General

The HF/UHF deviation meter by G3BIK [4] described here is simple to construct, of relatively low cost and based on readily available components. It is housed in a small RF-shielded plastic enclosure, and can be used with FM signals over a wide frequency range from about 3MHz to 450MHz. The power supply requirement is 15–20V DC at about 50mA – see later.

Fig 11.6.1 shows the block diagram of the instrument, the interconnections and signal routing, and Fig 11.6.2 gives the circuit diagram.

Fundamentally, the circuit is a type of superheterodyne receiver with an FM demodulator output which is displayed on a moving-coil meter showing kilohertz deviation. The instrument can also be used to monitor the demodulated audio signal on a small internal loudspeaker, and provision has been made for external access to the pulsed RF harmonics of the VFO as an elementary source of test signals (extending up to VHF) which could be useful for calibration or general receiver testing.

11.6.2   Circuit operation

A restricted-range signal f_2 (1.5MHz) is generated by the Colpitts oscillator (VFO) formed by TR1 and associated components. The variable capacitance diode in conjunction with RV1 allows variation of this frequency by about

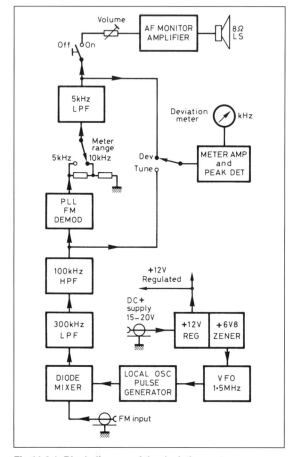

Fig 11.6.1. Block diagram of the deviation meter

signal is then demodulated by phase-locked loop IC2. The output at pin 7 of the PLL is a true replica of the input modulating signal and then attenuated by R57 and RV3 for the two meter ranges. The output is selected by S1 and then amplified by a low-pass active filter IC3a.

With S2 in the TUNE position, the IF signal at about 150kHz is passed to the meter amplifier IC3b/c. D7 with C58 acts as a peak detector and the resulting DC drives the meter. With S2 set to DEV, the demodulated signal is applied to the meter circuit.

An AF monitor is provided (IC4). The drive to this is via a push switch (S3) so that the user is deterred from using the monitor during measurement of deviation.

11.6.3   Power supply

A single supply philosophy is adopted for the deviation meter via an on-board 12V regulator, thus ensuring stability of deviation calibration and flexibility in the choice of external voltage supply.

All of the discrete transistors are fed from the full +12V regulated rail except the VFO which is further stabilised by a 6.8V zener diode. Split voltage supplies for IC1, IC2 and IC3 are provided by resistive dividers R50/51, R52/55 and R71/72 and are well decoupled.

Adequate decoupling of the DC supply connections is of the utmost importance in this circuit due to the pulsed nature of the local oscillator and mixer signals, hence the provision of low-value decoupling capacitors to filter out the higher frequencies from the supply rails and larger capacitors (microfarads) to deal with the lower frequencies.

11.6.4   Construction

The prototype circuit was constructed on SRBP copper stripboard of 0.1in hole spacing and dual parallel planes were allocated on the stripboard for each of the several DC supply and return rails.

Component layout is not critical provided that, as with any HF circuit, due attention is given to the shortness of component leads and interconnecting wires, and to mechanical rigidity. Sub-miniature 50Ω coaxial cable is employed for the interconnection between signal input socket and mixer, and miniature screened cable is used between all other panel-mounted components and the circuit board.

The RF screened enclosure is electrically bonded to the negative supply terminal, shown on the circuit diagram as the 0V rail, and the decoupling capacitors associated with the integrated circuits should be connected directly between the supply pins of the appropriate IC.

The panel-mounted miniature volume control was found to be not really necessary in practice, so this could be replaced by a preset potentiometer mounted internally on the circuit board.

±100kHz. The sine-wave output from this oscillator is buffered by TR2 and then amplitude limited by TR3–TR5 and D3, and then differentiated by TR6 and TR7 which results in a train of sharp pulses at the VFO repetition rate.

The pulses are then applied to a fast switching diode D4, which causes current pulses through the primary of pulse transformer T1. These pulses are rich in harmonics and extend well up into the VHF region. Note: the usable upper frequency is to a large extent determined by the switching diode. A microwave step-recovery diode would probably extend the frequency range but these devices are not cheap. Transformer T1 is wound in bifilar manner, it being important to get the transformer phasing correct.

The two phase-related outputs from the transformer are applied to the diode bridge mixer formed by D5 and D6, and here mixed with the FM signal (f_1) being measured. The mixing products are developed across R41 and the signal $f_1 - f_2$ (harmonic) filtered by the action of the various constituents of IC1 (range 100–300kHz). This

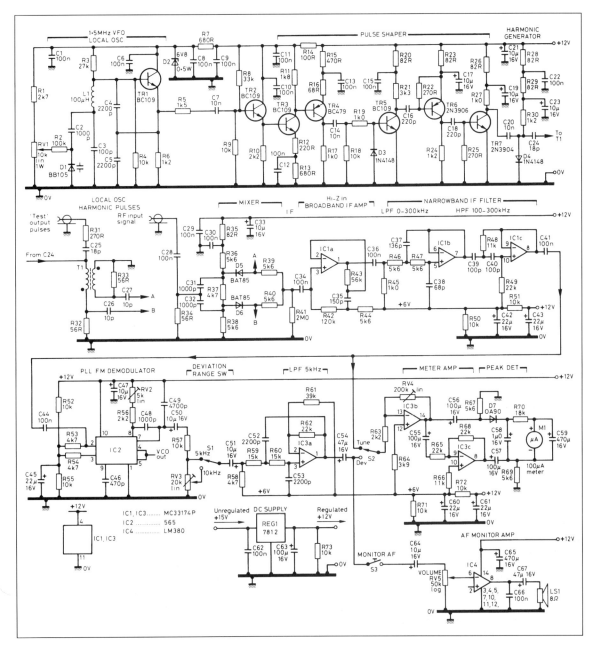

Fig 11.6.2. Circuit diagram of the deviation meter

As the upper operational frequency limit of the instrument is largely determined by the performance of the local oscillator harmonic generator diode D4, pulse transformer T1 and the D5/D6 diode mixer circuit, particular care should be taken to ensure shortness of component leads and symmetry of component layout for this section of the circuit.

A PCB pattern and component layout are given in Appendix 2.

11.6.5 Setting up

Before any attempt is made to use or calibrate the instrument, the free-running frequency of the phase-locked loop VCO must be set to 150kHz.

Table 11.6.1. Components list for the HF/UHF deviation meter

R1	2k7	R50–52, 55	10k, 0.5W	C49	4n7 ceramic
R2	100k	R59, 60	15k	C54, 67	47μ electrolytic
R3	27k	R61	39k	C55–57, 63	100μ electrolytic
R4, 9, 18, 57	10k	R64	3k9	C58	1μ electrolytic
R5	1k5	R70	18k	C59, 65	470μ electrolytic
R6, 24, 30	1k2	R71-73	10k, 0.5W	D1	BB105, BB405B or BB809
R7	680R, 0.5W	RV1	10k lin, 1W cermet		varicap
R8	33k	RV2	5k lin, min cermet	D2	6V8, 500mW zener
R10, 56, 63	2k2	RV3	20k lin, min cermet	D3, 4	1N4148
R11	1k8	RV4	200k lin, min cermet	D5, 6	BAT85
R12	220R	RV5	50k log carbon pot (with S3)	D7	OA90
R13	680R	C1, 6, 8–13,		TR1–3, 5	BC109, 2N3904 or similar
R14	100R	15, 22,		TR4	BC479, 2N3906 or similar
R15	470R	28–30, 34,		TR6	2N3906
R16	68R	36, 41, 44,		TR7	2N3904
R17, 19,		62, 66	100n ceramic	IC1, 3	MC33174P
27, 45	1k	C2, 48	1n ceramic	IC2	565
R20, 23, 26,		C3	100p silver mica/polystyrene	IC4	LM380
28, 29, 35	82R	C4, 5, 52, 53	2n2 polystyrene	REG1	12V, eg 7812
R21	3k3	C7, 14, 20	10n ceramic	L1	100μH RF inductor
R22, 25, 31	270R	C16, 18	220p ceramic	T1	Pulse transformer, 10mm
R32, 33, 34	56R	C17, 19, 21,			ferrite ring, 4t bifilar ECW
R36, 38, 39,		23, 33, 47,		LS1	8Ω miniature
46, 47	5k6	50, 51, 64	10μ electrolytic	M1	Meter, 100μA FSD,
R37, 53, 54,		C24, 25	18p silver mica/ceramic		scaled 0–10
58	4k7	C26, 27	10p silver mica/ceramic	S1, 2	SPDT miniature toggle
R40, 44, 67,		C31, 32	100p ceramic	S3	Pushbutton, n.o. (part of RV5)
69	5k6	C35	150p silver mica/ceramic		
R41	2M (2 × 1M)	C37	136p (2 × 68p)	Enclosure: ABS, RF shielded 190 × 110 ×
R42	120k	C38	68p ceramic/silver mica	60mm
R43	56k	C39, 40	100p silver mica	Socket (DC): 3.5mm chassis mounting
R48, 66	11k	C42, 43, 45,		Socket (RF): 50Ω BNC panel mounting
R49, 62, 65,		60, 61	22μ electrolytic	Socket (pulse): 50Ω BNC panel mounting
68	22k	C46	470p silver mica/ceramic	

Resistors are 0.25W, 5% and metal film unless specified otherwise.

Connect a frequency counter to either pin 4 or 5 of IC2 and adjust RV2 until the frequency is virtually 150kHz.

11.6.6   Calibration

As for the calibration of most measuring instruments, the crunch comes with the requirement for a signal source of known accuracy. The ideal source for this particular application would be an RF signal generator with a frequency range of 2–450MHz, and with a frequency modulation facility with calibrated deviation from zero to 30kHz at an audio frequency of 1kHz. Output attenuation down to 5μV PD across a 50Ω load is also required.

With the deviation meter switch turned on, set switch S2 (TUNE/DEV) to TUNE. Connect the signal generator to the input of the deviation meter, set the frequency of the generator to 50MHz and an output of 50μV PD at zero deviation. Rotate the VFO knob slowly until a maximum deflection is obtained on the meter. If the meter deflection is greater than full scale, adjust the signal generator attenuator to bring it back on to scale.

A number of maxima of differing amplitudes will be observed as the VFO knob is rotated, the choice of which is not critical. It is sufficient to opt for one which appears to be dominant and carefully tune for the peak. Switch from TUNE to DEV (S2) and the meter reading should fall to zero (no deviation on input signal).

Set the deviation switch of the meter (S1) to the 5kHz position. Frequency modulate the signal generator with a 1kHz signal at 5kHz deviation. The resultant meter deflection can now be adjusted with preset resistor RV4 until the meter reads full scale. Now switch S1 to the 10kHz setting and the meter will take up a lesser deflection. Adjust RV3 until a mid-scale reading is obtained. Assuming that the meter is scaled 0–10, then with S1 set for 10kHz, the scale reading is read as kilohertz deviation.

Change the signal generator to 10kHz deviation and note the meter reading. It should read full scale – if not, adjust RV3 slightly. Reduce the deviation in steps of 1kHz on the signal generator to confirm the true linearity of the indicating meter circuit.

While the signal generator is still connected it is prudent to determine the upper frequency limit of the meter.

Turn off the deviation on the signal generator and set S2 to TUNE. Progressively increase the carrier frequency in sensible increments, retuning at each step, until it is no longer possible to obtain a suitable maximum on the meter. If required, the frequency tuning range of the VFO may be conveniently measured at the TEST PULSES output socket.

The instrument is now ready for use.

11.6.7   Use

Apply the RF signal to be measured to the input socket via a coaxial cable or by plugging into the socket an elementary pick-up antenna of some 100–200mm length. In either case the instrument will behave correctly with an input as low as 5μV but a higher signal is preferred, eg 50μV.

With no modulation of the RF carrier and S2 set to TUNE, rotate RV1 for maximum deflection on the meter. Switch S2 to DEV and read the meter, altering S1 if necessary.

11.7   References

[1] 'A modulation meter for SSB', John Stebbings, G4BTV, *Radio Communication* March 1985.

[2] 'In Practice' ('You're still a bit wide, old man'), *Radio Communication* July 1988, p506.

[3] 'An automatic gain compression meter', Paul Brooking, G4SHH, *Radio Communication* December 1989.

[4] 'HF/UHF deviation meter', E Chicken, G3BIK, *Radio Communication* May 1989.

Chapter 12

Power supplies

12.1 Introduction

Most items of test equipment require DC power supplies and these are generally obtained from the AC mains, especially in view of the high cost of batteries. However, some portable equipment may well use rechargeable batteries. This chapter therefore considers circuits for the production of DC supplies and charging circuits for rechargeable batteries. Only low-voltage supplies are considered.

Good-quality components are not cheap but if used should provide a very reliable power supply which will give good service over the years. If components of doubtful origin are used then they may not be as reliable.

If power supplies are bought, then expect to pay a reasonable price or use ex-industrial units. These are likely to be designed for continuous use. The cheaper 'CB' supplies are *not* generally intended for continuous use and when they fail they may put excessive voltages on equipment, causing additional failures – you have been warned!

The component ratings used for the power supplies in this section are conservative. It may be possible to reduce ratings of the transformers and heatsinks if the power supply is not required to provide the maximum output continuously.

For further useful information on voltage regulator ICs the reader should consult some of the data books from various manufacturers (eg references [1] and [2]) and examine the applications therein. There is a lot of information to be picked up from these sources.

12.2 Basic DC power supplies

The basic problem is transforming to the correct voltage range and then conversion to DC. This step requires some thought and Fig 12.2.1 shows two arrangements for this conversion using full-wave rectification.

If the secondary voltage of the transformer is V_s (RMS) and the voltage drop across each diode is V_d (= 0.6V for silicon), then for Fig 12.2.1(a) the voltage across the smoothing capacitor (V_c) is given by:

$$V_c = (\sqrt{2} \times V_s) - 2V_d$$

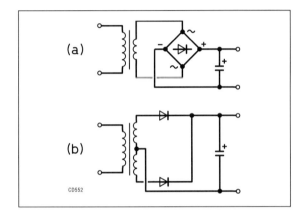

Fig 12.2.1. Two methods for obtaining full-wave rectification

For Fig 12.2.1(b) it is given by:

$$V_c = (\sqrt{2} \times V_s) - V_d$$

This is the voltage on *no load*. When a load is applied across the capacitor, ripple occurs and a voltage is obtained as shown in Fig 12.2.2.

In addition, the transformer has regulation – ie on heavy loads the output voltage will 'sag'. Providing one obtains a transformer from a reputable supplier, then the ratings quoted will be when on load, eg a '12V, 5A' transformer will have an RMS output voltage of 12V when providing an AC current of 5A. A regulation figure is usually quoted, which for this example may be 7%. This translates to an output voltage on *no load* of 12 × 1.07 = 12.84V (RMS).

The transformer must be specified. Assuming that the

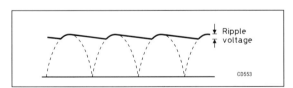

Fig 12.2.2. Typical output using capacitor smoothing with load

current for the DC load is I_{dc}, then for the circuit of Fig 12.2.1(a) the transformer current equals $1.61 \times I_{dc}$. For the circuit of Fig 12.2.1(b) the transformer current equals the DC current.

Toroidal transformers create less external magnetic field than their E-I lamination counterparts, and they are also less prone to the production of mechanical vibrations.

Rectifiers also have to be chosen – both the voltage and current ratings must be determined. In both cases of Fig 12.2.1 the average current per rectifier is approximately $0.5 \times I_{dc}$. In reality it is wise to choose a diode with a higher rating than this, especially as the peak charging current of the capacitor can be quite high. Choose a value at least equal to $1.25 \times I_{dc}$. The voltage rating of the diodes must also be determined. This should equal at least $\sqrt{2} \times V_s$ so choose a value in excess of this.

Do not forget that with high-current supplies the rectifiers usually need a heatsink, although in many instances the metal chassis is adequate. The average power dissipation per rectifier will be $0.5 \times I_{dc} \times V_d$ watts.

The capacitor ratings must now be determined, and this requires a capacitance value and a voltage rating. The voltage rating is the easiest and should be greater than the value of the maximum voltage across the capacitor. Electrolytic capacitors are one of the least reliable of electronic components and hence it is wise to choose a voltage value at least 25% greater than the expected maximum voltage if economically and practically feasible. The capacitance value is a little more complex. The value of acceptable ripple voltage V_r must be determined. The capacitance value is given approximately by:

$$C = \frac{I_{dc} \times 0.01 \times 10^6}{V_r} \; \mu F$$

This is only true for full-wave rectification and a 50Hz supply.

In some applications the basic smoothed supply is adequate, especially if the equipment contains its own regulators. If not, then the design principles for stabilised supplies are explained below. Do not forget that one must accept an output voltage with ripple, variations due to transformer loading (regulation) and input mains variations.

12.3   Stabilised DC power supplies

A stabilised supply is one where the output DC voltage is held within close limits (usually at most tens of millivolts) for quite large variations on the input side. This should take into account working from a low mains voltage (eg 225V), the transformer regulation and the ripple on the smoothing. The regulator is placed after the basic smoothing circuit – see Fig 12.3.1.

Integrated circuit regulators have now become firm

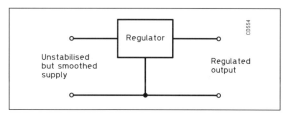

Fig 12.3.1. Basic regulator arrangement

favourites – those that have been around the longest need about a 3V drop across them. There is a newer breed of 'low-drop-out' voltage regulators that can manage with less than a 1V drop across them. What is important is that the minimum of any ripple voltage must allow for this voltage drop across the regulator to provide the stable output voltage. If for any reason the ripple is too great, part of it will appear at the regulator output. The familiar zener diode can be used as a regulator but low-power IC regulators in TO92 packages are comparable in price and give better performance.

IC regulators come in two forms, the fixed-voltage type and the variable-voltage type, and both provide comparable performances. The voltage regulator takes a sample of the output voltage and compares it with an internal reference voltage. It then either increases or decreases the output voltage, depending on what the load is doing. Fixed-voltage regulators have the sampling accomplished within the IC, while variable voltage regulators use an external sampling network made up from resistors.

The fixed-voltage type come in voltages (both negative and positive) such as 5, 12, 15 and 24V. They come also in various current ratings, typically 100mA, 500mA, 1.5A, 3A and 5A. The only additional components that may be required with these are decoupling capacitors – see the data sheets. The packages range from the plastic TO92 type, 8-pin DIL, plastic TO220 and TO3 types.

The variable-voltage types will provide output voltages between 1.2V and 37V, dependent on type, again either positive or negative voltages. They come in the same packages as the fixed-voltage types. Apart from possible decoupling capacitors, they normally require at least one resistor that is used to determine the output voltage.

There is a multiplicity of regulators available from various manufacturers with a variety of numbers. It is best to look through a supplier's catalogue – remember it is the output voltage and load current that will determine the type. They all generally provide protection against thermal overloads and short-circuits, and possibly against exceeding the output transistor's safe operating area. There are various ways in which a regulator can be used but Fig 12.3.2 shows the basic arrangement with capacitors as suggested by SGS and Texas Instruments. Further details are in the relevant data sheets. To protect a

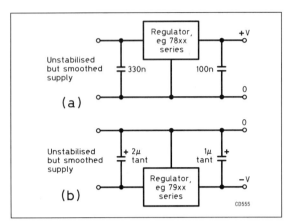

Fig 12.3.2. Typical regulator arrangement with decoupling. (a) Positive output regulator; (b) negative output regulator

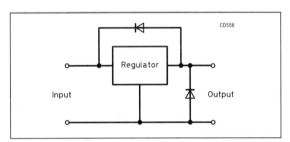

Fig 12.3.3. Regulator protection

regulator against reverse voltage spikes or where the output voltage decays more slowly than the supply, diodes can be added as per Fig 12.3.3.

12.4   Fixed 9V low-current power supply

This circuit will replace the familiar PP3 battery which is used in many items of portable test equipment and is suitable for some of the circuits described in earlier chapters. The circuit will supply 9V at up to about 140mA and uses the ubiquitous 723 regulator IC with short-circuit current protection.

Fig 12.4.1 shows the circuit diagram for this unit. A sample of the output voltage (provided by R1 and R2) is

Table 12.4.1. Components list for the fixed 9V, low-current power supply

T1	240/9-0-9V, 3VA	R1	390R, 1%
D1, 2	1N4001 or similar	R2	1k5, 1%
IC1	LM723, µA723 etc	R3	330R
C1	1000µ, 25V electrolytic	R4	4R7
C2	100p, 50V ceramic		

Resistors are 0.25W/0.5W, 5% unless specified otherwise.

compared with an internal reference, while R4 is the current-sense resistor which limits the output current. A PCB layout is given in Appendix 2.

12.5   Mid-point power supply

Sometimes it is necessary to generate a mid-point voltage in order to create complementary supplies. It is possible to use just a potential divider using equal resistors but this will have a low current capability. The circuit shown in Fig 12.5.1 uses an 741 operational amplifier and will source or sink 25mA. The output capability can be further increased by the use of an output buffer.

12.6   Low-current power supply with variable voltage and complementary output

This is a useful power supply for powering op-amp circuits and other test circuits which need a dual-voltage supply. The output is variable from ±0.05V to ±15V with one control and will supply up to 100mA per rail. The dual output is achieved using a RC4194N IC [3] which provides internal current limit and thermal shutdown protection. The short-circuit current output is ±300mA.

Fig 12.6.1 shows the circuit diagram – the output voltage is set by RV1. The circuit requires light loading – for this reason, LEDs and resistors can be added between +V and 0V, and between 0V and −V. The brightness will vary according to the output voltage and they will extinguish below about ±2.5V. No metering is shown and it is up to the user to add this if required.

A PCB layout is given in Appendix 2 which also allows RV1 to be replaced by a fixed resistor – useful if only a fixed output is required. Please note that R1 is

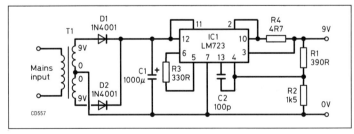

Fig 12.4.1. Fixed 9V, low-current power supply

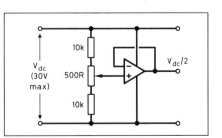

Fig 12.5.1. Mid-point power supply

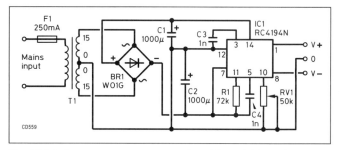

Fig 12.6.1. Low-current power supply with variable voltage and complementary output. Loading resistors and LEDs not shown

Table 12.6.1. Components list for the low-current power supply with variable voltage and complementary output

T1	240/15-0-15V, 6VA	RV1	50k lin pot
BR1	WO1G	C1, 2	1000μ, 25V
IC1	RC4194N	C3, 4	1n, 50V ceramic
R1	120k and 180k in parallel	F1	250mA fuse and holder
R2, 3	1k	LEDs	Red (2 off)

Resistors are 0.25W/0.5W, 5% unless specified otherwise.

formed by two resistors in parallel. Holes are included on the PCB for the LEDs and resistors (R2 and R3).

12.7 Fixed 5V or 12V, 1.5A and 5A power supplies

These power supplies use fairly standard components and the circuits are the same except for component values. Because of this, a single design is presented in Fig 12.7.1.

In both the 1.5A and 5A supplies it is suggested that the bridge rectifier is bolted to the metal chassis. The regulators should be mounted on heatsinks using heatsink compound.

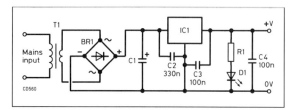

Fig 12.7.1. Fixed output voltage, regulated supply

The minimum suggested heatsink values are:

5V/1.5A, 2.5°C/W   12V/1.5A, 1.8°C/W
5V/5A, 1°C/W   12V/5A, 0.8°C/W

C2 and C3 should be placed as close to the regulator as possible while, if C4 is included, it should be placed across the output terminals of the power supply.

12.8 A versatile 12V, 1.5A power supply

For certain circumstances a power supply is required with equal positive and negative voltages but with greater current output than that described in Section 12.6. One way of achieving this is to use the circuit in Section 12.7 twice but using a single mains transformer with dual output windings. This probably represents the most versatile arrangement. The 12V, 1.5A supply is used as an example.

Fig 12.8.1 shows the general arrangement with individual outputs AB and CD, with no terminal grounded. There are thus initially two independent 12V outputs, and a ground can be applied separately to one of the output terminals of each supply. If B and C are connected there is then 24V between terminals A and D. If the junction BC is grounded then A is 12V above ground and D is 12V below ground, ie −12V. If A is grounded then D is at −24V, if D is grounded then A is at +24V.

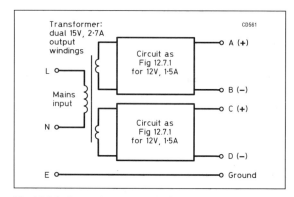

Fig 12.8.1. General arrangement for a versatile ±12V, 1.5A power supply

Table 12.7.1. Components list for the fixed 5V or 12V, 1.5A and 5A power supplies

Output	Transformer	BR1	C1	IC1	R1
5V, 1.5A	9V, 2.7A, 30VA	KBPC1005, KBPC102, KBU4D	4700μ, 25V	LM340T5, L7805CV, LM7805CT	220R, 0.25W
5V, 5A	9V, 8A, 80VA	MB151, 26MB10A, GBPC2501	15,000μ, 25V	LAS1905, LT1084CT5, IP3R18K05	220R, 0.25W
12V, 1.5A	15V, 2.5A, 30VA	KBPC1005, KBPC102, KBU4D	4700μ, 25V	LM340T12, LM7812CT, L7812CV	680R, 0.25W
12V, 5A	15V, 8A, 120VA	MB151, 26MB10A, GBPC2501	15,000μ, 25V	LAS1912, LT1084CT12, IP3R18K12	680R, 0.25W

For all versions, C2 is 0.33μ, 63V polyester; C3 and C4 are 100n, 50V ceramic; and D1 is a red LED.

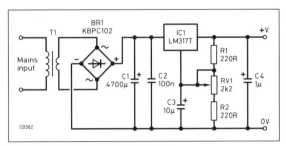

Fig 12.9.1. A 2.5/15V, 1.5A power supply

12.9   Variable-voltage 2.5–15V, 1.5A power supply

This circuit provides a variable output voltage between 2.5V and 15V with 1.5A available at all voltage settings. It uses what is known as a *variable-voltage regulator*, and the circuit is shown in Fig 12.9.1. Part of the output voltage is fed back via a potential divider formed by R1, RV1 and R2. This feedback ratio determines the output voltage.

In order to optimise load regulation, R1 should be as close to IC1 as possible while the ground end of R2 should be soldered as close as possible to the output terminal. C2, C3 and C4 aid ripple rejection and improve transient response.

This arrangement gives a continuously variable output. If only fixed steps are required then the resistors RV1 + R2 can be replaced by a single switchable resistor R′ which is obtained from the following formula:

$$V_o = 1.25(1 + R'/R_1)$$

The bridge rectifier should be fixed to a metal surface (eg metal enclosure) and the regulator mounted on a

heatsink of 1.5°C/W or better. Note that the heat generation is worst at low-voltage output.

If it is not necessary to go as low as 2.5V then the resistor chain can be recalculated and it may be possible to use a smaller heatsink.

12.10   Limited-voltage-range 12V, 10A power supply with foldback current limit

Sometimes it is necessary to test equipment with a given input voltage range but high current. For example, it may be required to test equipment over the voltage range of a typical 12V vehicle battery or to cope with slightly different voltage specifications. The circuit described will provide a variation from 11.2 to 13.7V.

The circuit is given in Fig 12.10.1, and uses a low-power regulator (IC1) which controls two darlington pairs (TR1 and TR2). Each of these can carry the total current but the resistors R2 and R3 help to make the devices share the load, the arrangement giving increased reliability. TR1 and TR2 can be spaced apart on the heatsink. Resistors R7, R8 and RV1 form the voltage sampling network. Resistors R6a/R6b form the current-sensing network and in conjunction with R4 and R5 provide foldback current limiting. The variable resistor RV1 will

Table 12.9.1. Components list for the variable-voltage 2.5–15V, 1.5A power supply

T1	240/15V, 2.7A, 40VA	C3	10µ, 25V
BR1	KBPC102 or similar	C4	1µ, 25V
IC1	LM317T	R1, 2	220R
C1	4700µ, 35V	RV1	2k2 potentiometer
C2	0.1µ, 50V ceramic		

Resistors are 0.25W/0.5W, 5% unless specified otherwise.

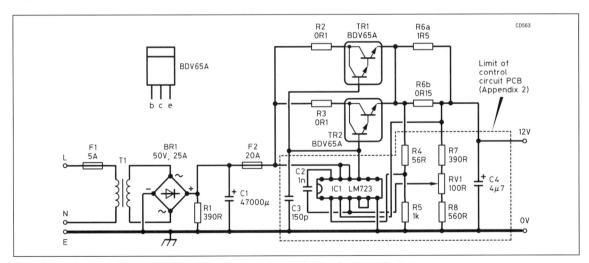

Fig 12.10.1. Limited-voltage-range 12V, 10A power supply with foldback current limit

Table 12.10.1. Components list for the limited-voltage-range 12V, 10A power supply with foldback current limit

F1	5A, HRC + holder	R1	390R, 3W wirewound
F2	20A, HRC + holder	R2, 3	0.1R, 10W wirewound
T1	240V/15V, 16A, 300VA	R4	56R
BR1	50V, 25A	R5	1k
TR1, 2	BDV65A	R6a	1R5, 15W wirewound
IC1	LM723 or equivalent	R6b	0.15R, 25W wirewound
C1	47000µ, 25V	R7	390R
C2	1n, 50V ceramic	R8	560R
C3	150p, 50V ceramic	RV1	100R cermet trimmer/pot
C4	4µ7, 254V tantalum	Heatsink, 0.8°C/W	

Resistors are 0.25W/0.5W, 5% unless specified otherwise.

Table 12.11.1. Components list for the lead-acid battery charging circuit

Type	Transformer	R2	R3	RV1
6V	9-0-9, 20VA	1k2	1k	100R cermet
12V	15-0-15, 30VA	2k4	470R	200R cermet

Common components are:

D1–3	1N5401	R1	240R
D4	Red LED	R4	100R
IC1	LM317K or equivalent	R5	0R68, 2W, wirewound
TR1	2N697 or equivalent	M1	0–1A meter
C1	1000µ, 25V electrolytic		
C2	220µ, 25V electrolytic		

Resistors are 0.25W/0.5W, 5% unless specified otherwise. R2 and R3 are 0.5W, 5%.

provide the output adjustment and can be either a trimmer or potentiometer.

When the output current reaches about 10A (dependent on tolerance of R6a/R6b), foldback current limit commences and the final short-circuit current is 5A. Fuses F1 and F2 should be of a high rupture capacity (HRC) type.

The bridge rectifier and current sense resistors should be mounted onto the metal case the supply is housed in and the series-pass darlington pairs TR1 and TR2 mounted (and spaced out) on a heatsink of 0.8°C/W or better. If the power supply is likely to be used for prolonged periods near maximum output, increase the thermal rating of the heatsink and ensure adequate ventilation. A small PCB is given in Appendix 2 for the control circuit. Note that this board can be adapted for other voltages and currents.

12.11 Lead-acid battery charging circuit

This circuit can be adapted for both 6V and 12V batteries. It is intended for recharging lead-acid batteries used in portable and/or test equipment. The circuit is given in Fig 12.11.1, and is a constant-voltage charger with maximum current determined by R5 – for the present design it is 1A. Transistor TR1 can be any general-purpose silicon NPN type. The circuit should be set while on open-circuit, the values for the two battery types being 6.9V and 13.8V respectively. If this does not appear to provide full

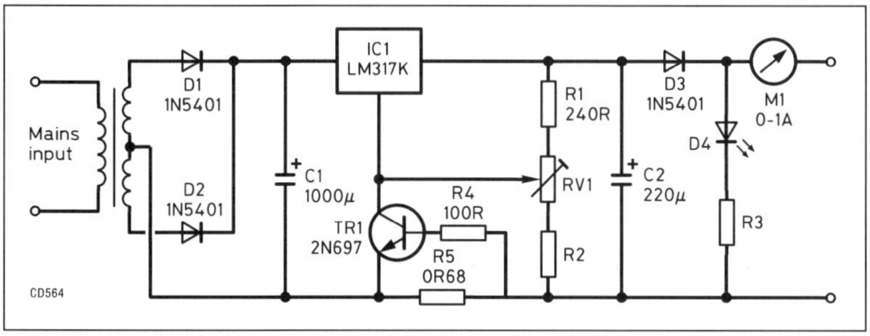

charging, then increase the output voltage slightly (via RV1).

IC1 is an LM317 which is used as a standard variable voltage regulator (see Section 12.9), the output being set via R1, RV1 and R2. However, the current is limited when the voltage across R5 exceeds about 0.6V and TR1 begins to turn on, subsequently lowering the drive current to IC1 which adjusts accordingly. The charger will stay in this constant-current mode until the battery voltage rises and the current required starts to drop below 1A. The charger then reverts to a constant-voltage mode.

A PCB layout is given in Appendix 2.

12.12 Nickel-cadmium battery discharging/charging circuit

12.12.1 General

Nickel-cadmium batteries suffer from the 'memory effect' if not used often, and the circuit described here provides both a discharge and a charging circuit. Please note that the setting up of the end-of-discharge voltage must be carried out accurately. Components must be altered according to the battery capacity (mAh) and the number of cells. An end-of-discharge cell voltage of 1.1V is assumed.

The circuit described here will charge a battery over a 12–14h period and discharge from a full charge in about 8h if the guidelines suggested are adhered to. When the battery is connected it will go immediately into a charge state unless pushbutton PB1 is pressed, whence a discharge cycle will commence until the end of discharge is detected – the battery will then be charged. If a mains failure occurs during the discharge process the circuit will revert to a slow charge state on resumption of

Fig 12.11.1. Lead-acid battery charger with current limit

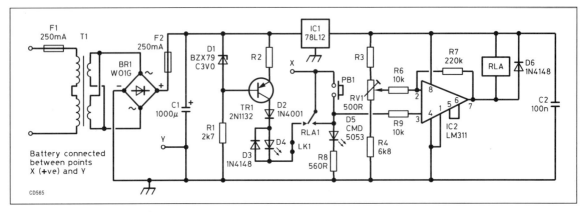

Fig 12.12.1. Ni-cad discharger/charger

the mains. Note that the terminals on the battery that must be used are those that supply power to the equipment – other charging terminals may have protection diodes incorporated and will not allow the discharge cycle.

12.12.2 Circuit description

The circuit is given in Fig 12.12.1. The mains power supply, T1, BR1 and C1 is standard. The charging circuit is provided by the constant-current source comprising D1, R1, R2 and TR1, with D2 preventing the battery discharging if the unit is off, and LED D4 illuminating during charging. The LED *must* be of the type specified or similar as it takes the full charging current. The LED specified can carry a current of up to 100mA. D3 protects the LED against reverse bias if the mains fails. R2 is calculated from $R2 = 2.4/I$ where I is the charging current, equal to the battery capacity divided by 10.

The remainder of the components form the control and discharge components. R5, LED D5 and R8 discharge the battery. The value of R5 is calculated from V/I where I is the value calculated above and V is the nominal battery voltage. It is suggested that the power rating of R5 is at least twice that given by $V^2/R5$. The battery voltage is monitored by IC2 and compared with a reference value provided by the potential divider R3, RV1 and R4. This sets up the changeover voltage from discharge to charge. The voltage reference is set for 1.1V per cell. Values for seven-, eight- and nine-cell batteries are given in the components list. R7 provides hysteresis so that no instability should be encountered from IC2 which is an LM311 voltage comparator of high gain. Capacitor C2 should be placed near the IC supply pins. Diode D6 removes the back EMF from relay coil RL1 when it switches.

12.12.3 Calibration

To set up the switch-over voltage, determine the voltage required which is the number of cells multiplied by 1.1V. Set this up on a suitable power supply (see earlier) using

Table 12.12.1. Ni-cad battery discharger/charger circuit

T1	240/15V, 3VA (8/9 cells)	R1	2k7
T1	240/12V, 3VA (7 cells)	R2	See text
F1, 2	250mA	R3	See below
BR1	WO1G	R4	6k8
D1	BZX79C3V0	R5	See text
D2, 6	1N4001	R6, 9	10k
D3	1N4148	R7	220k
D4	Yellow LED	R8	560R
D5	CMD5053	RV1	500R, 0.5W trimmer
TR1	2N1132 or equivalent	C1	1000m, 40V
IC1	78L12	C2	100n, 50V ceramic
IC2	LM311	RL1	SPCO, 12V, 720W coil
PB1	Pushbutton, push to make	Heatsink for TR1, 48°C/W	

R3 values: 7 cells, 2k7; 8 cells, 1k8; 9 cells, 1k. Resistors are 0.25W/0.5W, 5% unless specified otherwise.

a digital voltmeter. Remove link LK1, connect the supply across the battery charging terminal and turn the power on. Press PB1 and release – if the relay remains energised (LED D5 illuminating), then rotate RV1 very slowly until the relay drops. If the relay will not stay energised it is because the voltage at pin 2 is too low, so rotate RV1 and try again. Once the condition has been found where the relay remains energised, set up RV1 as previously described. As a final check, increase the power supply voltage by about 1.5V, and then gradually reduce and check that switch-over occurs as predicted. Persevere until the value is correctly set.

To test the value of charging current place an ammeter of the correct range across the charger terminals – this should indicate the value of charging current.

12.13 References

[1] 'Industry standard linear ICs', *SGS Databook*.
[2] 'Linear circuits, voltage regulators and supervisors', *Texas Instruments Data Book 3*.
[3] *RC4194 Data Sheet*.

Chapter 13

Reference data

13.1 General

It is inevitable that sooner or later anyone using the techniques discussed in previous chapters will require to identify components and connect units together. This chapter contains details of some of the more common forms of identification and connection.

More detailed and additional data is included in many of the standard electronic and radio reference books. For example, the *Radio Data Reference Book* published by the RSGB contains much useful information [1]. Alternatively useful data can be obtained from distributors' catalogues such as that from Farnell [2].

13.2 Component colour codes

The colour codes in Table 13.2.1 are applicable to resistors, capacitors and inductors and are occasionally used for small semiconductors such as diodes.

13.3 Resistor coding

There are basically two ways in which a resistor is coded – by colour or by alphanumerics.

Colour coding can be four, five or six bands. These are shown in Fig 13.3.1 with their significance. If there is no tolerance band then it is assumed to be 20%. When there are five bands, the fifth band represents a temperature

Table 13.2.1. Colour codes for components

Colour	Number	Multiplier	Tolerance
Black	0	1	
Brown	1	10	±1%
Red	2	100	±2%
Orange	3	1k	
Yellow	4	10k	
Green	5	100k	±0.5%
Blue	6	1M	±0.25%
Mauve	7	10M	±0.1%
Grey	8		
White	9		
Gold		1/10	±5%
Silver		1/100	±10%

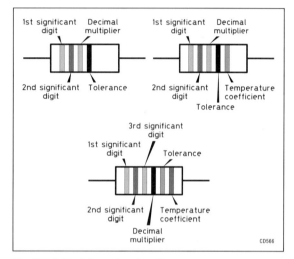

Fig 13.3.1. Resistor colour banding

coefficient. The increase to six bands allows the ohmic value to be read to three significant digits. The temperature coefficient coding is:

Brown	100ppm	Orange	50ppm
Red	50ppm	Yellow	25ppm

If the coding is alphanumeric then it should follow BS1852. To understand this it is easier to give examples:

0.22Ω is R22	220Ω is 220R
1.0Ω is 1R0	2.2kΩ is 2K2
2.2Ω is 2R2	22kΩ is 22K
22Ω is 22R	1MΩ is 1M
100Ω is 100R	2.2MΩ is 2M2

This system is normally used for low-value resistors.

In addition there is a letter denoting tolerance according to BS1852, IEC publication 62, which is defined by:

F is ±1%	K is ±10%
G is ±2%	M is ±20%
J is ±5%	Z is −20% +80%

Table 13.3.1. Resistor ranges

E6	10	15	22	33	47	68			
E12	10	12	15	18	22	27	33	39	47	56
	68	82								
E24	10	11	12	13	15	16	18	20	22	24
	27	30	33	36	39	43	47	51	56	62
	68	75	82	91						

Hence a resistor marked '4K7J' would have a value of 4.7kΩ, ±5%. The colour coding for this would be yellow, mauve, red, gold.

Resistors also come in various ranges of values, and these are classified according to BS2488 and IEC publication 63. The most common ranges are defined as shown in Table 13.3.1.

13.4 Capacitor coding

Capacitors are now generally alphanumerically coded but there have been attempts in the past at colour coding. All of the schemes are included here for reference.

Apart from the standards of 'pF', 'nF' and 'μF', they may be signified by just 'p', 'n' and 'μ'. Hence:

100p is 100pF	n22 is 220pF
2n2 is 2.2nF	100μ is 100μF

Another numeric system uses a three-digit code based on the value in picofarads: the first two digits are the significant numbers and the third the multiplier. Hence $102 = 10 \times 10^2 = 1000$pF and $473 = 47 \times 10^3 = 47$nF.

There is a colour coding on the top of some ceramic plate capacitors, and this is defined as follows:

Green	High K	
Yellow	Medium K	
Red/mauve	Low K, +100ppm/°C	
Black	Low K, 0ppm/°C	NPO
Orange	Low K, −150ppm/°C	N150
Mauve	Low K, −750ppm/°C	N750
Orange/orange	Low K, −1500ppm/°C	N1500

Apart from the tolerance coding under resistors the following two also apply for capacitance:

C is ±0.25pF	D is ±0.5pF

Table 13.4.1. Colour coding of the voltage rating of tantalum and polyester capacitors

Colour	Tantalum	Polyester
Black	10V	
Brown		100V
Red		250V
Yellow	6.3V	400V
Green	16V	
Blue	20V	
Grey	25V	
White	3V	
Pink	35V	

If capacitors are colour coded then they are normally polyester or tantalum types. If it is a polyester type then the value is read in picofarads, while if it is a tantalum bead type it is in microfarads. Fig 13.4.1 shows how the colour bands are organised. Additionally these have a colour coding for voltage rating, and this is shown in Table 13.4.1.

13.5 Inductor coding

Inductors may carry alphanumeric or colour coding. The alphanumeric coding is based on the value in microhenrys and arranged as a three-digit code as for resistors and capacitors. The only additional code that may occur is an 'n' for 'nH' (less than 100nH). From 100nH up to 1μH the code will be written as 'R22' for 22μH. From 1μH up to 10μH the code will be '8R2', ie 8.2μH. After this it becomes the number multipliers. The unit may also be placed where the decimal point should be, eg 'μH22' is 0.22μH, '5mH6' is 5.6mH.

If a colour coding is used (Fig 13.5.1), the first band is a broad silver identifier for inductor. The next two bands

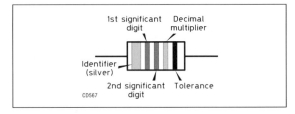

Fig 13.5.1. Inductor colour banding

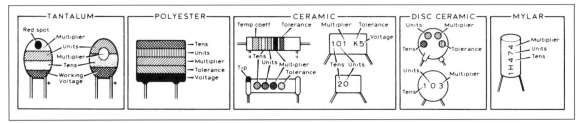

Fig 13.4.1. Various forms of capacitor coding

are the significant numbers, followed by the multiplier band and then a tolerance band. The base unit is the microhenry. In some inductors a gold band may be used at the position of the decimal point.

13.6   Discrete semiconductor coding

There are various methods of coding discrete semiconductor devices: some are manufacturer dependent, while others attempt to follow one of three forms of coding which are explained below. One of the biggest problems today is identifying transistors, as they come from such a variety of sources.

13.6.1   Pro-Electron numbering

This is the system most widely used in Europe. The coding consists of two letters followed by a serial number. The serial number consists of either three digits or one letter plus two digits, eg BC109 and BLX98.

The first letter is defined as follows:

A   Germanium
B   Silicon
C   Compound materials such as gallium arsenide
D   Compound materials such as indium antimonide
R   Compound materials such as cadmium sulphide

The second letter denotes the general function of the device as follows:

A   Detection diode, high-speed diode, mixer diode
B   Variable-capacitance diode
C   Transistor for AF applications (but not power type)
D   Power transistor for power applications
E   Tunnel diode
F   Transistor for RF applications (but not power type)
G   Multiple of dissimilar devices; miscellaneous devices
L   Power transistor for RF applications
N   Photo-coupler
P   Radiation-sensitive device such as a photo-diode, photo-transistor, photo-conductive cell or a radiation detector diode
Q   Radiation-generating device such as an LED
R   Controlling/switching device (eg thyristor) having a specified breakdown characteristic (but not power type)
S   Transistor for switching applications (not power types)
T   Controlling and switching power device (eg thyristor) having a specified breakdown characteristic
U   Power transistor for switching applications
X   Multiplier diode such as varactor or step-recovery diode
Y   Rectifier diode, booster or efficiency diode
Z   Voltage reference or voltage regulator diode, transient suppressor diode

The remainder of the type number is a serial number indicating a particular design or development and is one of the following two groups:

1   Device intended primarily for use in consumer applications (radio and TV, audio amplifiers, tape recorders, domestic appliances etc). The serial number consists of three figures.
2   Device intended mainly for other applications, eg industrial, professional and transmitting equipments. The serial number consists of one letter ('Z', 'Y', 'X', 'W' etc) followed by two figures.

Where there is a range of variants of a basic type of rectifier diode, thyristor or voltage regulator diode, the type number as defined above is often used to identify the range; further letters and figures are added after a hyphen to identify individual types within the range. These additions are as follows:

Rectifier diode and thyristors
The group of figures indicates the rated repetitive peak reverse voltage V_{RRM} or the rated repetitive peak off-state voltage V_{DRM}, whichever value is lower in volts for each type. If there is a final letter 'R', this denotes a reverse polarity version, ie stud is anode.

Voltage regulator diodes, transient suppression diodes
The first letter indicates the nominal percentage tolerance in the operating voltage V_Z as follows:

A is ±1%	D is ±10%
B is ±2%	E is ±15%
C is ±5%	

The letter is omitted on transient suppressor diodes. The succeeding group of figures indicates the typical operating voltage V_Z for each type at the nominal operating current I_Z rating of the range. For transient suppressor diodes the figure indicates the maximum recommended stand-off voltage V_R. The letter 'V' is used to denote the position of the decimal point.

In addition to the above, small-signal devices sometimes have a letter after them, and this defines an h_{fe} range as follows:

A is h_{fe} between 125 and 260
B is h_{fe} between 240 and 500
C is h_{fe} between 450 and 900

13.6.2   The JEDEC system

This is a system which originated in the USA. Devices can be registered and then allocated coding such as 1Nxxxx, 2Nxxxx etc, as follows:

First symbol	A number '1', '2', '3' etc
Second symbol	A single letter 'N'
Third symbol	Registration number (xxxx)

The first symbol is defined as follows:

1   Two-pin device such as diodes and rectifiers
2   Three-pin device such as transistors and thyristors
3   Four-pin device such as dual-gate MOSFETs

13.6.3   Japanese Industrial Standard (JIS-C-7012)

This designation code applies to discrete semiconductors (eg transistors, diode and rectifiers) and follows the sequence below. The code is made from five symbols:

First symbol   Digits '0', '1', '2' or '3'
Second symbol   Letter 'S'
Third symbol   Letter ('A', 'B' etc)
Fourth symbol   Digits (group of two or three)
Fifth symbol   Letter 'A', 'B', 'C' etc

The first symbol indicates the type of semiconductor as follows:

0   Photo-transistor
1   Signal, rectifier or varactor diode
2   Bipolar, junction FET (single gate), thyristor etc.
3   As 2 but with two gates

The second symbol indicates that the device is diffused from semiconductor elements.

The third symbol indicates polarity and application of the device as follows:

A   High-frequency PNP transistor
B   Low-frequency PNP transistor
C   High-frequency NPN transistor
D   Low-frequency NPN transistor
F   P-gate thyristor
G   N-gate thyristor
J   P-channel FET
K   N-channel FET

Note that when the first symbol is only a '0' or '1', ie photo-transistors and diodes, only numbers are used for the third symbol.

The fourth symbol consists of numbers of 11 or more which are given according to the sequence of registration with JIS.

The fifth symbol indicates a revision of the product originally introduced.

13.7   Logic families

There are a multitude of logic ICs available, and Table 13.7.1 classifies them into families.

The 74 series are usually pin-for-pin compatible with other members of the family but the characteristics of the IC must be considered if trying to substitute, ie operating levels (CMOS or TTL), operating speeds and drive currents etc. The 74HC4xxx series are pin-for-pin compatible with the 4000 series CMOS ICs.

Table 13.7.1. Logic IC families

Type no	Family	Comments
74xx	Standard TTL	Standard
74ACxx	Advanced CMOS	High speed, reduced power, CMOS voltage levels
74ACT	Advanced CMOS	As AC type but TTL input voltage levels
74ASxx	Advanced Schottky	Improved-speed LS type TTL
74ALSxx	Advanced LS TTL	Twice the speed, half the power of LS TTL
74Cxx	CMOS	Low power, high noise immunity
74Fxx	Fast TTL	High-speed switching
74HCxx	High-speed CMOS	Low power, speeds similar to LS TTL, CMOS voltage levels
74HCTxx	High-speed CMOS	As HC type but TTL levels
74LSxx	Low-power Schottky TTL	Same speed as standard but one fifth power
74Sxx	Schottky TTL	Faster than LS TTL, takes more power
4xxx/45xx	CMOS	Low power, high noise immunity, 3–15V operation, medium speed
1000xxx	ECL	For use in very-high-speed systems

13.8   Metric/SWG wire equivalents

Enamel copper wire (ECW) used today may be quoted in either metric or wire gauge (SWG). Table 13.8.1 gives the nearest equivalents and characteristics of the wire.

Table 13.8.1. Metric equivalents of SWG

Diameter (mm)	SWG (approx)	Nominal resistance (Ω/m @ 20°C)	Typical current rating (mA)
0.2	35/36	0.54	48
0.224	34/35	0.43	61
0.25	33	0.35	76
0.315	30	0.22	120
0.4	27	0.14	194
0.5	25	0.087	304
0.56	24	0.069	381
0.71	22	0.04	613
0.8	21	0.034	779
0.9	20	0.027	972
1.0	19	0.022	1210
1.25	18	0.014	1910
1.5	16/17	0.0096	2740
1.75	15	0.007	3675
2.0	14	0.005	4840

Note: The current carrying capacity of wires can vary considerably – this depends mainly on the amount of ventilation around the wire, the permissible temperature rise, whether it is coiled and how many layers there are. The figures quoted are very conservative and represent a current density of about 1.5A/mm^2. For *well-ventilated wiring* the value can be tripled – this would represent a current density approaching 5A/mm^2.

Table 13.9.1. Characteristics of various coaxial connectors

Connector type	Impedance (Ω)	Typical upper frequency (GHz)	Typical peak voltage rating (V)	Notes
BNC	50 and 75 types	4	500	Bayonet coupling. Common on connecting leads of instruments
TNC	50 and 75 types	4	500	Screw coupling version of BNC type
N	50 and 75 types	10	1000	Screw coupling. VHF and UHF uses
UHF PL259 etc	Not constant	0.2	500	Screw coupling. Typical for HF and video, some instruments
Min UHF	Not constant	2	450	Screw coupling
PET100	50	1.5	3000	Screw coupling. RF and high voltage
F	75 (not constant)	1	350	Screw coupling. Satellite TV cable etc
SMA	50	18	450	Screw coupling. High performance, extended frequency range
SMB	50	4	500	Snap on. Suitable for use within equipment
TV	60–75	1	Low power	Push fit. Domestic TV connector
Min TV	50	1	Low power	Miniature version of above connector

Table 13.10.1. Coaxial cable equivalents

European	American
UR43	RG58B/U
UR57	RG11A/U (stranded)
UR67	RG213
UR70	RG59B/U (solid core)
UR76	RG58C/U
UR95	RG174A/U (stranded)

13.9 Coaxial connectors

There are various types of coaxial connector suitable for the different coaxial cables, some requiring adapters to accommodate the cable. Table 13.9.1, which is not exhaustive, gives a list of some common coaxial connectors and their characteristics. A typical lead for instruments is UR43 cable with BNC plugs at either end. It is worth a look in a catalogue such as reference [2] for typical illustrations of the various types of connectors. Various adapters also exist for conversion between the various types of connector, or alternatively one can make short adapter leads.

Putting a connector onto the end of a piece of cable can be rather intricate. References [3] and [4] show the exploded views of some connectors and how they should be assembled.

A word of warning – the common UHF connector (PL259/SO239) is available from many sources but the quality can be somewhat variable – look to see what is being bought, especially the insulation material. A reputable supplier will always offer a good product.

13.10 Common coaxial cable equivalents

Table 13.10.1 gives the approximate equivalents between the European UR and American RG series of coaxial cable.

13.11 References

[1] *Radio Data Reference Book*, 5th edn, G R Jessop, G6JP, and R S Hewes, G3TDR, RSGB, 1985.
[2] *Farnell Electronic Components Catalogue*.
[3] *Microwave Handbook*, Vol 2, ed M W Dixon, G3PFR, RSGB, 1991.
[4] *ARRL Handbook for the Radio Amateur*, various editions, ARRL, Chapter 37.

Appendix 1

Surplus test gear

There are numerous items of test gear around, of varying vintage, which may use valves or semiconductors. While there is nothing wrong with valves it will become harder to obtain these items for maintenance purposes. The trend should therefore be to buy test gear utilising semiconductors wherever possible.

The test gear is available from various sources, the most common being the ubiquitous radio rally. Test equipment has been made by a plethora of manufacturers and has probably had a varied life. The important items to get hold of are the handbook and, if at all possible, the service manual. Remember, from the radio rally there is unlikely to be much of a guarantee on the equipment, and it may well have to be bought 'as seen'. Alternatively there are the second-hand equipment suppliers who will provide the equipment newly calibrated and with some form of guarantee. However, one has to pay for this facility.

At the end of the day it is still the purchaser's responsibility to make sure that the equipment bought is suitable for the work to be undertaken. It is also up to the purchaser to haggle for the best deal possible!

The following list is by no means comprehensive but is based on what has been seen advertised. It therefore gives a guide to the most common equipment appearing on the surplus market.

Advance

Type C	Signal generator
Type J	AF generator
Type E	RF signal generator, 100kHz–100MHz
OS2000	Oscilloscope, 30MHz

Airmec

210(A)	Modulation meter, 3–300MHz
301(A)	Millivoltmeter
304A	Oscillator, 50kHz–100MHz
319A	Wattmeter
352	Sweep signal generator, 20Hz–200kHz
409	Modulation meter
853	Wave analyser, 30kHz–20MHz
858	Oscillator, 30kHz–30MHz

Avo

B150	Universal bridge
	Valve tester
	Transistor tester

Bradley

CT471	Electronic multimeter

Farnell

SG	Synthesised signal generator, 520MHz

Cossor

CDU150	Oscilloscope, dual beam, 35MHz

Dynamco

D7100	Oscilloscope

General Radio

1209B	Oscillator
1360B	Microwave oscillator, 1.7–4.1GHz
1363	VHF oscillator, 56–500MHz
1311A	Audio oscillator, 50Hz–10kHz

Gould/Advance

QS250A-S2	Dual-beam oscilloscope, 10MHz
OS3001	Oscilloscope
TC311	Timer/counter

Hewlett Packard

HP141T	Spectrum analyser frame, used typically with HP8552B and HP8553B
HP302A	Wave analyser
HP400D	Valve voltmeter
HP430C	Microwave power meter
HP606A	Signal generator
HP620A	SHF signal generator, 0.7–11GHz
HP1746A	Oscilloscope, three Y-inputs, 100MHz
HP3582	Spectrum analyser
HP5328B	Frequency counter, 100MHz
HP8614A	Signal generator, 800–2400MHz
HP8698B	Sweep generator, 0.4–110MHz

Levell

TG200DM	Oscillator, 1Hz–1MHz

Lyons

SQ10	Sine/square oscillator, 10Hz–1MHz

Marconi

CT401	RF meter, calibrated 0–500W
OA090B	White noise test set
TF144H	AM signal generator, 10kHz–72MHz (Services code 452A)
TF791	Deviation meter
TF801	AM signal generator, 10–470MHz (Services code CT394B)
TF868A/B	Universal bridge
TF893A	AF power meter, 10W, 20Hz–20kHz
TF995A/2	AM/FM signal generator, 1.5–220MHz (Services version CT402)
TF995B/2	AM/FM signal generator, 200kHz–220MHz (Services code CT520A)
TF995B/5	As above but for mobile radio testing
TF1020A	RF power meter and dummy load, 0–150W, 0–300W, DC–1500MHz
TF1041	Valve voltmeter
TF1060/2	UHF signal generator, 450–1200MHz
TF1064	Signal generator, 68–108MHz, 118–185MHz, 450–470MHz
TF1065	TX/RX output test set
TF1066	AM/FM signal generator, 10–470MHz
TF1073	RF attenuator
TF1099	Sweep generator, 20MHz
TF1101	RC oscillator, 20Hz–200kHz
TF1205/S	RF dummy load, 1.3kW, oil filled
TF1245A	*Q* meter. Usually used with oscillators TF1246 (40kHz–50MHz) or TF1247 (20–300MHz)
TF1300	Valve voltmeter
TF1313A	0.1% universal bridge for LCR, mains operated
TF1331	Oscilloscope
TF2002AS	AM/FM signal generator, 10kHz–72MHz (Services code CT572)
TF2008	AM/FM signal generator, 10kHz–510MHz
TF2015	AM/FM signal generator, 10–510MHz, small size
TF2016	AM/FM signal generator, 10kHz–120MHz
TF2103	Battery oscillator, sine/squarewave, 10Hz–1MHz
TF2168	UHF attenuator
TF2210	Oscilloscope, dual trace, 100MHz
TF2300	AM/FM modulation meter, 4–1000MHz FM, 4–350MHz AM
TF2301A	Modulation meter
TF2303	AM/FM modulation meter, 25–225MHz and 380–520MHz
TF2500	Audio power meter, 10Hz–1MHz, to 25W
TF2501	RF power meter with load, 3W, DC–1GHz
TF2502	RF power meter with load, 10W, DC–1GHz
TF2503	RF power meter with load, 100W, DC–1GHz
TF2603	RF millivoltmeter, 1mV–3V, 50kHz–1.5GHz
TF2604	AC/DC electronic voltmeter, AC 20Hz–1500MHz
TF2700	Universal bridge for LCR. Battery operated
TF2703	Transistor tester
TF2950	Mobile radio test set, AM/FM, 65–84MHz, 84–108MHz, 140–180MHz, 420–470MHz

Philips

PM3200	Oscilloscope, 10MHz
PM3217	Oscilloscope, dual trace, 50MHz
PM3232	Oscilloscope, 10MHz
PM3233	Oscilloscope, dual beam, 10MHz

Pye

MM1	Modulation meter, 68–510MHz
SG1U	UHF signal generator, six-channel
SG3V	VHF signal generator, 70–170MHz
SG5U	UHF signal generator, 370–470MHz

Racal

409	Modulation meter
850	VHF calibrator
852	Radiotelephone calibrator
952	Crystal calibrator
9036	Universal counter, 32MHz
9059	Frequency meter
9522	Frequency counter, 30MHz
9901	Counter/timer, 50MHz
9903	Counter/timer, 50MHz
9905	Counter/timer, 200MHz
9913	Frequency meter, 200MHz
9915	Frequency meter, 520MHz

Rohde and Schwarz

BN4242/2	Sweep signal generator, 50kHz–12MHz
BN15241	Test receiver, 0.17–4.4GHz
BN41001	Power signal generator, 0.1–30MHz
BN41409	AM/FM signal generator, 4–300MHz
BN41022	UHF signal generator, 300–1000MHz
BN41103	Decade signal generator, 0–50MHz
BN41104	Decade signal generator, 0.3–500MHz
SWOB2	Polyskop, spectrum analyser, to 1200MHz

SE Labs

SM111	Oscilloscope, dual trace, 18MHz
SM202	Timer/counter, DC to 150MHz

Scopex

4S-6	Oscilloscope, single trace, 6MHz

| 4D-10 | Oscilloscope, dual trace, 10MHz |
| 4D-25 | Oscilloscope, dual trace, 25MHz |

Solartron

| 4D10 | Oscilloscope, dual trace, 10MHz |
| CD1400 | Oscilloscope, dual trace, 15MHz |

Taylor

| 68A | AM signal generator, 100kHz–240MHz |

TechTest

| 250 | Synthesised signal generator, 80–105MHz, 140–170MHz, 440–475MHz |

Telequipment

S31	Oscilloscope, single trace, 6MHz
S32	Oscilloscope, single trace
S43	Oscilloscope, single trace
S51A	Oscilloscope, single trace
S54	Oscilloscope, single trace, 10MHz
D43	Oscilloscope, dual trace
D61	Oscilloscope, dual trace, 10MHz
D83	Oscilloscope, dual trace, 50MHz

Tektronix/Telequipment

| 453 | Oscilloscope, dual trace, 50MHz |

454A	Oscilloscope, dual trace, 150MHz
D465	Portable oscilloscope, double beam, 100MHz
475	Oscilloscope, dual trace, 200MHz
491	Spectrum analyser, 10–2000MHz
515A	Oscilloscope
564	Storage oscilloscope
585A	Oscilloscope
647	Oscilloscope
D755	Portable oscilloscope, dual trace, 50MHz (Services spec of D75 and D83)
858A	Oscilloscope
2213A	Oscilloscope, dual trace, 60MHz
7633	Storage oscilloscope
7834	Storage oscilloscope

Wandel and Goltermann

| RE50 | White noise receiver |
| RS50 | White noise generator |

Wayne Kerr

B521	Component bridge
CT375	Component bridge
44C/WKC/1	Measuring set, 20Hz–120kHz
S121	Oscillator, 10Hz–120kHz

Appendix 2

PCB/layout patterns

This appendix contains PCB and component layouts for some of the projects in this book. The component layout is viewed from the component side while the copper pattern is that viewed from the copper side.

While every endeavour has been made to ensure that these patterns are correct, neither the author, the originator or the RSGB can accept any liability from any mistakes or consequential damage. It is up to the constructor to ensure that any component used is fit for the purpose it is to be used for.

In making the boards/masters, always take time to examine the board thoroughly before etching to ensure that there is no break in the tracks etc. If there is, the fault can be touched up with an appropriate fine pen. Examine the board during etching to see if any bridges are being left – if they are, then scratch through any etch resist with a sharp pointed implement, eg a craft knife.

Copyright notice

Project	Chapter	Originator of PCB	Page
DC micro/milliammeter	2	G4FZH	144
High-input-impedance AC voltmeter	2	G4FZH	145
198kHz receiver and standard frequency source	4	G4FZH	146
600MHz frequency counter	4	G4FZH	148
Mk2 FET dip oscillator	5	G3WPO	154
VHF dip oscillator	5	G3XGP	143
Simple Spectrum Analyser	5	G4PMK	151
Modulated RF noise bridge	7	G4FZH	154
Wheatstone bridge	9	G4FZH	155
Linear-scale capacitance meter	9	G4FZH	156
Basic crystal tester	9	G4FZH	165
Square-wave generator	10	G4FZH	144
Low-frequency oscillator	10	G4FZH	157
Two-tone burst oscillator	10	G4FZH	158
Ramp generator	10	G4FZH	159
440–550kHz sweep generator	10	G4FZH	160
9–10.7MHz sweep generator	10	G4FZH	161
Crystal-based frequency marker	10	G4FZH	162
HF/UHF deviation meter	11	G4FZH	163
9V, 130mA DC power supply	12	G4FZH	165
0–15V, 100mA, complementary output power supply	12	G4FZH	166
12V, 10A control PCB	12	G4FZH	167
Lead-acid battery charging unit	12	G4FZH	167
Ni-cad discharger/charger	12	G4FZH	168

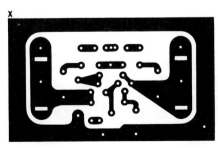

Fig A2.1. VHF dip oscillator PCB

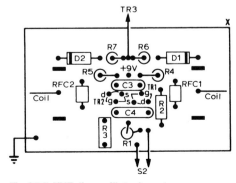

Fig A2.2. VHF dip oscillator layout

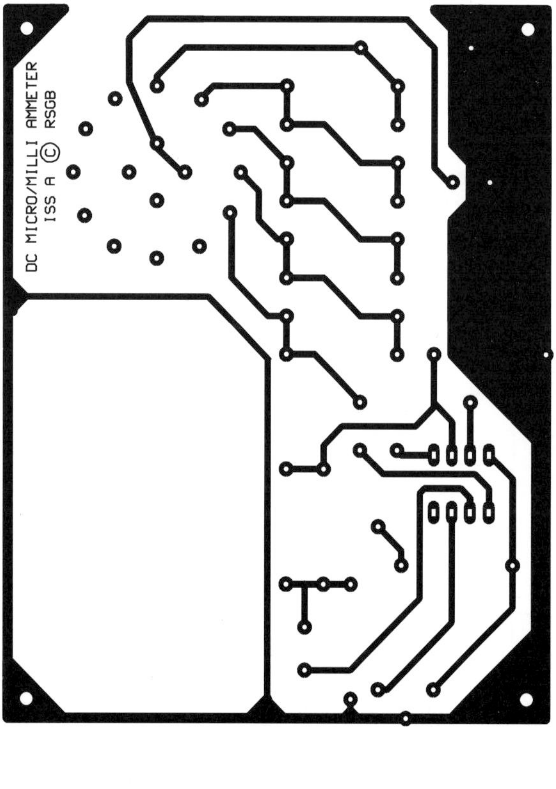

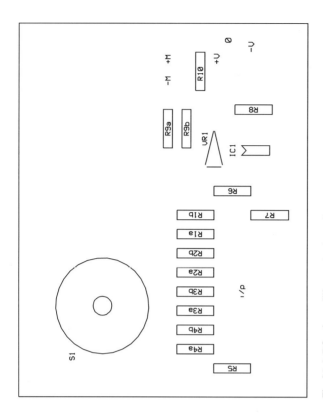

Fig A2.4. DC micromilliammeter layout

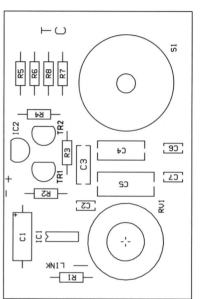

Fig A2.6. Square-wave generator layout

Fig A2.3. DC micro/milliammeter PCB

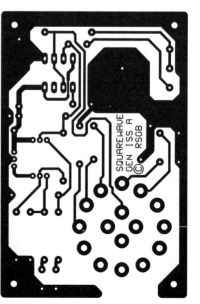

Fig A2.5. Square-wave generator PCB

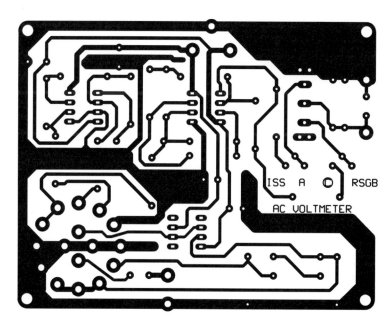

Fig A2.7. AC voltmeter PCB

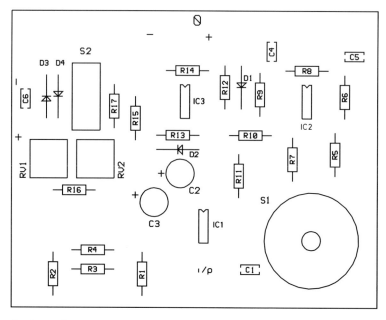

Fig A2.8. AC voltmeter layout

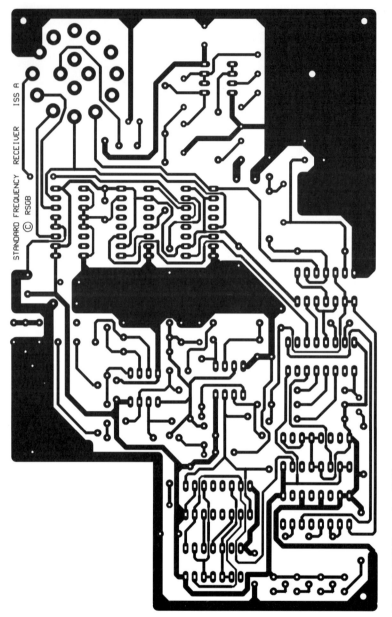

STANDARD FREQUENCY RECEIVER   ISS A

© RSGB

Fig A2.9. 198kHz receiver PCB

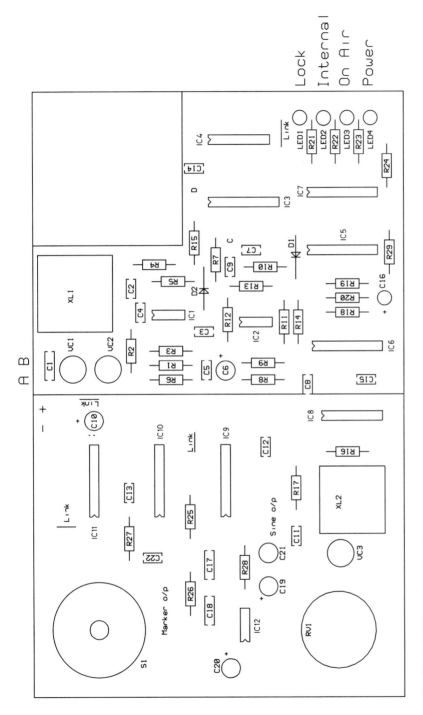

Fig A2.10. 198kHz receiver layout

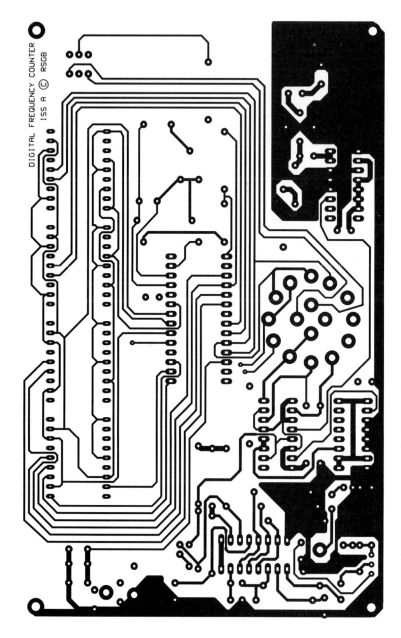

Fig A2.11. 600MHz frequency counter PCB (bottom layer)

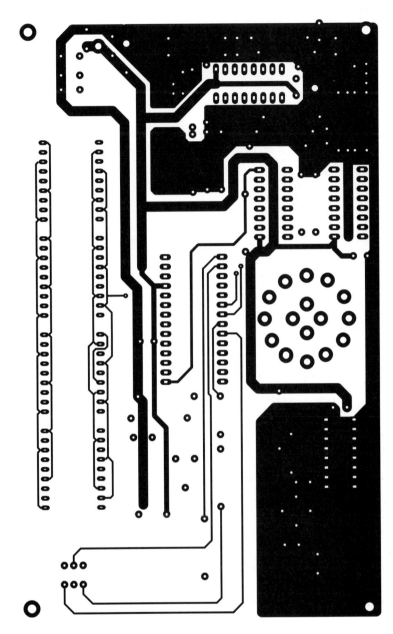

Fig A2.12. 600MHz frequency counter PCB (upper layer)

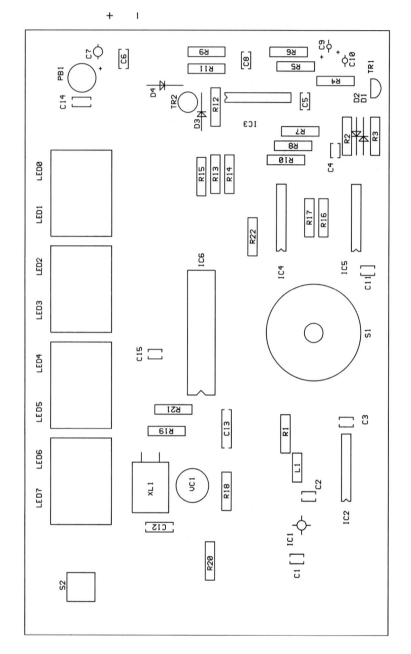

Fig A2.13. 600MHz frequency counter layout

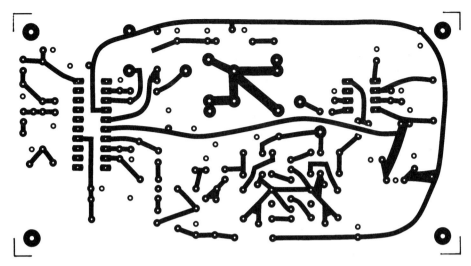

Fig A2.14. Simple Spectrum Analyser RF board PCB

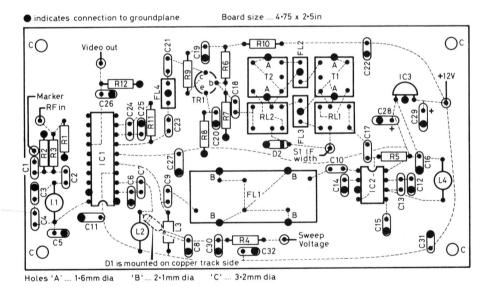

Fig A2.15. Simple Spectrum Analyser RF board layout. Note that the BB109 D1 is mounted on the underside of the board

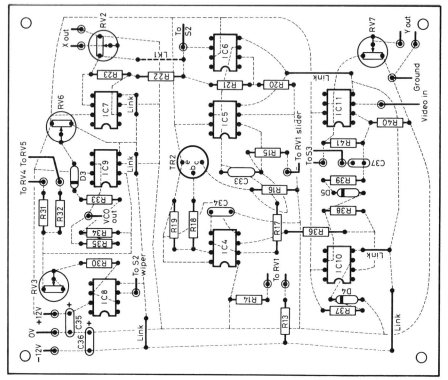

Fig A2.17. Simple Spectrum Analyser video/sweep board layout

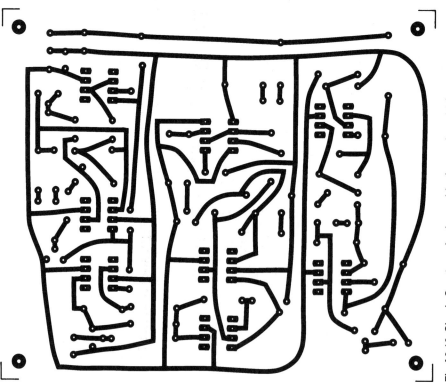

Fig A2.16. Simple Spectrum Analyser video/sweep board PCB

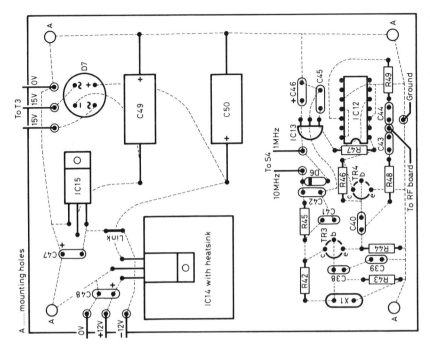

Fig A2.19. Simple Spectrum Analyser marker generator/power supply board PCB

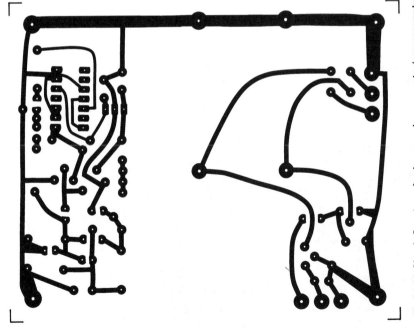

Fig A2.18. Simple Spectrum Analyser marker generator/power supply board PCB

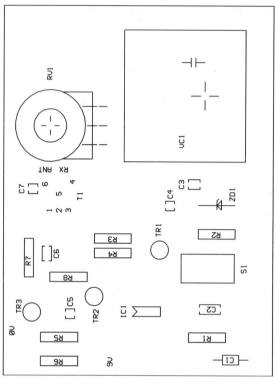

Fig A2.21. Modulated RF noise bridge layout

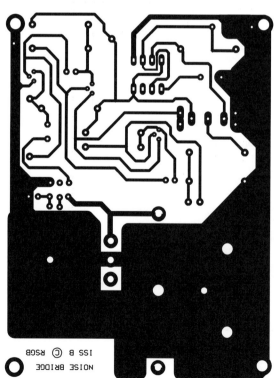

Fig A2.20. Modulated RF noise bridge PCB

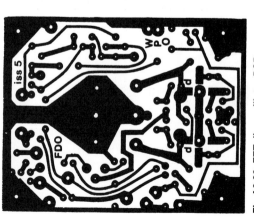

Fig A2.23. FET dip oscillator layout

⊙ indicates connection pin

Fig A2.22. FET dip oscillator PCB

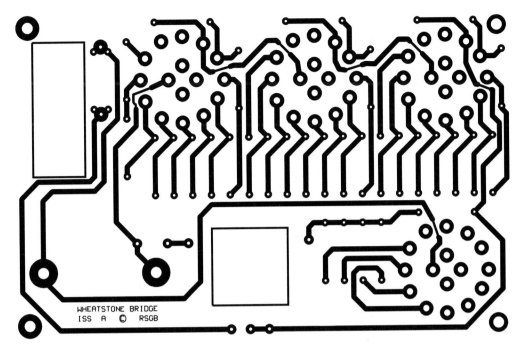

Fig A2.24. Wheatstone bridge PCB

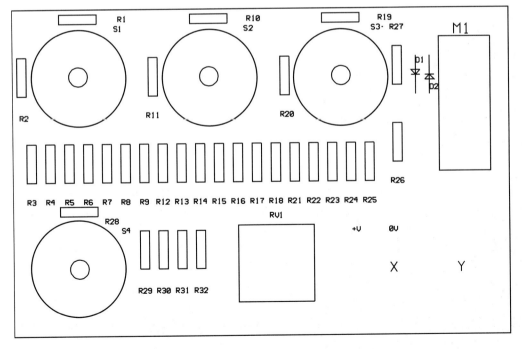

Fig A2.25. Wheatstone bridge layout

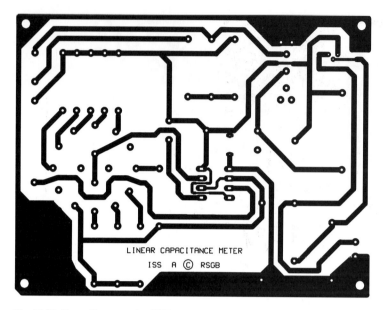

Fig A2.26. Capacitance meter PCB

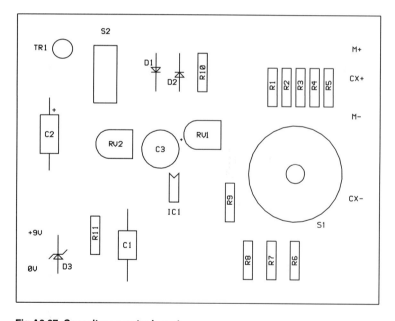

Fig A2.27. Capacitance meter layout

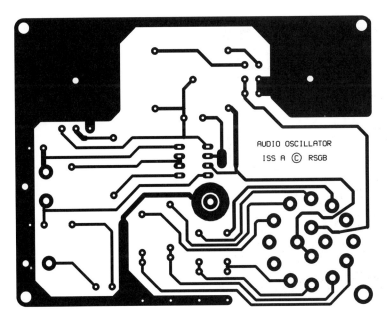

Fig A2.28. Low-frequency oscillator PCB

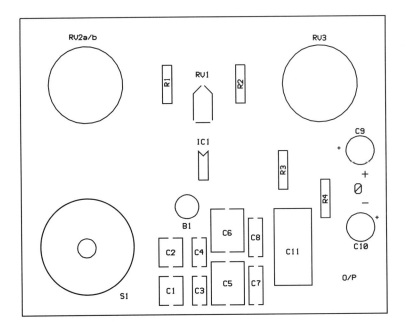

Fig A2.29. Low-frequency oscillator layout

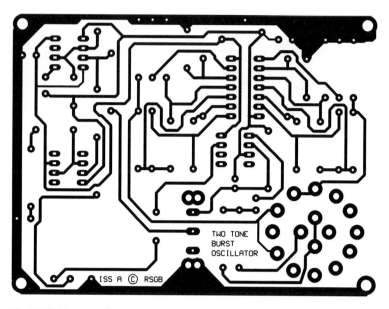

Fig A2.30. Two-tone burst oscillator PCB

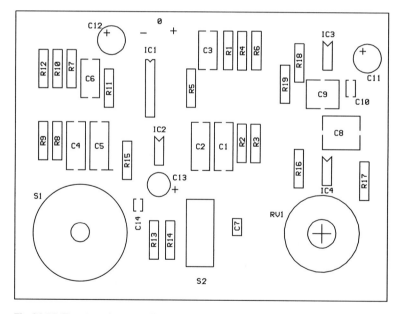

Fig A2.31. Two-tone burst oscillator layout

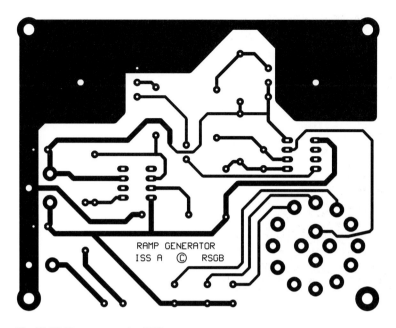

Fig A2.32. Ramp generator PCB

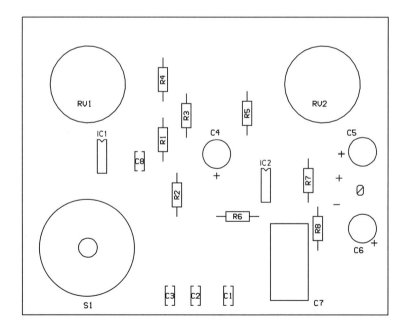

Fig A2.33. Ramp generator layout

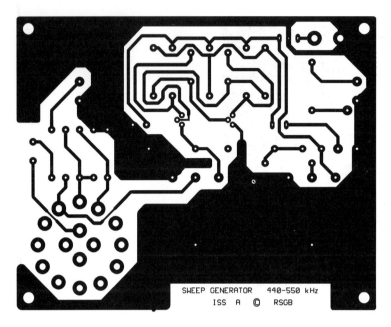

Fig A2.34. 440–550kHz sweep generator PCB

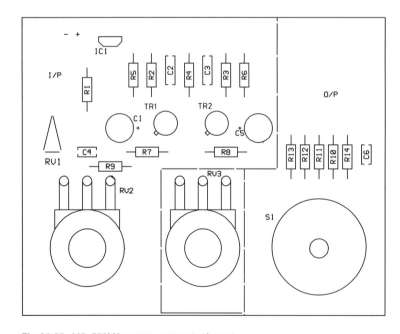

Fig A2.35. 440–550kHz sweep generator layout

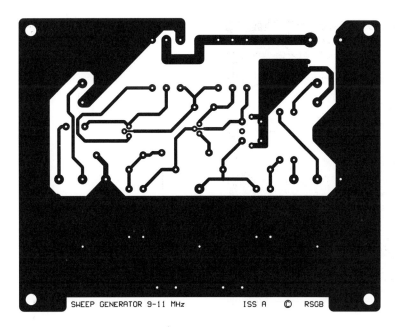

Fig A2.36. 9–10.7MHz sweep generator PCB

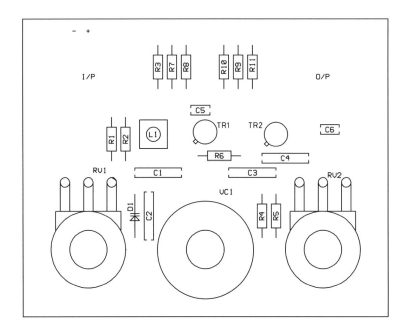

Fig A2.37. 9–10.7MHz sweep generator layout

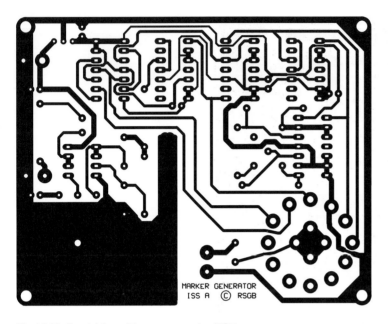

Fig A2.38. Crystal-based frequency marker PCB

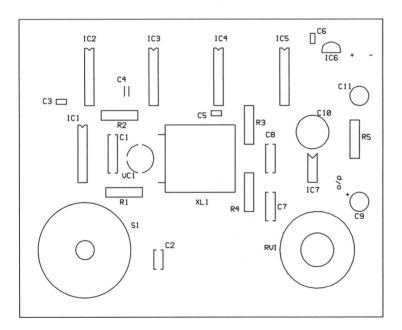

Fig A2.39. Crystal-based frequency marker layout

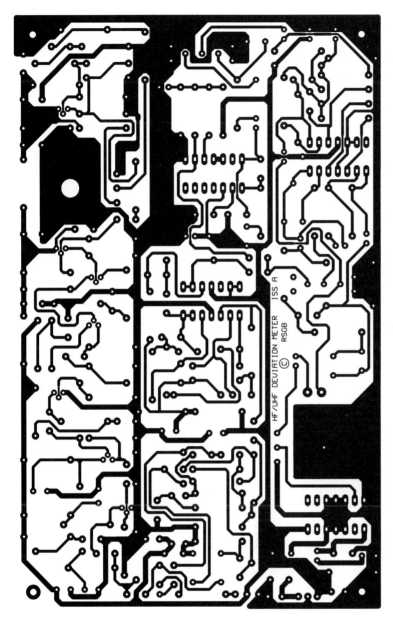

HF/UHF DEVIATION METER ISS A
© RSGB

Fig A2.40. HF/UHF deviation meter PCB

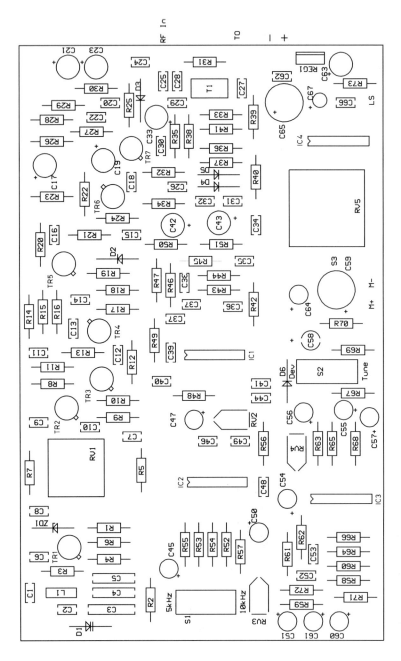

Fig A2.41. HF/UHF deviation meter layout

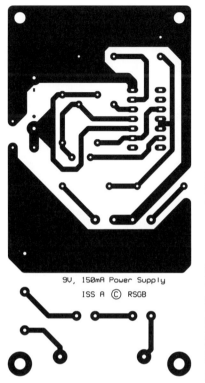

Fig A2.44. 9V, 130mA DC power supply PCB

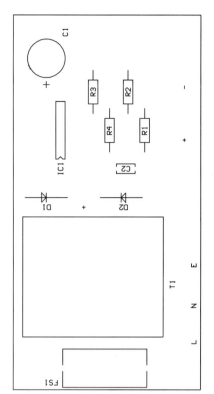

Fig A2.45. 9V, 130mA DC power supply layout

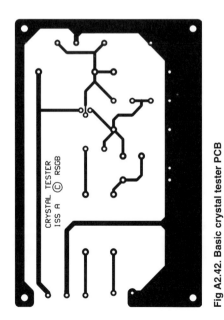

Fig A2.42. Basic crystal tester PCB

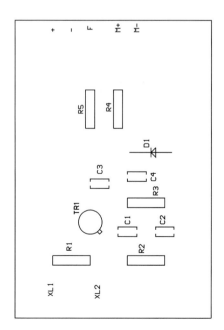

Fig A2.43. Basic crystal tester layout

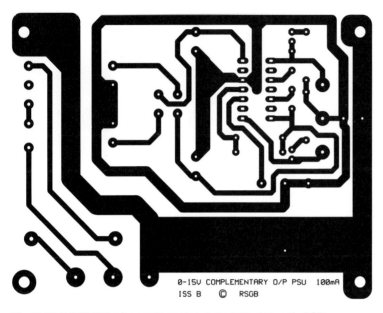

Fig A2.46. 0–15V, 100mA, complementary output power supply PCB

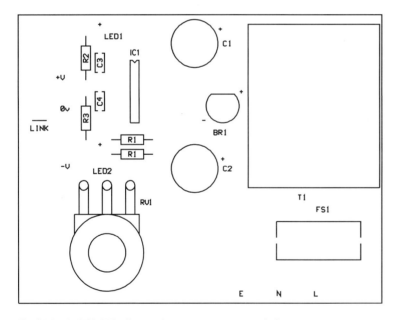

Fig A2.47. 0–15V, 100mA, complementary power supply layout

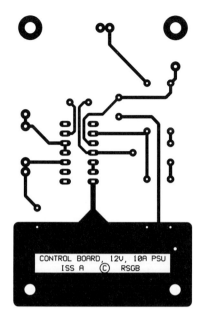

Fig A2.48. 12V, 10A control PCB

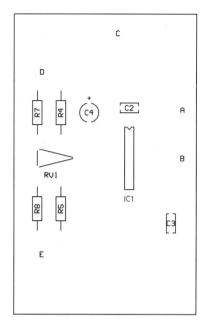

Fig A2.49. 12V, 10A control layout

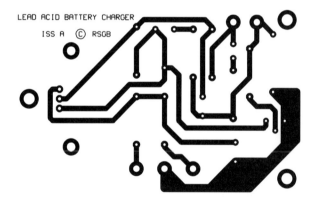

Fig A2.50. Lead-acid battery charging unit PCB

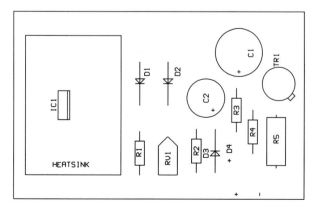

Fig A2.51. Lead-acid battery charging unit layout

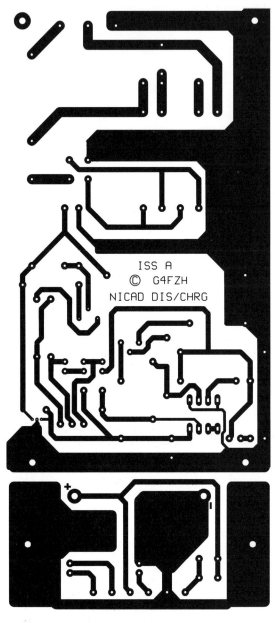

Fig A2.52. Ni-cad discharger/charger PCB

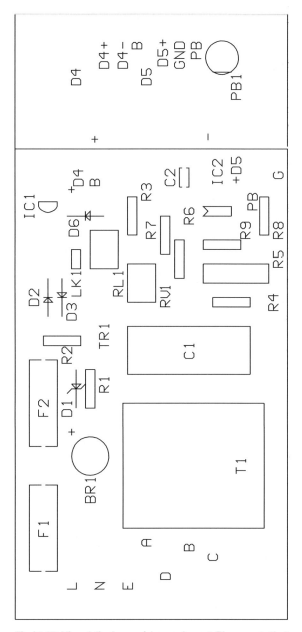

Fig A2.53. Ni-cad discharger/charger layout. Please note that this PCB is designed in two parts. The smaller part can be mounted remotely, adjacent to battery connecting terminals

Index